AUTOMOTIVE

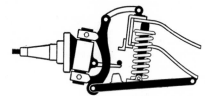

CHASSIS

and BODY

Construction, Operation, and Maintenance

SECOND EDITION

William H. Crouse

McGRAW-HILL BOOK COMPANY, INC.

New York   Chicago   San Francisco   Dallas   Toronto   London

ABOUT THE AUTHOR

Behind William H. Crouse's clear technical writing is a background of sound mechanical engineering training as well as a variety of practical industrial experiences. He spent a year after finishing high school working in a tinplate mill, summers, while still in school, working in General Motors plants, and three years working in the Delco-Remy Division shops. Later he became Director of Field Education in the Delco-Remy Division of General Motors Corporation, which gave him an opportunity to develop and use his natural writing talent in the preparation of service bulletins and educational literature.

During the war years, he wrote a number of technical manuals for the Armed Forces. After the war, he became Editor of Technical Education Books for the McGraw-Hill Book Company. He has contributed numerous articles to automotive and engineering magazines and has written several outstanding books: *Automotive Mechanics, Electrical Appliance Servicing, Everyday Automobile Repairs, Everyday Household Appliance Repairs,* and *Understanding Science.*

William H. Crouse's outstanding work in the automotive field has earned for him membership in the Society of Automotive Engineers and in the American Society for Engineering Education.

How to study this book

THIS IS one of a series of five books covering in detail the construction, operation, and maintenance of automobiles. The five books are designed to give you the complete background of information you need to become an automotive mechanic. Furthermore, the comprehensive coverage of the subject matter in the books should make them a valuable addition to the library of anyone interested in any phase of automobile engineering, manufacturing, sales, services, and operation.

GETTING PRACTICAL EXPERIENCE

Of course, these books alone will not make you an automotive mechanic, just as books alone do not make an airplane pilot or a dentist or an architect. Practice also is required, practice in handling automotive parts and automotive tools, and in following automotive servicing procedures. The books will give you the theoretical background you need, but you should seek out means of getting practice also. If you are taking a regular course in automotive mechanics, you will get practical experience in the school automotive shop. But if you are not taking a regular course in a school, you may still be able to make use of the facilities of any nearby school with an automotive shop. Perhaps you will meet others who are taking an automotive mechanics course and can talk over any problems you have. This often clears up difficult points. A local garage or service station is a good source of practical information. If you can get acquainted with the automotive mechanics there, so much the better. Watch them as they work, notice how they do things. Then go home and think about it. Perhaps the mechanics will allow you to handle various parts and possibly even help some with some of the servicing jobs.

SERVICE PUBLICATIONS

While you are in the service shop, try to get a chance to study the various publications that are received there. Automobile manufacturers and suppliers of parts, accessories, and tools publish shop manuals, service bulletins, and parts catalogues. All of these are designed to help service personnel do a better job. In addition, numerous automotive magazines are published which deal with the problems and methods of automotive service. All of these publications will be of great value to you; study them carefully.

Such activities will help you gain practical experience in automotive mechanics. Sooner or later this experience, plus the knowledge that you have gained in reading the five books in the McGraw-Hill Automotive Mechanics Series, will permit you to step into the automotive shop on a full-time basis. Or, if you are already in the shop, you will be equipped to step up to a better and a more responsible job.

CHECKING UP ON YOURSELF

Every few pages in the book you are given a chance to check the progress you are making by answering a series of questions. You will notice that there are two types of tests, progress quizzes and chapter checkups. Each progress quiz should be taken just after you have completed the pages preceding it. The quizzes allow you to check yourself quickly as you finish a "lesson." On the other hand, the chapter checkups may cover several "lessons" since they are review tests of entire chapters. In view of this, you should review the entire chapter by rereading it or at least scanning it to check important points before trying the test. If any of the questions stump you, reread the pages in the book that will give you the answer. This sort of review is very valuable and will help you to fix in your mind the essential information you will need when you go into the automotive shop. Do not write in the book. Instead, write down your answers in a notebook.

KEEPING A NOTEBOOK

Most of the questions require a written answer. It would be well for you to keep a notebook and for you to write the answers in the notebook. Also, you can write down in the notebook important facts that you pick up from reading the book or from working in the shop. As you do this, you will find that the notebook will become a valuable source of information to which you can refer. Use a loose-leaf, ring-binder type of notebook so you can insert or remove pages and thereby add to and improve your notebook.

GLOSSARY AND INDEX

There is a list of automotive terms in the back of the book, along with their definitions. Whenever you have any doubt about the meaning of some term or the purpose of some automotive part, you can refer to this list, or glossary. Also, in the back of the book you will find an index. This index will help you to look up anything in the book that you are not sure about. For example, if you want to refresh your mind on how some component works, you can find it quickly by looking in the index to find out what pages the information is on.

AUTOMOTIVE TOOLS AND COMPONENTS

In *Automotive Engines*, one of the five books in the McGraw-Hill Automotive Mechanics Series, there is a chapter on automotive tools. This chapter is an important one and should be studied along with any of the books in the Automotive Mechanics Series. In other words, the information in the chapter on tools applies to all service operations on the car, and not just to engine service. The book, *Automotive Engines*, also has a chapter on automotive components that describes briefly the operation of all the mechanisms in the automobile. You should refer to this chapter if you want a short explanation of any component.

And now, good luck to you. You are engaged in the study of a fascinating, complex, and admirable mechanism—the automobile. Your studies can lead you to success in the automotive field, the field where opportunities are great. For it is the man who knows—the man who can do things—who moves ahead. Let this man be you.

WILLIAM H. CROUSE

Contents

Contents

[ix]

Contents

Contents

Preface to second edition

RAPID technological developments in the automotive field, as well as advancements in educational methods required to keep pace with these new developments, have made advisable a new edition of *Automotive Chassis and Body*. This revision includes material on the new automotive equipment introduced in the past three years and related servicing techniques. Insofar as possible, this new material has not been appended to the old; instead, it has been integrated into the pattern of the text so that the student sees the new material as part of the complete presentation.

The comments and suggestions of teachers and students who have used the earlier edition have been carefully analyzed and acted upon where possible during the revision of the text. Reports of their experience in the actual use of the text for classroom and home study have been of paramount importance to the author in his efforts to make the book of maximum usefulness. Improvements that have been made in the present edition, therefore, should be credited to these users, and acknowledgment of their helpful suggestions is herewith gratefully extended.

WILLIAM H. CROUSE

Acknowledgments

DURING the several years that the five books in the McGraw-Hill Automotive Mechanics Series (of which this is one) were in preparation, the author was given invaluable aid and inspiration by many, many people in the automotive industry and in the field of education. The author gratefully acknowledges his indebtedness and offers his sincere thanks to these many people. All cooperated with the aim of providing accurate and complete information that would be useful in the training of automotive mechanics. Special thanks are due to the following organizations for information and illustrations that they supplied: AC Spark Plug Division, Buick Motor Division, Cadillac Motor Car Division, Chevrolet Motor Division, Delco Products Division, Delco-Remy Division, Detroit Diesel Engine Division, Frigidaire Division, Oldsmobile Division, Pontiac Motor Division, Saginaw Steering Gear Division, and United Motors Service Division of General Motors Corporation; Allen Electric and Equipment Company; American Exporter's Automotive World; Akron Equipment Company; American Motors Corporation; Barrett Equipment Company; Bear Manufacturing Company; Bendix Products Division of Bendix Aviation Corporation; Black and Decker Manufacturing Company; Carter Carburetor Company; Chrysler Sales Division, De Soto Division, Dodge Division, and Plymouth Division of Chrysler Corporation; Clayton Manufacturing Company; Henry Disston and Sons, Inc.; Eaton Manufacturing Company; E. I. du Pont de Nemours & Company, Inc.; Electric Auto-Lite Company; Federal-Mogul Corporation; E. Edelmann and Company; Federal Motor Truck Company; Ford Motor Company; Gemmer Manufacturing Company; B. F. Goodrich Company; Greenfield Tap and Die Corporation; Hall Manufacturing Company; Jam Handy Organization, Inc.; Hercules Motors Corporation; Hobart Brothers; Hotpoint, Inc.; Houde Engineering Division of Houdaille-Hershey Corporation; International Harvester Company; Kaiser Motors Corporation; K-D Manufacturing Company; Kelsey-Hayes Wheel Company; Kent-Moor Organization, Inc.; Johnson Bronze Company; King-Seeley Corporation; Lincoln-Mercury Division of Ford Motor Company; Linde Air Products Company; Mack-International Motor Truck Corporation; Metalizing Company of America; Alexander Milburn Company; Monmouth Products Company; Monroe Auto Equipment Company; Muskegon Piston Ring Company; New Britain Machine Company; North American Electric Lamp Company; Perfect Circle Company; Ramsey Accessories Manufacturing Company; Rottler Boring Bar Company; A. Schrader's Son Division of Scovill Manufacturing Company, Inc.; Sealed Power Corporation; South Bend Lathe Works; Spicer Manufacturing Corporation; Standard Oil Company; Storm Manufacturing Company, Inc.; Studebaker-Packard Corporation; Sun Electric Corporation; Sunnen Products Company; Thompson Products, Inc.; United Specialties Company; United States Rubber Company; Van Norman Company; Warner Electric Brake Manufacturing Company; Waukesha Motor Company; Weaver Manufacturing Company; Wilkening Manufacturing Company; and Zenith Carburetor Company.

Special thanks are also due to the staff and instructors at General Motors Institute; they supplied the author with much excellent information and gave him great assistance during certain phases of the work on the McGraw-Hill Automotive Mechanics Series. To all these organizations and the people who represent them, sincere thanks!

WILLIAM H. CROUSE

1: Fundamental principles

THIS CHAPTER discusses the fundamental principles of the various operating components of the automobile. These principles will help you to understand why and how the engine, brakes, steering system, and other components operate. Further, when you know the principles, you will find it much easier to understand the machines operating on these principles.

§1. Purpose of this book   In this book we hope to give you a great deal of interesting information on that part of the automobile called the *chassis*. The chassis includes the frame, wheels and supporting springs, steering mechanism, brakes, engine, and the power train, or the mechanisms that carry the engine power to the wheels. Other books in the McGraw-Hill Automotive Mechanics Series describe the engine (*Automotive Engines*) and the power-train components (*Automotive Transmissions and Power Trains*). The remainder of the chassis components are described in this book: springs, shock absorbers, steering systems (including power steering), brakes (including power brakes), tires, and frames. There are also chapters on automotive body repair and automotive air conditioning.

The man who wants to get into the automotive business, as well as the automotive mechanic, the automotive engineer, the man working at the higher level in automotive manufacture, sales, service, or operation, should find much of interest in this book. With the information in this book at his finger tips, he can do a better job for himself and for his employer. And he is equipped for the bigger job up ahead. The man who knows the facts and who can use those facts in a practical way is the man who moves on to better things. This book is designed to help you be that man.

§2. Why we talk about principles first   Before we start describing the various chassis components covered in this book, we want to discuss the "principles," or "physical laws," that make these com-

[1]

ponents operate. When we release a stone from our hand, it drops to the ground. When a vacuum exists in the engine cylinder, air rushes in as the intake valve opens. When we step on the brake pedal, liquid is forced through tubes into the brake mechanisms at the wheels so that braking action takes place; but if air gets into the tubes, then the braking effect will be poor. Why do these and many other things happen? Because of those physical laws we mentioned a moment ago. Because, for instance, air acts one way and a liquid another when pressure is applied on it. The principles we are about to discuss explain why these things happen. And when we understand *why* a mechanism works, it is much easier to remember *how* it works and how to service and repair it. Actually, we are all acquainted with these physical principles and use them every day. There's really nothing very complicated about them.

§3. Gravity Take gravity, for example. Gravity makes the stone we release from our hand fall to the earth. Gravity is the attractive force that all objects have toward each other. The earth attracts the stone and it is pulled toward the earth. When a car is being driven up a hill, a good part of the engine power is being used to overcome gravity and raise the car against the gravitational attraction. Likewise, a car can coast down a hill with the engine off because of the gravitational attraction of the earth on the car.

We usually measure gravitational attraction in terms of "weight." For instance, we note that an object, when put on a scale, "weighs" 10 pounds. We simply mean that the object has enough mass for the earth to register that much pull on it. It is the gravitational attraction, or the pull of the earth, that gives an object its weight.

§4. Atmospheric pressure The air has weight, just as any other material object has weight. Normally we do not think of air as having weight because we cannot see it and we have become accustomed to feeling its weight and movement—as we do, for instance, when it blows in our face.

However, since the air is an "object," it does have weight; that is, the air is pulled toward the earth by gravitational attraction. At sea level, and at average temperature, a cubic foot of air weighs about eight-hundredths (0.08) of a pound, or about 1¼ ounces (Fig. 1-1). This seems like a very small weight. However, we know that the blanket of air (or the atmosphere) that surrounds the

[2]

earth is many miles thick. This means that there are, in effect, many thousands of cubic feet of air, piled one on top of another, all adding their weight. The actual weight of this air, or its downward push, amounts to about 15 pounds per square inch at sea level. This is another way of saying that the atmospheric pressure (the pressure or downward push of the air) is 15 pounds per square inch (usually abbreviated *psi*). And 15 psi means 2,160 pounds per square foot [1] (Fig. 1-2). In other words, atmospheric pressure at sea level amounts to more than a ton on every square

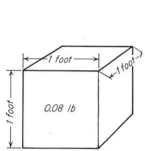

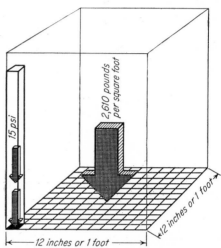

Fig. 1-1. A cubic foot of air at sea level and at average temperature weighs about 0.08 pound.

Fig. 1-2. A pressure of 15 pounds per square inch means 2,160 pounds per square foot.

foot of the earth's surface or on any object on the earth at sea level. Since the human body has a surface area of several square feet, atmospheric pressure on the body amounts to several tons!

When a person first comes across this fact about atmospheric pressure, he usually wonders why all that pressure doesn't crush him. The reason is that the internal pressures of the body balance the external pressure of the air. Fish are subjected to much greater pressures—more than 100,000 psi several thousands of feet down in the ocean. But their internal pressure balances the outside pressure. They manage to live and swim about, just as we live and

[1] 1 square foot = 144 square inches. 144 × 15 = 2,160.

walk about on earth, even though a great weight of air exerts its pressure on us.

§5. Changes in atmospheric pressure Atmospheric pressure is continually changing. It changes with the weather. It also changes as you move up from sea level by climbing a mountain or by flying in a plane. In the next section, on vacuum, we shall learn how atmospheric pressure is measured so that men can predict what the weather will be. The reason changing atmospheric pressure is tied in with the weather is that the changing pressure helps to get the air moving from one place to another. For instance, air over the ocean picks up a great deal of moisture. Suppose that to the east of this moist air, there is a sunshiny area of dry land. The sun heats the air above the dry land. As air is heated, it expands and becomes lighter. (It contracts, or becomes heavier, when it is cooled.[2]) The lighter air tends to rise, the heavier air to sink. As the lighter air rises, the heavier, cooler, moister air from the ocean moves in under it. This brings rain and changing weather to the land.

When you climb a mountain or fly upward in an airplane, you find that the atmospheric pressure is reduced. You put more and more of the air below you as you go up. There is less and less air above you to press down on you. At 30,000 feet above the earth's surface, for instance, the air pressure is less than 5 psi. At 100,000 feet altitude, the air pressure is only about 0.15 psi. A man could not live at this height unless he wore a "space suit" which maintained a pressure around him and kept him supplied with enough air to breathe.

§6. Vacuum Vacuum is the absence of air or other matter. If we could travel far above the earth's surface, hundreds of miles or more into space, we should find no atmosphere at all. No air. At this distance from the earth, there are only a very few particles of air, widely scattered. This is a vacuum.

But we do not need to leave the earth to find a vacuum. We can produce a vacuum anywhere on earth with a long glass tube closed at one end, plus a dish of mercury (a very heavy metal that is liquid at normal temperatures). To produce a vacuum, we com-

---

[2] A cubic foot of air at 100°F weighs 0.070 pound. A cubic foot of air at 0°F weighs 0.085 pound. As the air is cooled, it contracts, so there is more air in a cubic foot (actually 0.015 pound more).

pletely fill the tube with mercury, and then close the end tightly. Next, we turn the tube upside down, put the end into the dish of mercury, and open this end. When we open the end, part of the mercury will run out of the tube, leaving the upper part of the tube empty (Fig. 1-3). Since no air can enter this upper part of the tube, the upper part of the tube contains nothing—that is, it contains a vacuum.

The device shown in Fig. 1-3 is a barometer; it can be used to measure atmospheric pressure. You might wonder why all the mercury doesn't run out of the tube when it is turned upside down—

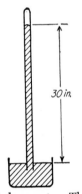

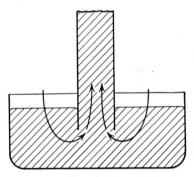

FIG. 1-3. A barometer. The mercury in the tube will stand at about 30 inches above the surface of the mercury in the dish at an atmospheric pressure of 15 psi.

FIG. 1-4. In a barometer the pressure of the air, acting on the surface of the mercury and through the mercury, holds the mercury up in the sealed tube.

that is, why some of the mercury stays in the tube. The reason is that atmospheric pressure holds it up in the tube. The atmospheric pressure presses down on the surface of the mercury in the dish, and this push, transmitted through the mercury, holds the mercury up in the tube (Fig. 1-4). You could compare this to putting your hand, palm down, into soft mud. As you push down on the mud, the downward pressure causes some of the mud to squirt up between your fingers.

The barometer indicates atmospheric pressure, as we mentioned. When air pressure goes up, the air pushes harder on the mercury and forces it higher up in the tube. But when air pressure goes down, then there is a weaker push and the mercury settles to a lower level in the tube. The barometer can foretell the coming of a storm. A storm is normally accompanied by a lowered atmospheric pressure, brought on by the presence of heated, and lighter, air. Thus, when the barometer "drops" (mercury goes down in the tube), chances are a storm is coming.

§**7. Vacuum machines**   The barometer is one "machine" for producing vacuum. There are a great many devices, pumps of one sort or another, that produce vacuum. The automobile engine is, in one sense, a vacuum machine. During its operation, a partial vacuum is created in its cylinders by the downward moving pistons during intake strokes. As this happens, atmospheric pressure pushes air toward the vacuum. The air passes through the carburetor where it picks up a charge of fuel. Thus, the vacuum causes a charge of air-fuel mixture to be delivered to the engine cylinder during the intake stroke.[3]

As long as we are talking about the automobile engine, we might add that the engine is also a compression machine. After the intake stroke, the piston moves up during the compression stroke and compresses the air-fuel charge to one-seventh, or less, of its original volume.

§**8. Some characteristics of air**   We have seen that air can expand, or thin out. We have also noted that air can be compressed, or packed into a smaller volume. Air is a mixture of several gases. About 20 percent is oxygen, and the rest is mostly nitrogen. Air, or any gas or mixture of gases, is composed of tiny particles called molecules (or combination of atoms). These atoms or molecules are so tiny that there are literally billions upon billions of them in a cubic inch of gas. For example, in a cubic inch of hydrogen gas at atmospheric pressure and 32°F, there are about 880 billion billion atoms (Fig. 1-5). That is 880,000,000,000,000,000,000 atoms. Despite the fact that there are so many of them, the space is not crowded because the atoms are so very tiny. In fact, the space is almost empty. We can prove this by increasing the pressure. For example, suppose our cubic inch of hydrogen gas is contained in a rigid box and we fitted a square piston to the box. Then suppose we pushed down on the piston with a force of 150 pounds (Fig. 1-6). We would find that the pressure would squeeze the atoms of hydrogen closer together so the volume would be reduced to $\frac{1}{10}$ cubic inch.

[3] See *Automotive Engines* for a discussion of how the engine operates.

[6]

We would also find that the temperature of the hydrogen gas would increase. Why do these things happen?

§9. Pressure The atoms, or molecules, of gas are in constant motion. They have a relatively large space to move around in, so they dart about in a constant turmoil. If the gas is enclosed in a container, then molecules of the gas are constantly bumping into the inner sides of the container. There will be billions of these bumps every second in our cubic inch container (Fig. 1-5). These billions of bumps—this constant bombardment—add up to the total push we know as pressure. Now, when we compress the cubic inch

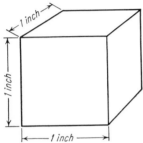

Fig. 1-5. A cubic inch of hydrogen gas at atmospheric pressure (15 psi) and at 32°F contains about 880 billion billion atoms.

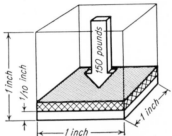

Fig. 1-6. Increasing the pressure to 150 psi decreases the volume of gas to ⅒ cubic inch.

into one-tenth of a cubic inch (Fig. 1-6), we have squeezed the gas molecules much closer together. Since the molecules are closer together, and have much less room to move around in, they are going to bump into the walls of the container more often. In fact, they bump into the walls 10 times as often. This is another way of saying that the pressure has increased by 10 times as much. This is actually what has happened. We started out with a pressure of 15 psi (Fig. 1-5), and increased it 10 times—that is, to 150 psi (Fig. 1-6).

§10. Heat We have noted that increasing the pressure on a gas decreases its volume. This also increases its temperature. For actually, temperature, or heat, is nothing more nor less than speed of molecular motion. When the molecules move fast, the object is hot. When the molecules move slowly, the object is cold. In a piece of ice, the molecules are moving so slowly that they all more or less

[7]

hang together. The ice remains a solid. But if the ice is heated, it melts. That is, the molecules begin to move a little faster and they can no longer hang together to form a solid: the ice turns to water. If the water is heated, the molecules are set into more rapid motion. Finally, they move so fast that they begin to jump clear of the liquid: the water boils, or turns to vapor.

When the cubic inch of gas is compressed to one-tenth of an inch, the molecules are not only pushed more closely together, but they are set into more rapid motion. This is because of the more frequent collisions between molecules and more frequent collisions with the walls of the container. Since the gas molecules are in more rapid motion, the gas is hotter. Soon, however, this extra heat is absorbed by the walls of the container and passes from the walls to the outer air. The rapidly moving molecules, as they bombard the walls of the container, set the molecules of the container into more rapid motion—that is, the container is heated. Outside molecules of air, as they pass the container, or bump into the outer walls of the container, are then set into more rapid motion. Soon, the heat produced by compressing the gas has all dissipated to the container walls and then to the outside air.

§11. Pressure increase with heat   If we heat a container of air, we find that the pressure inside the container increases. Suppose we start again with a cubic inch of air (Fig. 1-5). At 32°F, this cubic inch of air is at atmospheric pressure or 15 psi. If we heated the container of gas to 100°F, we would find that its pressure would increase to about 17 psi. In heating the gas, we have caused the molecules to move faster. They bombard the walls of the container harder and more often, thus registering a higher push, or pressure.

CHECK YOUR PROGRESS

Progress Quiz 1

The following questions have two very definite purposes. First, they give you a chance to review what you learned as you read the past few pages. Second, they give you a chance to check up on yourself, that is, to find out how well you are remembering what you read. It is much like the battery man when he has a battery on charge. He checks it periodically to see how it is taking the charge. Likewise, there are quizzes throughout the book that let you check yourself to see how you are taking your "charge" of information. If you don't do too well on the following checkup, don't be discouraged. It simply means that you should review the past few pages. Most good students reread their "lessons" several times to make sure they remember the important points covered.

Completing the Sentences

The sentences below are incomplete. After each sentence there are several words or phrases, only one of which will correctly complete the sentence. Write down each sentence in your notebook, selecting the proper word or phrase to complete it correctly.

1. The attractive force that all objects have toward each other is called   *pressure*   *vacuum*   *gravity*   *heat*
2. At sea level and at average temperature, a cubic foot of air weighs about   *0.008 pound*   *0.08 pound*   *0.8 pound*   *8.0 pounds*   *15 pounds*
3. At sea level and at average temperature, the atmospheric pressure is about   *0.08 psi*   *0.15 psi*   *1.5 psi*   *15.0 psi*
4. At sea level and at average temperature, the atmospheric pressure is about   *2 pounds per square foot*   *15 pounds per square foot*   *2,160 pounds per square foot*
5. As air is heated, it tends to   *contract and become heavier*   *expand and become lighter*   *expand and become heavier*
6. Absence of air or other matter is called   *gravity*   *vacuum*   *pressure*   *volume*
7. When the pressure on a gas is increased, the gas is   *cooled*   *expanded*   *compressed*   *atomized*
8. The pressure of a gas against the walls of a container is the result of   *gravity*   *vacuum*   *bombardment of molecules*   *contraction*
9. When the pressure on a gas is increased so that the gas is compressed, it is also   *cooled*   *heated*   *expanded*
10. If we heated a sealed container of gas, we would find that the pressure inside the container   *is reduced*   *is increased*   *does not change*

HYDRAULICS

§12. **Meaning of the word "hydraulics"** In its simplest sense, hydraulics has to do with certain characteristics of liquids such as water and oil. Our special interest, so far as the automotive chassis is concerned, is related to the effects of pressure applied to a liquid.

[9]

This is called hydraulic pressure. Hydraulic pressure is used in the braking system, in shock absorbers, and in power-steering systems. It is also used in automatic transmissions (control circuits, fluid coupling, and torque converter), in engines (hydraulic valve lifters, oil pump, fuel pump, water pump), and so on.

§13. Incompressibility of liquids We have seen that increasing the pressure on a gas will compress the gas into a smaller volume

GAS CAN BE COMPRESSED

LIQUID CANNOT BE COMPRESSED

Fɪɢ. 1-7. Gas can be compressed when pressure is applied. However, liquid cannot be compressed by application of pressure. (*Pontiac Motor Division of General Motors Corporation*)

(Fig. 1-6). However, increasing the pressure on a liquid will not reduce its volume; its volume stays the same even though the pressure on it is greatly increased (Fig. 1-7). A liquid cannot be compressed into a smaller volume; it is incompressible. This might be explained as follows. The molecules of the liquid are rather close together—as opposed to a gas, in which the molecules are relatively far part. Putting pressure on a gas can "squeeze out" some of the space between the molecules. But in a liquid, there is no extra space that can be "squeezed out" by the application of pressure. The

[10]

molecules are already as close together as we can get them; putting pressure on the liquid will not force them closer together.

§14. Transmission of motion by liquid   Since liquid is not compressible, motion may be transmitted by liquid. For example, Fig. 1-8 shows two pistons in a cylinder, with a liquid separating them. When the applying piston is pushed into the cylinder 8 inches, as shown, then the output piston will be pushed along in the cylinder for the same distance, or 8 inches. In this illustration, you could substitute a solid connecting rod between piston A and piston B and get exactly the same effect.

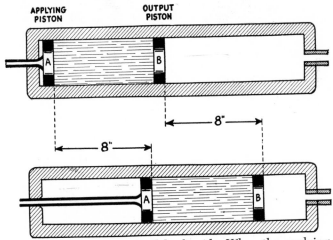

FIG. 1-8. Motion may be transmitted by liquids. When the applying piston is moved 8 inches in the cylinder, the output piston is also moved 8 inches. (*Pontiac Motor Division of General Motors Corporation*)

The motion may also be transmitted from one cylinder to another by a tube, or pipe (Fig. 1-9). Here, the applying piston is in cylinder A and the output piston is in cylinder B. As the applying piston is moved into its cylinder, liquid is forced from cylinder A into cylinder B. This causes the output piston to be moved in its cylinder. If both pistons are of the same size, then the output piston will move the same distance as the applying piston.

§15. Transmission of pressure by liquid   The pressure that is applied to a liquid is transmitted by the liquid in all directions and to every part of the liquid. For example, in Fig. 1-10 a piston with an area of 1 square inch is shown applying a force of 100 pounds. This is

[11]

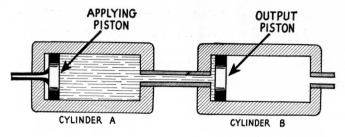

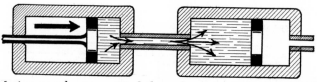

FIG. 1-9. Motion may be transmitted through a tube from one cylinder to another by liquid, or hydraulic, pressure. (*Pontiac Motor Division of General Motors Corporation*)

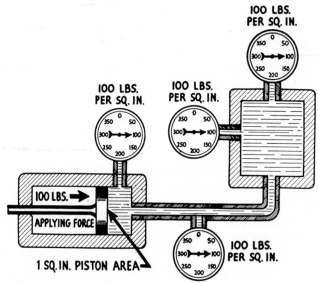

FIG. 1-10. The pressure applied to a liquid transmitted equally in all directions. (*Pontiac Motor Division of General Motors Corporation*)

a force of 100 psi (pounds per square inch). If we attached pressure gauges to various parts of the system, as shown, to measure the pressure on the liquid, we would find that the pressure on the liquid would be the same at all points. Note that regardless of the point where the pressure measurement is taken, we get the same reading.

The pressure is usually referred to in terms of pounds per square inch (or psi). Thus, when a piston is applying pressure to a liquid, we can calculate the psi if we know the force being applied by the piston, and the area of the piston in square inches. For instance,

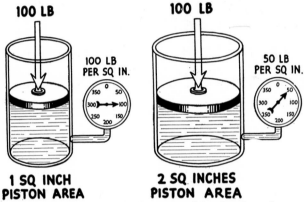

FIG. 1-11. Pressure in the system is determined by dividing the applying force by the area of the applying piston. (*Pontiac Motor Division of General Motors Corporation*)

in Fig. 1-11, when a one-square-inch piston applies a force of 100 pounds, the pressure on the liquid is 100 psi. But if the area of the piston is 2 square inches, and the piston is applying a force of 100 pounds, then the pressure on the liquid is only 50 psi. That is, each square inch of the piston is applying only 50 pounds. So the psi is determined by dividing the applied force by the area of the piston in square inches.

When we have an input-output system (Fig. 1-12), we can determine the force applied to any output piston by multiplying the pressure in psi by the area of the output piston in square inches. For example, the pressure shown in Fig. 1-12 is 100 psi. The output piston to the left has an area of 0.5 square inch. Thus, the output force on this piston is 100 times 0.5 or 50 pounds. The center

[13]

output piston has an area of 1 square inch and its output force is therefore 100 pounds. The right-hand output piston has an area of 2 square inches and its output force is therefore 200 pounds (100 × 2). If the area of the output piston were 500 square inches, then the output force, with 100 psi applied, would be 50,000 pounds. You can see that hydraulic pressure can be used to apply tremendous loads by making the output piston much larger than the input piston. In big presses used in manufacturing automotive

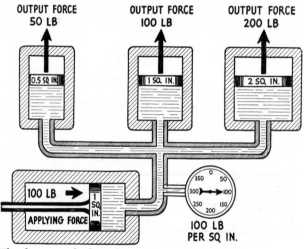

FIG. 1-12. The force applied to the output piston is the pressure in the system in psi times the area of the output piston. (*Pontiac Motor Division of General Motors Corporation*)

and airplane parts, pressures of hundreds of thousands of pounds are produced by this means.

FRICTION AND LUBRICATION

§16. **Friction**   Friction is the resistance to motion between two objects in contact with each other. Friction acts to prevent one object from sliding on another. In the automobile, many parts are sliding on or rotating within other parts. Thus, some of the power developed by the engine must be used up in overcoming this friction. This is, in effect, wasted power because it does not contribute to moving the car. On the other hand, friction is very valuable in the car brakes; here, the friction between brake drums and brake shoes slows or stops the car when the brakes are applied.

[14]

§17. Some characteristics of friction Friction varies with the pressure applied between the sliding surfaces, the roughness of the surfaces, and the material of which the surfaces are made. Suppose, for example, that a platform with its load weighs 100 pounds and it takes 50 pounds of pull to move it along the floor (Fig. 1-13). If you reduced the load so the platform with load weighed only 10 pounds, you would find that it required only 5 pounds pull to move it along the floor. *Friction varies with the load.*

If you went over the floor and the sliding part of the platform with sandpaper and smoothed them off, you would find that it

Fɪɢ. 1-13. Friction varies with the load applied between the sliding surfaces.

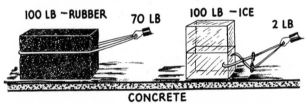

Fɪɢ. 1-14. Friction varies with the type of material.

would require less pull to move the platform on the floor. *Friction varies with the roughness of the surfaces.*

Friction varies with the type of material, too. For example, if you dragged a 100-pound bale of rubber across a concrete floor, you might find that it required a pull of 70 pounds (Fig. 1-14). But to drag a 100-pound cake of ice across the same floor might require a pull of only 2 pounds.

§18. Coefficient of friction Engineers need a more exact way to express frictional differences than to say that one surface has a high friction and another surface a low friction. They therefore developed the idea of the *coefficient of friction.* This is simply a figure that accurately states how much friction there is between two surfaces. For example, wood dragged on cast iron has a fairly high friction. A 100-pound block of wood might require a pull of

[15]

Coef. frict = $\frac{pull}{weight}$

50 pounds to move it over a cast-iron slab (Fig. 1-15). To state this in terms of the coefficient of friction, you divide the pull by the weight, or 50 divided by 100. This gives a coefficient of 0.5. Knowing the coefficient, you could then determine how much pull would be required to pull a wood block of any weight over cast iron.

COEFFICIENT OF FRICTION   **COEFFICIENT OF FRICTION**

50 ÷ 100 = 0.5   **20 ÷ 100 = 0.2**

WOOD ON CAST IRON   **BRONZE ON CAST IRON**

FIG. 1-15. The coefficient of friction is the force required to move an object divided by the weight of the object.

All you have to do is multiply the weight by the coefficient. For instance, a 250-pound block would require a pull of 125 pounds (250 × 0.5 = 125).

The other example shown in Fig. 1-15 is that of a 100-pound block of bronze being dragged over a cast-iron slab. Here, the pull required is 20 pounds. This gives a coefficient of friction of 0.2. If the bronze block weighed 40 pounds, you could determine how much pull would be required to move it, knowing the coefficient of friction. It would be 40 times 0.2, or 8 pounds.

§19. Friction of rest and motion   It requires more force to start an object moving than it does to keep it in motion (Fig. 1-16). In the example shown, it takes two men to get the object started, but once it is started, one man alone can keep it moving. Thus, the friction of an object at rest is greater than the friction of an object in motion.

Engineers do not usually refer to these two kinds of friction as friction of rest and friction of motion. Instead, they call them *static friction* and *kinetic friction*. The word *static* means at rest. The word *kinetic* means in motion, or moving. Thus, static friction is friction of rest and kinetic friction is friction of motion.

[16]

McGRAW-HILL
Automotive Mechanics Series
BY WILLIAM H. CROUSE

Automotive Engines
Automotive Fuel, Lubricating, and Cooling Systems
Automotive Chassis and Body
Automotive Transmissions and Power Trains
Automotive Electrical Equipment

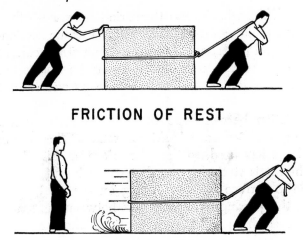

FRICTION OF REST

FRICTION OF MOTION

Fig. 1-16. Friction of rest is greater than the friction of motion. In the example shown, it takes two men to overcome the friction of rest, but only one to overcome the friction of motion after object starts moving.

§20. Causes of friction One explanation of friction is that it is caused by surface irregularities. That is, it is caused by high spots on the two surfaces in contact that tend to catch on each other and hinder the motion between the two objects. When the surfaces are smoothed off, the high spots are cut down and there is less tendency for them to catch on each other; friction is reduced. On the other hand, if the force between the two surfaces is increased, then the high spots are pressed harder against each other so the friction is increased. The fact that static friction is greater than kinetic friction can be explained along the same lines. When the surfaces are at rest, the force or weight between them tends to press the high spots of one surface into the other surface. Then, it takes considerable pull to move all the high spots of one surface up and out of the low spots of the other surface. But once moving, the high spots do not have a chance to "settle" into the opposing surface; less force is required to keep the surfaces moving. That is, kinetic friction is less than static friction.

§21. Friction in the car brakes We have mentioned that friction is used in the car braking system. The friction between the brake drums and brake shoes slows or stops the car. This friction slows

[17]

the rotation of the wheels, and then friction between the tires and road slows the motion of the car. Note that it is the friction between the tires and road that results in the stopping of the car. That being the case, would the car stop more quickly if the wheels were locked (so the tires skidded on the road)? The answer is that the car would not. If the brakes are applied so hard that the wheels lock, then the friction between the tires and road is kinetic friction (friction of motion as the tires skid on road). When the brakes are applied a little less hard, so the wheels are permitted to continue rotating, then it is static friction that works between the tires and road. The tire surface is not skidding on the road, but is rolling on it. Since this produces static friction between the road and tires, there is considerably greater braking effect. The car will stop more quickly if the brakes are applied just hard enough to get maximum static friction between the tires and road. If the brakes are applied harder than this, then the wheels will lock, the tires will slide, and the lower kinetic friction will result.·

§22. Classes of friction   Up to now, we have been discussing *dry* friction, or the friction between two dry surfaces. There are two other classes of friction, greasy friction and viscous friction. It is the latter two that we find most often in the moving parts of the automobile.

1. Greasy friction.   If we thinly coat the moving surfaces of two objects with grease or oil, we will find that the friction is greatly reduced. It is assumed that this thin coat tends to fill in the low spots of the surfaces. Therefore, the surface irregularities have less tendency to catch on each other. However, high spots will still catch and wear as the two surfaces move over each other. In automobile engines, greasy friction may occur when starting. At this time, most of the lubricating oil has drained away from bearings, piston rings, and cylinder walls. Thus, when these surfaces first start to slide over each other, there is only a thin film to protect them against wear. Of course, the lubricating system quickly starts to pump oil to the moving surfaces to provide additional protective lubrication.

2. Viscous friction.   Viscosity is a term that refers to the tendency of liquids, such as oil, to resist flowing. A heavy oil is thicker, or more viscous, than a light oil. It flows more slowly (has higher viscosity or higher resistance to flowing). Viscous friction is the friction, or resistance to motion, between adjacent layers of liquid. As applied to machines, viscous friction occurs during relative motion between two lubricated surfaces (Fig. 1-17). This picture illustrates, in greatly exaggerated view, an object W moving over a stationary object, the two being separated by lubricating oil. The oil is shown in five layers, A to E, for simplicity.

Layer A adheres to the moving object W and moves at the same speed as W (as indicated by the arrow). A layer of oil E adheres to the stationary object and is therefore stationary. Thus, there must be relative motion between the layers of oil A and E. This can be

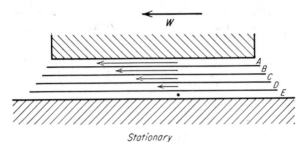

Stationary

Fɪɢ. 1-17. Viscous friction is the friction between layers of liquid moving at different speeds or, in the illustration, between layers A, B, C, D, and E. W represents a moving object.

pictured as a slippage between many layers of oil between A and E. The nearer a layer is to the stationary layer E, the less it moves. This is shown by the progressively shorter arrows in layers B, C, and D. There is slippage between these layers. But there is resistance to this slippage and this is called *viscous friction*.

§**23. Friction and wear** When dry or viscous friction exists, the moving parts are in contact with each other, as we already mentioned. This means that the high spots are interfering with each other. They catch on each other, and particles of the material are torn off. In other words, wear takes place. These tiny particles then add to the wear by scratching and gouging the moving surfaces. Soon, the roughness of the surfaces is increased, and wear goes on at a progressively swifter pace. To prevent this sort of wear, moving parts in machines are covered with coatings of oil (or grease). The oil holds the moving surfaces apart so that only viscous friction results; wear is kept to a minimum.

[19]

§24. Bearings Various devices, called bearings, are used to support the moving parts in machines and at the same time supply the moving parts with lubricating oil. Machine bearings are classified as either friction bearings or antifriction bearings. These two names are somewhat misleading since it would indicate that one type has friction while the other has not. Actually, the friction bearing does have greater friction, but both are low-friction devices. Figure 1-18 shows graphically the difference between friction and antifriction bearings. In the friction bearing, one body slides over another; the load is supported on layers of oil as shown in Fig. 1-17. In the antifriction bearing, the surfaces are separated by balls or

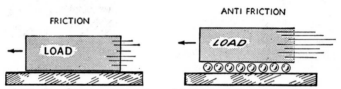

FIG. 1-18. Graphic representation of friction and antifriction bearings.

rollers so that there is rolling friction between the two surfaces and the balls or rollers.

§25. Friction bearings Friction bearings have sliding contact between the moving surfaces. The load is supported by layers of oil. There are three types of friction bearing (Fig. 1-19), journal, guide, and thrust. The journal type is symbolized by two hands holding a turning shaft, as shown in the upper left. The hands support the shaft just as the surrounding bearing supports a shaft journal in an engine. Crankshaft, connecting rod, camshaft, and piston-pin bearings are but a few examples of this type of bearing used in the engine.

The bearing surface between the piston and cylinder wall is of the guide type (center, Fig. 1-19).

The thrust type of friction bearing checks endwise movement of the shaft (right, Fig. 1-19). The flats on the ends of the bearing are parallel to flats at the ends of the shaft journal. As the shaft attempts to move endwise, the flats, or thrust faces, prevent it.

§26. Antifriction bearings Figure 1-20 shows three types of antifriction bearing, ball, roller, and tapered roller. There are other

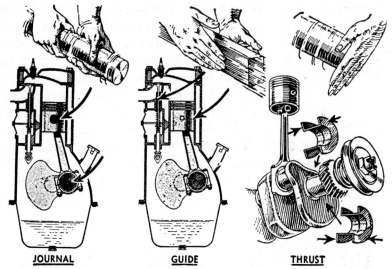

JOURNAL   GUIDE   THRUST

Fig. 1-19. Three types of friction bearings in an automotive engine.

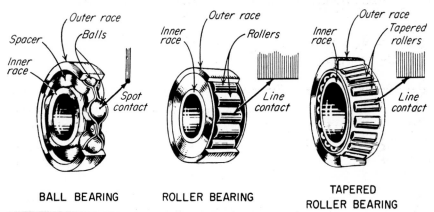

BALL BEARING   ROLLER BEARING   TAPERED ROLLER BEARING

Fig. 1-20. Antifriction bearings.

types, including a spherical roller, thrust, double-row ball, and so on. But all operate on the same principle of interposing a rolling object between the moving surfaces.

The ball bearing has an inner and an outer race in which grooves have been cut. Balls roll in these two race grooves. The balls are held apart by a spacer assembly. When one race is held stationary —for instance, by mounting it in a housing—and the other rotates— as it might when on a shaft—the balls roll in the two races to permit low-friction rotation.

[21]

The roller bearing is similar to the ball bearing except that it has rollers, either plain or tapered. The rollers roll between the inner and outer races. In the ball bearing, there is spot contact between the balls and races. In the roller bearing, there is line contact between the rollers and races.

Antifriction bearings are usually lubricated by grease. Grease is essentially oil mixed with a solidifying agent (called "soap"). The solidifying agent does not contribute directly to the lubricating of the balls or rollers. But it does hold the oil in the bearing so that the bearing receives proper lubrication.

CHECK YOUR PROGRESS

Progress Quiz 2

Here is your chance to check up on yourself once again to find out how well the facts you have been reading have stuck with you. The past few pages have covered some principles that are directly related to the operation of certain chassis units. Understanding these principles will help you understand how the chassis units work. Reread the past few pages if any of the questions that follow stump you. Remember that most good students reread their lessons several times to make sure they have memorized the important facts.

Completing the Sentences

The sentences below are incomplete. After each sentence there are several words or phrases, only one of which will correctly complete the sentence. Write down each sentence in your notebook, selecting the proper word or phrase to complete it correctly.

1. Air is compressible but liquid is not because, in the liquid, the molecules are about as close together as   *in the air*   *they can be* *in a vacuum*
2. Since it is incompressible, liquid can be used to transmit *pressure and motion*   *pressure and friction*   *static and kinetic friction*
3. When a pressure is applied to a liquid, it will be found that the pressure   *increases with distance*   *is reduced with distance* *is the same at all points*
4. The resistance to motion between two objects in contact with each other is called   *friction*   *braking*   *coefficient* *static friction*

[22]

5. Friction between two surfaces varies with the   *thickness and pressure*   *pressure, weight, and pull*   *pressure, roughness, and material*
6. The pull required to move an object, divided by the weight of the object, is called   *static friction*   *kinetic friction*   *coefficient of friction*
7. Two kinds of friction are   *at rest and static*   *moving and kinetic*   *static and kinetic*
8. Three classes of friction are   *dry, greasy, and viscous*   *greasy, thin, and thick*   *dry, wet, and viscous*
9. Comparing friction and antifriction bearings, the one with the lower friction is the   *friction bearing*   *antifriction bearing*
10. Two types of antifriction bearings are   *guide and thrust*   *ball and sleeve*   *ball and roller*

CHAPTER CHECKUP

NOTE: Since the following is a chapter review test, you should review the chapter before taking it.

You have completed a chapter in the book, and have taken an important step forward into a better future for you. The chapter you have just finished may seem somewhat abstract and less interesting than the following chapters that deal with specific chassis units. But the general principles we have been discussing are important for you to know. When you know them, you will find you can answer many puzzling questions about how and why the chassis units perform as they do. The following test will help you to review, and remember, the important facts you have just read in the chapter. Write down your answers in your notebook. The act of writing down the answers is another aid to your memory.

Completing the Sentences

The sentences below are incomplete. After each sentence there are several words or phrases, only one of which will correctly complete the sentence. Write down each sentence in your notebook, selecting the proper word or phrase to complete it correctly.

1. Atmospheric pressure results from   *absence of vacuum*   *compression of gas*   *gravity*
2. As a solid, a liquid, or a gas, is heated, its molecules   *move faster*   *stop moving*   *move slower*
3. Since the pressure in a closed container of gas results from the bombardment of the container walls by the gas molecules, crowding

more molecules in a container (by compressing the gas) will increase the   *pressure*   *vacuum*   *gravity*   *volume*

4. In view of the statement in the previous question, increasing the speed of the molecules—by heating the gas—will increase the *pressure*   *vacuum*   *gravity*

5. Due to the fact that, in a liquid, there is no extra space between the molecules that can be squeezed out, liquid is   *compressible*   *incompressible*   *incompatible*   *solid*

6. The pressure applied to a liquid by a piston, in psi, is the force on the piston divided by the   *distance it moves*   *piston area in square inches*   *piston diameter*

7. Comparing the two kinds of friction (static and kinetic), other things being equal, static friction is always   *less*   *equal*   *greater*

8. When you apply the brakes on your car so hard that you lock the wheels so they do not turn (and the tires thus skid), the friction between the tires and road is   *static friction*   *kinetic friction*

9. Comparing the three classes of friction, other things being equal, the class that offers the lowest friction is   *dry friction*   *greasy friction*   *viscous friction*

10. In comparing the actions of friction and antifriction bearings, you will note that the main difference is between   *sliding and slipping contact*   *spot and line contact*   *sliding and rolling contact*

Problems

Work out the following problems in your notebook.

1. If the air pressure were 20 psi, how much pressure would there be per square foot?   *2880 psf*

2. A piston with an area of 5 square inches is forced into a cylinder filled with liquid with a force of 100 pounds. What is the psi? *20#*

3. A piston with an area of ½ square inch is forced into a cylinder filled with liquid with a force of 100 pounds. What is the psi? *200 psi*

4. A pressure of 200 psi is applied to an output piston which has an area of 3 square inches. What is the force on the output piston? *600#*

5. A pressure of 200 psi is applied to an output piston which has an area of ½ square inch. What is the force on the output piston? *100 psi*

6. An input piston of ½ square inch area is forced into a liquid-filled cylinder with a force of 400 pounds. An output piston in a connected cylinder has an area of 3 square inches. What is the force on the output piston?   *600#*

[24]

7. The coefficient of friction between a certain type of brass and cast iron is 0.25. How much force would be required to pull a block of brass weighing 100 pounds over a cast-iron slab?
8. It requires a force of 75 pounds to move a block of wood weighing 150 pounds across a metal slab. What is the coefficient of friction?

Definitions

In the following, you are asked to define certain terms. Write down the definitions in your notebook, and then check your answers with the textbook.

1. Explain what atmospheric pressure is in terms of gravity. In terms of molecular motion.
2. Explain how the barometer works.
3. Why does increasing the temperature of the gas in a closed container increase the pressure?
4. In what way does a liquid differ from a gas, so far as compressibility is concerned?
5. Friction varies with what three conditions?
6. Give an explanation of the cause of friction.
7. List and explain the three classes of friction.

SUGGESTIONS FOR FURTHER STUDY

If you are interested in the basic principles discussed in the chapter, you may wish to study them further. Almost any modern high-school physics textbook will give you much additional information on the principles covered in the chapter. Your local library probably has several physics textbooks you will find of interest. If you have a chance, you could talk over various points that may not be clear to you with your local high-school science or physics teacher. Teachers are always willing to help anyone who is really interested in gaining more knowledge.

2: Automotive chassis fundamentals

§27. Purpose of this chapter This chapter provides an introduction to the various components, or subassemblies, that make up the automobile. In effect, it establishes the relationship between these

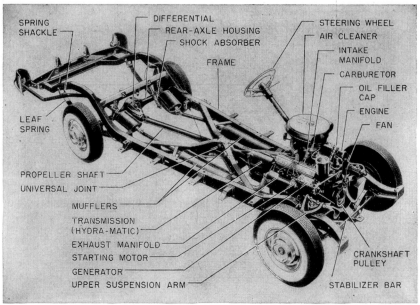

FIG. 2-1. A typical automotive chassis. (*Cadillac Motor Car Division of General Motors Corporation*)

various parts, and shows how they work together in the complete car. Later chapters describe the chassis components, explain how they operate, and tell how to service and repair them.

§28. Components of the automobile Before we begin our studies of the chassis units, we might take a quick look at the complete automobile. It is made up of five basic parts, or components:

[26]

1. The power plant or engine which is the source of power that makes the car wheels rotate and the car move. (This includes the electric, fuel, cooling, and lubricating systems.)
2. The frame which supports the engine, wheels, and body.
3. The power train which carries the power from the engine to the car wheels and which consists of the clutch, transmission, propeller shaft, differential, and axles.
4. The car body.
5. The car body accessories which include the heater, lights, radio, windshield wiper, convertible-top raiser, and so on.

Figures 2-1 and 2-2 illustrate two automobile chassis. The chassis is made up of the engine, frame, power train, wheels, steering, and braking systems. Other books in the McGraw-Hill Automotive

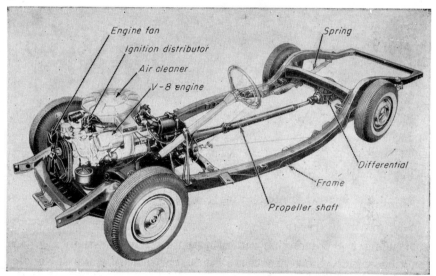

Fig. 2-2. Chassis of a passenger car. (*Mercury Division of Ford Motor Company*)

Mechanics Series (*Automotive Engines* and *Automotive Transmissions and Power Trains*) cover the engine and power-train components. The other chassis parts are covered in the pages that follow.

§**29. Frame**   The frame (Fig. 2-3) provides support for the engine, body, wheels, and power-train members. It is usually made of box, tubular, and channel members carefully shaped and then welded or riveted together. Cross members reinforce the frame and also

[27]

provide support for the engine and wheels. The frame is extremely rigid and strong so that it can withstand the shock blows, twists, vibrations, and other strains to which it is put on the road.

The engine is attached to the frame in three or four places. Noise and some vibration are inherent in engine operation. To prevent this noise and vibration from passing to the engine frame, and from there to the occupants of the car, the engine is insulated from the frame by some form of rubber pad or washer at each point of sup-

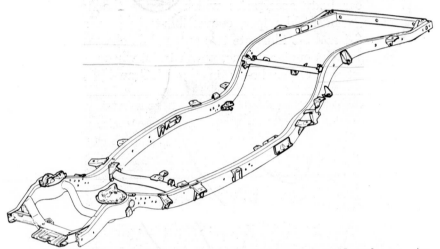

Fɪɢ. 2-3. Typical automobile frame. The frame curves upward at the rear (to right) to provide room for the rear springs. The frame narrows at the front to permit the front wheels to turn for steering. (*Ford Division of Ford Motor Company*)

port. One type of engine mounting support is shown in Fig. 2-4. In this engine, there are two biscuit-shaped rubber mountings at the front, and a single, long, narrow, rubber mounting pad at the back. Engine mounting lugs are supported in the rubber, and the mounting bolts pass through these rubber mountings so that there is no metal-to-metal contact. As a result, the rubber absorbs vibration and engine noise so that they are not carried to the engine frame.

§**30. Springs** The car wheels are suspended on springs that support the weight of the vehicle (Figs. 2-5 and 2-6). The springs absorb road shock as the wheels encounter holes or bumps and prevent, to

[28]

a large extent, any consequent jarring action or up-and-down motion from being carried through the frame and body. Springs are coil type, leaf type, torsion bar or rod (Fig. 2-10), or air suspension. Figure 2-6 shows the coil springs used in a front-suspension system. The coil spring is a heavy steel coil. The weight of the frame and

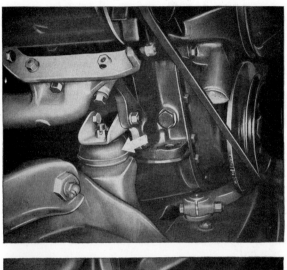

FIG. 2-4. Engine supports, indicated by arrows. At top, one of the two biscuit-shaped mountings at the front of the engine. At bottom, long, narrow mounting pad at rear of engine. (*Studebaker-Packard Corporation*)

body puts an initial compression on the spring. The spring will further compress when the wheel passes over an obstruction in the road (Fig. 2-7). It will expand if the wheel encounters a hole in the road (Fig. 2-8).

The leaf spring has been made in a number of forms, but the one that has been most commonly used is the semielliptical type

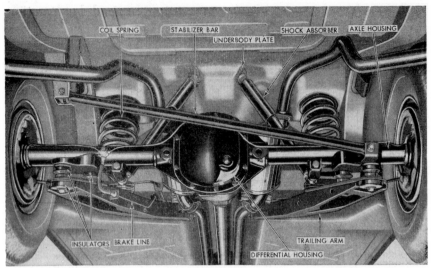

Fɪɢ. 2-5. Rear suspension system using coil springs. (*Lincoln Division of Ford Motor Company*)

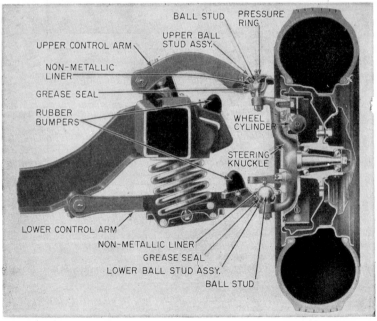

Fɪɢ. 2-6. Passenger car front suspension using coil springs. Frame, wheel, and other parts partly cut away to show suspension parts. (*Pontiac Motor Division of General Motors Corporation*)

[30]

FIG. 2-7. Coil spring compresses as wheel encounters a bump in the road. Note how upward movement of the wheel raises spring support or lower control arm, thus causing spring to compress. (*Ford Motor Company*)

FIG. 2-8. Coil spring expands as wheel encounters a hole in the road. Note how downward movement of wheel lowers the lower control arm and thus permits spring to expand. (*Ford Motor Company*)

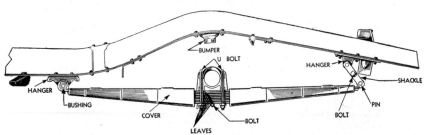

FIG. 2-9. Manner of attaching semielliptical spring to car frame and axle housing. This is a rear spring. (*Chevrolet Motor Division of General Motors Corporation*)

(Fig. 2-9). The leaf spring is made up of a series of flat plates, or leaves, of graduated length, one on top of another. The spring assembly acts as a flexible beam and is usually fastened at the two ends to the car frame and at the center to the wheel axle. Some cars have used only one leaf spring at the rear and one at the front, each spring supporting two wheels. With this design, the center of the

[31]

spring is attached to the frame and each end of the spring supports a wheel. The action is similar on all leaf springs. When the wheel encounters a bump, the spring bends upward to absorb the blow. When the wheel drops into a hole, the spring bends downward. Thus, the leaf spring does the same job as the coil spring in the vehicle.

Springs are usually insulated mechanically from the frame by means of rubber bushings and pads. This prevents road vibration from being transmitted to the frame and body.

§31. Shock absorbers Springs alone cannot provide a satisfactorily smooth ride. Therefore, an additional device, called a shock absorber, is used with each spring. To understand why springs alone would not give smooth riding qualities, let us consider the action of a coil spring. The same actions would take place with a leaf type of spring. The spring is under an initial load provided by the car weight, and this gives the spring an original amount of compression. When the wheel passes over a bump, the spring becomes further compressed. After the bump is passed, the spring attempts to return to its original position. However, it overrides its original position and expands too much. This behavior causes the car frame to be thrown upward. Having expanded too much, the spring attempts to compress so that it will return to its original position, but in compressing it again overrides. In doing this the wheel may be raised clear of the road, and the car frame consequently drops. The result is an oscillating motion of the spring that causes the car to rebound or bounce up and down several times after a bump has been encountered. If, in the meantime, another bump is encountered, a second series of reboundings will be started. On a bumpy road, and particularly in rounding a curve, the oscillations might become so serious as to cause the driver to lose control of the car.

Shock absorbers (Fig. 2-6) prevent these spring oscillations. Figure 2-11 shows one type of shock absorber in sectional view. This is the direct-acting, or telescope, shock absorber. One end of the shock absorber is attached to the frame, the other to the lower control arm (at front as shown in Fig. 2-6) or to the axle housing or spring (at rear). Thus as a wheel moves up or down in relation to the frame, the shock absorber will shorten or lengthen (see Fig. 2-11). When the shock absorber shortens, the piston rod forces the piston down

[32]

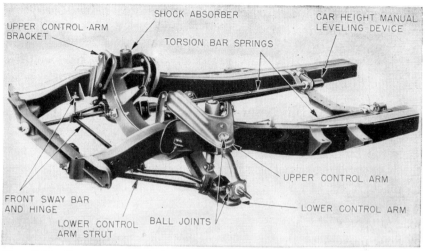

Fig. 2-10. Passenger car front suspension using torsion rods. The rods are locked at the rear to the frame and are attached at the front to the inner or pivot ends of the lower control arms. They twist varying amounts as varying loads are applied to permit the front wheels to move up and down. This action is similar to that of other springs. (*Chrysler Division of Chrysler Corporation*)

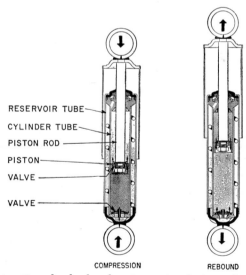

COMPRESSION   REBOUND

Fig. 2-11. Direct-acting shock absorber in sectional view, showing action during compression and rebound. Fluid movement is shown by arrows. Fluid under high pressure is shown darker than fluid not under pressure. (*Plymouth Division of Chrysler Corporation*)

[33]

into the cylinder tube, thereby putting the fluid below the piston under high compression. The fluid is forced through small orifices or openings in the piston and into the upper part of the cylinder tube. On rebound, when the wheel moves downward after passing a bump or dropping into a hole in the road, the shock absorber is extended (Fig. 2-11). As this happens, the piston moves into the upper part of the cylinder tube, thereby forcing fluid from the upper into the lower part of the tube.

As the fluid is forced in one direction or the other, it must pass through small orifices. This slows the motion of the piston and tends to place restraint on the spring action. That is, the *shock* of the wheel meeting a bump or hole is *absorbed*. The orifices have spring-loaded valves which open varying amounts to allow varying speeds of fluid movement through the orifices. This permits rapid spring motion while still imposing a restraining action. At the same time, it prevents excessive pressure rise in the fluid that might otherwise occur when large bumps in the road are encountered by the wheels. Also, the restraining action prevents excessive oscillations of the wheel after it passes a bump or hole.

Various arrangements of linkage are used. Although they are considerably different in general arrangement, all operate basically in the same manner. These linkage arrangements will be explained in more detail in the following paragraphs and in Chapters 5 and 7.

§32. Steering system   To guide the car, it is necessary to have some means of turning the front wheels so the car can be pointed in the direction the driver wants to go. The steering wheel in front of the driver is linked by gears and levers to the front wheels for this purpose. A simplified drawing of a steering system is shown in Fig. 2-12. The front wheels are supported on pivots so they can be swung to the left or right. They are attached by steering knuckle arms to tie rods. The tie rods are, in turn, attached to a pitman arm. As the steering wheel is turned in one direction or the other, gearing in the steering-gear assembly causes the end of the pitman arm to swing to the left or right. This movement is carried by the tie rods to the steering-knuckle arms, and wheels, causing them to swing to the left or right.

Figure 2-13 shows, in cutaway view, a steering-gear assembly. The steering shaft has a special sort of worm gear on its lower end.

[34]

Meshing with the teeth of this worm gear is a special gear called a *sector*. The sector is attached to one end of a shaft. The other end of the shaft carries the pitman arm. When the steering wheel is turned, the worm on the steering shaft rotates. This causes the sector to move toward one end or the other of the worm. The sector movement causes the sector shaft to rotate, and this rotary motion

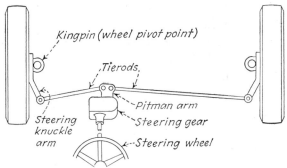

FIG. 2-12. Simplified drawing of a steering system as seen from above.

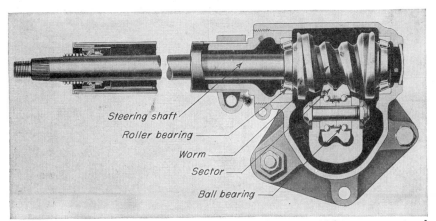

FIG. 2-13. One type of steering gear using a roller sector (shown in sectional view) with an hourglass worm gear. (*Chevrolet Motor Division of General Motors Corporation*)

is carried to the pitman arm, causing it to swing to the left or right, as already described. Figure 2-14 shows, in top and horizontal views, a front-suspension and steering system.

Practically all steering systems use a worm gear on the lower end of the steering shaft. But there are several types of device on the pitman-arm shaft. Some steering gears use studs that ride between the worm-gear teeth; others use a half nut, a plain gear, ball bearings, and so on. In addition, there are several devices now using hydraulic pressure to assist in steering. These are called power-steering devices and they take most of the effort out of steering; hydraulic pressure supplies most of the effort. Steering and power-steering mechanisms are discussed in detail in the chapters on steering systems.

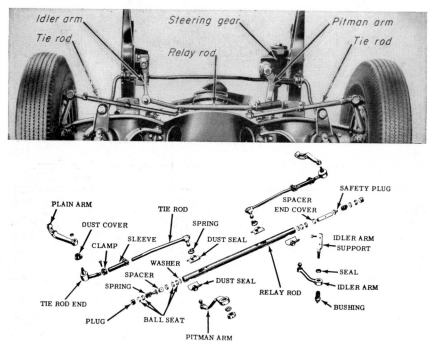

FIG. 2-14. Phantom view (top) and a disassembled view (bottom) of a typical steering mechanism and linkage. (*Chevrolet Motor Division and Oldsmobile Division of General Motors Corporation*)

§33. Brakes Brakes are necessary to slow or stop the car. Most braking systems in use today are hydraulic (§§12 to 15). A typical braking system is shown in Fig. 2-15. The brake pedal, when pushed down, forces a piston to move in a cylinder. This imposes hydraulic pressure on a fluid in the cylinder. The fluid is forced, under pressure, through tubes and into cylinders at the wheels. The wheel cylinders contain pistons that are forced to move as the fluid enters the cylinders under pressure. The piston movement then causes brake shoes to move so that the brakes are applied.

[36]

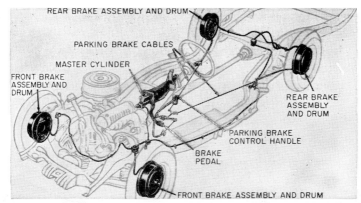

Fig. 2-15. Phantom view of a typical hydraulic braking system. (*Ford Division of Ford Motor Company*)

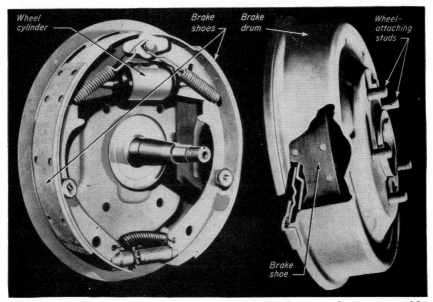

Fig. 2-16. Brake-shoe assembly (at left) and brake drum in place on assembly (at right). The drum is partly cut away to show a shoe. The studs are for attaching the wheel to the drum. (*Oldsmobile Division of General Motors Corporation*)

Figure 2-16 shows a brake-shoe assembly (on the left) and the brake drum placed on the outside of the shoes (on the right). The shoes are curved to conform with the inner diameter of the brake drum. They are covered with a tough asbestos lining that can withstand wear and high temperatures. The shoes are attached to

[37]

a backing plate and thus have only limited in-out movement. The brake drum is attached to the wheel and rotates with the wheel. When the shoes are forced into contact with the brake drum, the friction between them causes a dragging, or braking, effect on the drum so that the drum, and wheel, are slowed or stopped. Figure 2-17 shows a brake wheel mechanism with the wheel cylinder in sectional view. Note that hydraulic pressure, applied in the cylinder between the two pistons, forces the pistons outward. This, in turn,

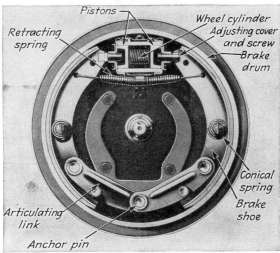

FIG. 2-17. One type of hydraulic brake mechanism at wheel. Wheel cylinder is in sectional view to show the pistons. (*Chevrolet Motor Division of General Motors Corporation*)

forces the two brake shoes to move outward and into contact with the brake drum.

Many vehicles now use power brakes. In these, vacuum and air pressure supplies most of the brake-applying effort. That is, as the driver pushes down on the brake pedal, vacuum is applied on one side of a piston and air pressure is applied on the other. This causes the piston to move in a cylinder. The piston then takes over most of the effort required to build up the hydraulic pressure in the lines to the wheel cylinders. Details of this and other braking mechanisms are discussed in a later chapter (Chap. 14).

§34. Tires Tires are of the air-filled, or pneumatic, type. Their function is to transmit the driving power of the wheels to the road

[38]

through frictional contact. They also absorb a considerable part of the road shock resulting from small bumps and holes and prevent these shocks from being carried to the frame and the body of the car. As the tires roll over small bumps, they flex; and the outer surface, or tread, moves inward against the cushion of air inside the tires.

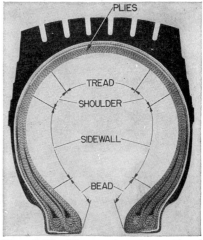

Many tires use inner tubes, many do not. In recent years, practically all new cars have been equipped with tubeless tires. With either type, the tire has a coating of rubber—of varying degrees of thickness—that is baked or vulcanized onto an inner structure of fabric or cord (Fig. 2-18). The fabric or cord provides a flexible but tough tire structure. The outside coating of

FIG. 2-18. Tire casing in sectional view to show construction. (*B. F. Goodrich Company*)

rubber is designed to withstand the wear caused by road friction; it also provides a good, high-friction contact with the road. The

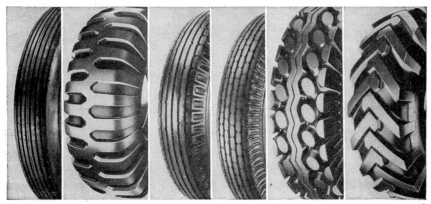

FIG. 2-19. Several types of tire-tread design. (*B. F. Goodrich Company and United States Rubber Company*)

part of the tire that makes contact with the road is called the *tread.* Tires are supplied with a variety of tread designs (Fig. 2-19) that aid in improving friction and thus reducing the chances of slippage.

Some special tread patterns are made for off-the-road operation, such as in farm-tractor or construction work. In these, the tread design has heavy ribs or buttons that bite deep into the mud or soft earth and provide adequate traction.

In the tubeless tire, the tire beads seal tightly against the wheel-rim flanges to hold the air pressure. The wheel rim is sealed and an air valve is mounted in it. The inner tube used in other tires is made of rubber—either natural or synthetic—and it retains the air

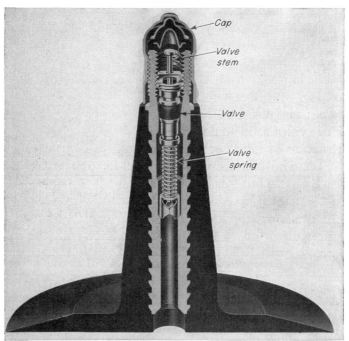

FIG. 2-20. Cross-sectional view of a typical tire valve. (*A. Schrader's Son Division of Scovill Manufacturing Company, Inc.*)

pressure. When air is forced into the tube, it expands outward against the inner face of the tire casing. Thus, in either the tubeless or the tube tire, it is air pressure that supports the vehicle load. The valve through which the air is introduced (Fig. 2-20) is spring-loaded. When air is being put into the tire (or tube), the valve is held off its seat. But at other times, the spring holds the valve tightly against its seat so the air is sealed into the tire (or tube).

§35. Body   The body (Fig. 2-21) is designed to contain and protect not only the engine and other car components but also the passengers within the car. Much thinking and engineering work have gone into making the body sturdy and thus safe. Also, since the appearance of the body is one of the important factors in sales appeal, an attempt has been made to shape the contours so that the external structure will have a pleasing appearance and at the same time will provide ample room for the driver and passengers. It will be noted that most modern cars have flowing lines, with few noticeable sharp angles. Curves are more pleasing to the human eye than sharp angles.

One factor that has received much attention in recent years is *streamlining*. To streamline a car means to shape it in such a manner

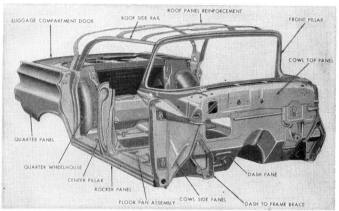

Fig. 2-21. Construction of a typical passenger car body. (*Mercury Division of Ford Motor Company*)

that it offers less resistance to the passage of the body through air. As car speed increases, the resistance of the air also increases. The air resistance increases approximately as the cube of the car speed. Thus, as car speed increases, a larger and larger part of the total driving power is being used to overcome the effects of air resistance. Streamlining helps to reduce this air resistance so that greater power economy is achieved at higher speeds.

The body is made up of a basic framework of rigid members onto which are fastened metal panels. It is usually supported on the frame by rubber-insulated bolts that prevent vibration and noise from traveling to the car body and hence to the passengers.

The details of door suspension, latches, locks, window-operating mechanisms, no-draft ventilation, air-conditioning, and other devices

[41]

that add to the comfort of the passengers are covered in later chapters.

CHAPTER CHECKUP

NOTE: Since the following is a chapter review test, you should review the chapter before taking it.

The following questions will help you determine how well you remember what you have been reading. If you have any trouble answering the questions, you should reread the past few pages. Don't be discouraged if questions stump you. That simply means you should review the chapter. Most good students read their "lessons" several times. As you do this, and take the tests in the book, you will gradually find your mind is becoming keener, more alert. You will be able to pick out the important facts you should remember. This is because you are improving your studying habits, and learning what is most important in the material you are reading. Answering the questions helps you by pointing out the important facts to remember.

Write the answers in your notebook. This is an aid to your memory. Also, you build up a valuable compilation of important information in your notebook that you can refer to later.

Correcting the Parts Lists

The purpose of this exercise is to give you practice in spotting unrelated items in a list. For example, in the list *Parts of the automobile include engine, frame, filling station, brakes, wheels,* you can see that *filling station* does not belong because it is the only thing named that is not part of an automobile. In each of the lists, one item is named that does not belong. Write down each list in your notebook, *but do not write down* the item that does not belong.

1. Parts of the chassis include frame, springs, shock absorbers, windshield, steering system, brakes, engine.
2. Parts of the shock absorber include pistons, valves, coupler, valve springs.
3. Parts of the steering system include worm gear, pitman arm, fan belt, tie rods, steering wheel.
4. Parts of the brake system include brake shoes, master brake cylinder, engine cylinders, wheel cylinders.
5. Parts of the tire include the inner tube, valve, piston, casing.

Picking Out the Right Answer

Several answers are given for each question or statement listed below. Read each statement carefully, then decide which of the several answers

[42]

or phrases is the correct one. Write down the statement or question in your notebook, including the correct answer.

1. At how many places is the engine ordinarily attached to the frame?
   one or two   *two or three*   *three or four*   *four or five*
2. The frame provides support for the engine, body, power-train members and   *road*   *tires*   *wheels*
3. What is the purpose of the shock absorbers?   *attach spring to frame*   *dampen spring oscillations*   *tighten the mounting*   *attach frame to wheel*
4. As the steering wheel is turned, a worm gear on the steering shaft causes the end of the   *kingpin*   *steering gear*   *pitman arm*   to swing toward one side or the other of the car.
5. Movement of the brake pedal forces brake fluid from the master brake cylinder, through brake lines, and into the   *brake shoes*   *brake cables*   *wheel cylinders*   *pedal rod*

Listing Parts

In the following, you are asked to list parts that go into various automotive components discussed in the chapter. Write down these lists in your notebook.

1. List the various parts attached to the frame.
2. List the major parts that make up a typical front-suspension system.
3. List the major parts that make up a shock absorber.
4. List the parts that make up a steering system.
5. List the parts that make up a braking system.

Purpose, Construction, and Operation of Components

In the following, you are asked to write down the purpose, construction, or operation of certain components of the automobile discussed in the chapter. If you have any difficulty in writing down your explanations, turn back to the chapter and reread the pages that will give you the answer. Then write your explanation. Don't copy, try to tell it in your own words. This is a good way to fix the explanation firmly in your mind. Write in your notebook.

1. Describe the construction of an automotive frame.
2. Describe the operation of the coil spring used in a front-suspension system.
3. Describe the operation of a shock absorber.
4. Describe the purpose and operation of a car-steering system.
5. Describe the operation of a hydraulic braking system.

[43]

SUGGESTIONS FOR FURTHER STUDY

If you would like to study the engine and power train, there are several things you can do. You can read the other books in the McGraw-Hill Automotive Mechanics Series (*Automotive Engines, Automotive Transmissions and Power Trains, Automotive Electrical Equipment,* and *Automotive Fuel, Lubricating, and Cooling Systems*). Also, you can inspect your own and your friends' cars as well as cars in the school automotive shop or in any friendly service garage where work on these automotive components is done. Many school automotive shops have cutaway models of the various components that help you to understand their construction and operation. In addition, the manuals issued by automotive manufacturers usually have many illustrations and explanations of how these parts work.

While examining various cars, you should note carefully the manner in which the different parts are attached to the car frame, how the springs and shock absorbers are attached, and so on. Write down in your notebook any important facts you come across.

3: Automotive springs and suspension

THIS CHAPTER describes the various springs and suspension systems used in automotive vehicles, with the exception of shock absorbers. Chapter 4 discusses shock-absorber construction and operation in detail, while Chap. 7 describes the servicing of springs and suspension systems.

§36. Function of springs   The car frame supports the weight of the engine, power-train components, body, and passengers. The frame,

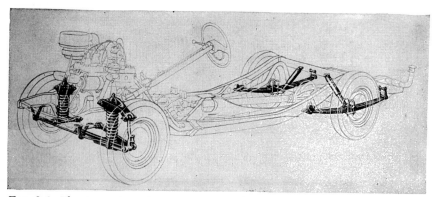

FIG. 3-1. Phantom view of an automotive chassis, showing location of the coil springs (at left, or front of car) and of the leaf springs (at right, or rear of car).

in turn, is supported by the springs. The springs are placed between the frame and the wheel axles. Figure 3-1 shows an automotive chassis using coil springs at the front and leaf springs at the rear. Regardless of the type of spring, all of them work in a similaı manner. The weight of the frame, body, and so on, applies an initial compression to the springs. The springs will further compress, or will expand, as the car wheels encounter irregularities in the road. Thus, the wheels can move up and down somewhat independently of the frame. This allows the springs to absorb a good part of the up-and-down motion of the car wheels. This motion therefore is not transmitted to the car frame and from it to the passengers. Figures 2-7 and 2-8 show how coil springs compress and expand as the wheels encounter bumps or holes in the road.

§37. Types of springs   The automobile uses four basic types of springs, coil, leaf, torsion bar, and air (in air suspension). Most

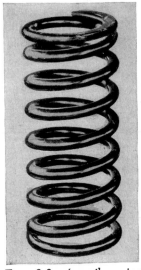

FIG. 3-2. A coil spring used in a front-suspension system.

cars use coil springs at the two front wheels. Some cars use coil springs at the rear wheels (Fig. 2-5 shows a coil spring at a rear wheel). Other cars use leaf springs at the rear wheels. A few cars and many heavy-duty vehicles also use leaf springs at the front wheels. Both the torsion-bar suspension system (§47) and the air-suspension system (§48) have recently come into use.

1. Coil springs. The coil spring is made of a length of special spring steel (usually round in cross section) which is wound in the shape of a coil (Fig. 3-2). The spring is formed at high temperature—while the steel is white-hot—and it is then cooled and properly heat-treated so as to give it the proper characteristics of elasticity and "springiness." Spring characteristics are discussed in a later section.

2. Leaf springs. The leaf spring is made up of a series of flat steel plates of graduated length, placed one on top of another as shown in Fig. 3-3. The plates, or leaves, are held together at the center by a center bolt which passes through holes in the leaves. Clips placed at intervals along the spring keep the leaves in alignment. Instead of clips, as shown in Fig. 3-3, some leaf springs are sheathed in a metal cover (Fig. 2-9). The longest, or master, leaf is rolled at both ends to form spring eyes through which bolts are placed to attach the spring ends. On some springs, the ends of the

[46]

second leaf are also rolled part way around the two spring eyes to reinforce the master leaf.

In operation, the leaf spring acts much like a flexible beam. An ordinary solid beam strong enough to support the car weight would not be very flexible. This is because, as the beam bends (Fig. 3-4), the top edge tries to become longer while the lower edge tries to

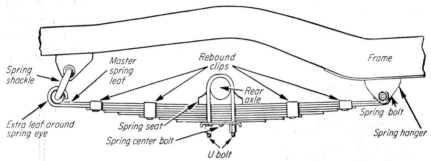

Fig. 3-3. A typical leaf spring, showing attachments to frame and also method of attachment to axle.

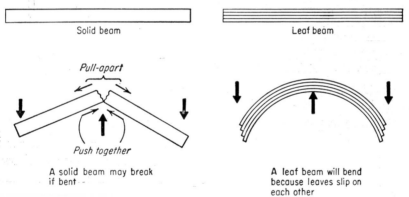

Fig. 3-4. Comparing the effects of bending a solid beam and a leaf beam, or spring.

become shorter. There is a pull-apart effect at the upper, or elongating, edge, and a push-together, or shortening effect, along the lower edge. The result is that the upper edge pulls apart if the beam is overloaded, and the beam breaks. However, there would be a different action if the beam were made of a series of thin leaves, one on top of another (right in Fig. 3-4). The leaves would slip over each other to take care of the pull-apart and push-together tendencies of the two edges of the beam. You can see how much the

[47]

leaves will slip over each other if the beam is sharply bent (lower right in Fig. 3-4). All leaves are of the same length, and the amount that the inner leaves project beyond the outer leaves (when curved) indicates the amount of slippage.

In the actual leaf spring, the leaves are of graduated length. To permit them to slip, various means of applying lubricant between the leaves are used. In addition, some leaf springs have special inserts of various materials placed between the leaves, to permit easier slipping. The clips shown on the spring in Fig. 3-3 are called

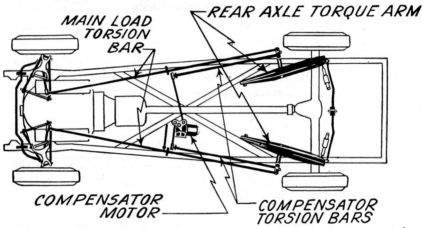

FIG. 3-4a. Simplified sketch of torsion-rod or -bar suspension system as used on Packard.

rebound clips because they prevent excessive leaf separation during rebound after the wheel has passed over an obstruction in the road. In addition, springs may be covered with a metal sheath as shown in Fig. 2-9 to retain lubricant and prevent the entrance of moisture and dirt.

3. *Torsion bar.* In the torsion-bar suspension, the springing action is produced by torsion, or a twisting effort, on long bars. Figure 3-4a is a simplified sketch of a torsion-bar suspension system. There are two main torsion bars, one on each side of the frame. Each torsion bar supports two wheels. At the front, the torsion bar has a lever pointing outward. This lever is connected to the front-suspension lower support. At the rear, the torsion bar has a lever pointing inward. This lever is attached to the center of the rear-axle torque arm. Note that the load of the car twists the torsion bar in one direction at the front and in the other direction at the rear.

[48]

The bar will twist more or less according to the load imposed on it, thus providing the springing action. For instance, when the front wheel rides up over a bump, the torsion bar twists more. Note that, in the system shown in Fig. 3-4a, this increased torsion on the bar at the front causes a similar increase at the back. The increase at the rear then tends to counteract the lifting effect of the bump at the front. That is, there is a leveling-off effect because of the tie-in between the front and rear wheels through the torsion bar.

The system shown also has a compensating system which uses an electric motor and a pair of compensator torsion bars. The purpose of these parts is to compensate for any change in loading. Thus, if the rear of the car is heavily loaded so that it tends to ride lower than the front end, a leveling switch causes the compensator motor to operate. The motor, through a series of gears, changes the torsion on the compensator bars. This action then brings the car back to level again.

Other torsion-bar suspension systems make use of separate torsion bars for each wheel (§47). On these, the wheel end has a lever attached in such a way as to support the wheel. The other end of the torsion bar is fastened rigidly to the car frame. The bar is then twisted more or less in accordance to the loading at the wheel.

§38. Leaf spring installation   The leaf spring most commonly used in automotive vehicles is a semielliptical spring. It has the shape

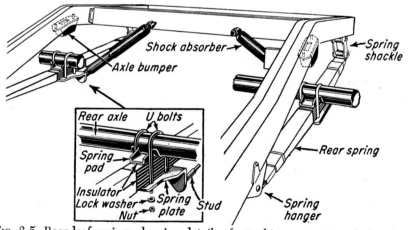

Fig. 3-5. Rear leaf springs showing details of attaching spring to axle housing

[49]

of half an ellipse, and that is the reason for its name. Figures 2-9, 3-3, and 3-5 show springs of this type. The method of attachment shown in these illustrations is a common one for leaf springs. The center of the spring is attached to the axle housing with two U bolts so that the spring is, in effect, hanging from the axle housing. A spring plate or straps are used at the bottom of the spring, while a spring pad is used between the axle and spring. There may also be an insulating strip of rubber or similar material to reduce noise transference from axle to spring.

1. Spring hanger. One end of the spring is attached to a hanger on the frame by means of a bolt and bushing in the spring eye

FIG. 3-6. Details of attaching spring to hanger of spring suspension shown in previous illustration.

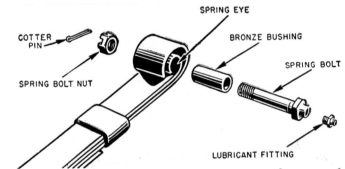

FIG. 3-7. Bushing and bolt for attaching spring eye to hanger on frame.

(Fig. 3-6). The spring, as it bends, causes the spring eye to turn back and forth with respect to the spring hanger. The attaching bolt and bushing must permit this rotation. Some forms (Fig. 3-7) have a hollow spring bolt with a lubricating fitting that permits lubrication of the bushing. Other designs do not require lubrication. Many designs have a bushing made up of an inner and an outer metal shell. Between these two shells is a molded rubber bushing. The weight is carried through the rubber bushing. The rubber also acts to dampen vibration and noise and thus prevents them from

[50]

entering the car frame. Figure 3-8 shows one type of rubber-bushed mounting.

2. *Spring shackle.* As the spring bends, the distance between the two spring eyes changes. If both ends of the spring were fastened rigidly to the frame, then the spring would not be able to bend. To permit bending, the spring is fastened at one end to the frame through a link called a *shackle*. The shackle is a swinging support attached at one end to the spring eye and at the other end

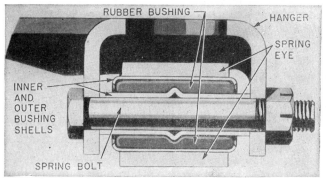

Fig. 3-8. Details of bushing in spring eye through which the spring eye is attached to the hanger on the car frame. (*Chevrolet Motor Division of General Motors Corporation*)

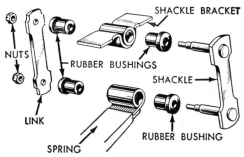

Fig. 3-9. Details of a rubber-bushed spring shackle.

to a supporting bracket on the car frame. Spring shackles can be seen in Figs. 2-9, 3-3, and 3-5. A spring shackle is shown in disassembled view in Fig. 3-9. The two links provide the swinging support that the spring requires, and the bolts attach the links to the shackle bracket on the frame and the spring eye. The rubber bushings insulate the spring from the frame to prevent transference of

[51]

noise and vibration between the two. A link-type shackle very similar to this unit is shown in sectional view in Fig. 3-10.

Another type of shackle is shown in Fig. 3-11. This shackle is made up of two internally threaded steel bushings, two threaded hollow steel pins, a draw bolt, shackle links, and cork or rubber washers. The steel bushings are installed in the spring eye and the frame bracket, and the threaded steel pins are screwed into them. The shackle links are held on the pins by the draw bolt. The cork or rubber washers protect the threaded pins from dirt and retain the lubricant in the shackle.

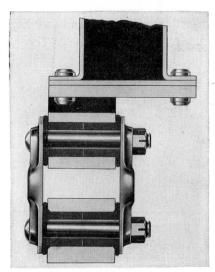

FIG. 3-10. Sectional view of a rubber-bushed, link-type spring shackle. (*Chevrolet Motor Division of General Motors Corporation*)

A U-type shackle is shown in partial sectional view in Fig. 3-12. The bushings are threaded on the inside and screw onto the threaded legs of the shackle. Lubricant fittings are provided for each bushing.

Shackles with lubrication fittings require periodic lubrication. However, the rubber-bushed shackles, such as are shown in Figs. 3-9 and 3-10, must not be lubricated. Oil or grease on the rubber bushings will cause them to soften and deteriorate.

§39. Sprung and unsprung weight In the automobile, the terms "sprung weight" and "unsprung weight" refer to the part of the car that is supported on springs and the part that is not. The frame and the parts attached to the frame are sprung—that is, their weight is supported on the car springs. However, the wheels, wheel axles, rear-axle housing, and differential are not supported on springs; they represent unsprung weight. Generally speaking, unsprung weight should be kept as low as possible, because the roughness of the ride increases as unsprung weight increases. For example, consider a single wheel. If it is light, it can move up and down

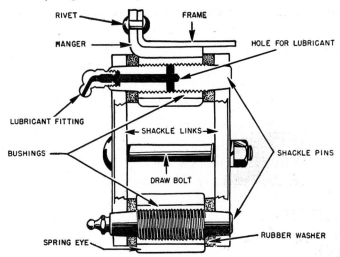

Fɪɢ. 3-11. Sectional view of link-type spring shackle showing method of lubricating bushings.

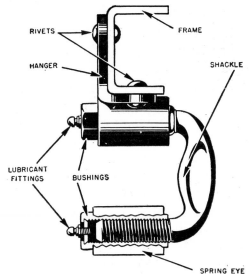

Fɪɢ. 3-12. U-type spring shackle.

as road irregularities are encountered without causing much reaction to the car frame. But if the weight of the wheel is increased, then its movement would become more noticeable to the car occupants. To take a ridiculous example, suppose the unsprung weight at the wheel is equal to the sprung weight above the wheel. In such

[53]

a case, the sprung weight would tend to move almost as much as the unsprung weight. The unsprung weight, which must move up and down as road irregularities are encountered, would tend to cause a like motion of the sprung weight. This is the reason for keeping the unsprung weight as low as possible so that it represents only a small portion of the total weight of the car.

§40. Characteristics of springs   The ideal spring for automotive suspension would be one that would absorb road shock rapidly and then return to its normal position slowly. Such an ideal is not possible, however. An extremely flexible, or soft, spring would allow too much movement, while a stiff, or hard, spring would give too rough a ride. However, satisfactory riding qualities are attained by using a fairly soft spring in combination with a shock absorber (Chap. 4).

Softness or hardness of a spring is referred to as its "rate." The rate of a spring is the weight required to deflect it 1 inch. The rate of automotive springs is almost constant throughout their operating range, or deflection, in the car. This is an example of Hooke's law, as applied to coil springs: the spring will compress in direct proportion to the weight applied. Thus, if 600 pounds will compress the spring 3 inches, 1,200 pounds will compress the spring 6 inches.

§41. Hotchkiss and torque-tube drives   Before we discuss rear-suspension systems further, we should note that the rear springs may have an additional job to do besides supporting the car load. This additional job may be to absorb *rear-end torque*. Whenever the rear wheel is being driven, through the power train, by the engine, it rotates as shown in Fig. 3-13 (for forward car motion). It is a fundamental law of nature that for every action there must be an equal and opposite reaction. Thus, when the wheel rotates in one direction, the wheel-axle housing tries to rotate in the opposite direction, as shown (Fig. 3-13). The twisting motion thus applied to the axle housing is called *rear-end torque*. Two different rear-end designs are used to combat this twisting motion of the axle housing, Hotchkiss drive and torque-tube drive (Fig. 3-14).

1. Hotchkiss drive. In the Hotchkiss drive, the twisting effect, or torque, is taken by the springs. Note that the spring (Fig. 3-13) is firmly attached to the axle housing. The torque applied by the housing to the spring tends to lift the front end of the spring (on

[54]

the left in Fig. 3-13 or on the right in Fig. 3-14). At the same time, it tends to lower the rear end of the spring. The spring does flex

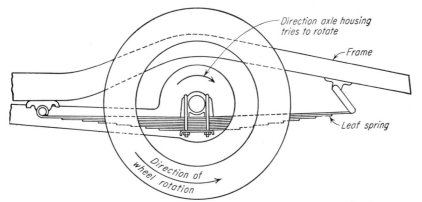

FIG. 3-13. Axle housing tries to rotate in direction opposite to wheel rotation.

a little to permit a slight amount of housing rotation. The spring thus absorbs the rear-end torque or twisting effort.

2. *Torque-tube drive.* Inside the torque-tube drive (Fig. 3-14), a rigid tube surrounds the propeller shaft. (The propeller shaft carries the power developed by the engine from the transmission to the rear-wheel axles). The rigid tube is attached to the transmission at the front and to the axle housing— actually differential housing—at the rear. The axle housing, in attempting to rotate, tries to bend the tube, but the tube resists this effort. The twisting effort of the housing, or rear-end torque, is thus absorbed by the torque tube.

NOTE: Another book in the Mc-Graw-Hill Automotive Mechanics Series (*Automotive Transmissions*

FIG. 3-14. Hotchkiss drive (top) compared with torque-tube drive (bottom).

and Power Trains) describes these drives as well as the operation of the propeller shaft, differential, and other power-train components, in detail.

[55]

§42. Rear suspension We have illustrated and discussed rear-suspension systems in some detail. Figures 2-9, 3-3, and 3-5 show various rear suspension systems using leaf springs. Methods of attaching the springs through hangers and shackles have also been

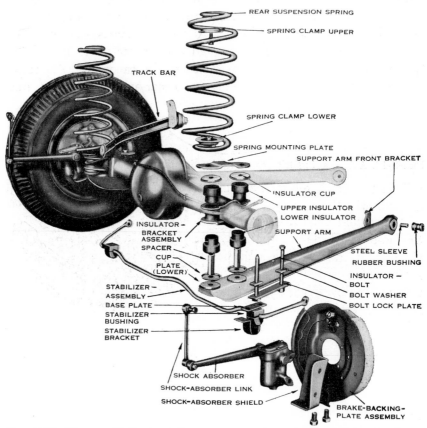

FIG. 3-15. Disassembled view of a rear-suspension system using coil springs. (*Oldsmobile Division of General Motors Corporation*)

shown and described (§38). No additional bracing is needed with leaf springs.

However, with coil springs, the rear-suspension system requires some method of holding the axle housing in place. Figure 2-5 shows a rear suspension using a coil spring, and Fig. 3-15 shows a disassembled view of a similar unit. The coil springs are assembled between spring mounting plates on the axle housing and spring seats in the car frame. The two rear-axle support arms are attached between the rear-axle housing and the car frame and permit upward or downward movement of the axle housing with respect to the car frame. They prevent relative forward or backward movement. The track bar (in upper left) is connected to the axle housing and to the car frame and prevents sideward movement of the housing assembly with respect to the car frame. The shock absorbers are attached at the rear wheels through shields bolted to the brake-backing-plate assembly and are linked to the car frame. The stabilizer shaft is connected between the two rear-axle support arms and helps to reduce rolling action of the car on turns.

Fɪɢ. 3-16. Manner of attaching leaf spring to frame and axle housing on heavy-duty truck. Note the upper spring which is an auxiliary, or helper, spring; it comes into use when heavy loads are applied. (*International Harvester Company*)

§**43. Heavy-duty suspension** Figure 3-16 shows the spring arrangement used at the rear of a heavy-duty truck. Note that the spring is above the axle housing (and not slung below it as in other suspension systems previously described). Note also that there is an auxiliary, or helper, spring above the main spring. This helper spring comes into action only when the truck is heavily loaded or when the wheel encounters a large road bump. Then, as the main spring goes through a large deflection, the ends of the helper spring encounter the two bumpers on the frame. The auxiliary spring then deflects and adds its tension to the tension of the main spring. Figure 14-47 illustrates a heavy-duty front-suspension system.

[57]

§44. Front suspension   The suspension of the front wheels is more complicated than the suspension for the rear wheels. Not only must the front wheels move up and down with respect to the car frame for spring action, but also, they must be able to swing at various angles to the car frame for steering. In the pages that follow, we discuss the various types of suspension systems used on modern cars. Chapter 5 covers steering systems.

In order to permit the front wheels to swing to one side or the other for steering, each wheel is supported on a spindle which is part of a steering knuckle. The steering knuckle is then supported,

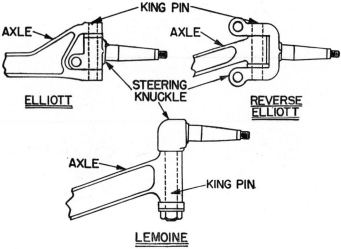

FIG. 3-17. Elliott, reverse Elliott, and Lemoine steering-knuckle arrangements.

through a kingpin, by the front-axle beam or by a steering-knuckle support. There are three types of steering knuckles and supports, the Elliott, reverse Elliott, and the Lemoine (Fig. 3-17). In the Elliott, there is a yoke on the end of the axle and the steering knuckle fits between the two legs of the yoke. In the reverse Elliott, the yoke is on the steering knuckle. The Lemoine arrangement makes use of an L-shaped spindle and steering knuckle. The reverse Elliott arrangement is the most commonly used on automotive vehicles.

Despite what we just said about kingpins in front-suspension systems in the previous paragraph, you would look in vain for king-pins in many late-model cars. This is because these cars use a ball-joint front suspension (§46) which has no kingpin. Nevertheless,

[58]

the front-wheel alignment of these kingpin-less cars is checked and adjusted just as though they actually had kingpins. In the alignment-checking instructions, reference is made to the "apparent" or theoretical kingpin inclination (see §§57 and 124).

§45. **Independent front suspension** Practically all passenger cars now use the independent type of front suspension in which each front wheel is independently supported by a coil or leaf spring. The coil-

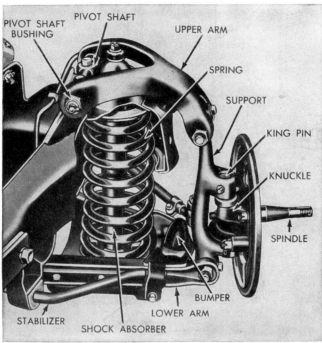

FIG. 3-18. Front suspension system at one wheel with frame cut away to show spring and shock absorber locations. Wheel is assembled on, and turns on, spindle. (*Ford Motor Company*)

spring arrangement is most common. Figure 3-1 shows, in phantom view, essential parts of an independent front-suspension system using coil springs. Figure 3-18 shows the details of a similar front suspension for one wheel. Figure 3-19 shows another front-suspension system in disassembled view. (See also Figs. 3-21 and 3-22 as you read the explanation that follows.) All of these suspension systems operate in a similar manner. The coil spring is retained between an upper spring seat in the car frame and a lower spring seat that is part of the lower suspension arm—also called the lower *control* arm. One end of the lower suspension arm is attached to the car frame through a pivot. The other end of the lower suspension arm is attached to the lower end of the steering-knuckle support, also through a pivot. The upper end of the steering-knuckle

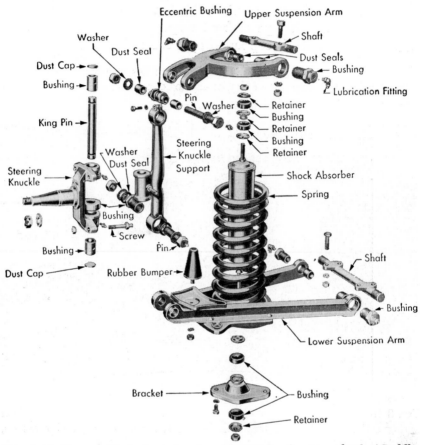

Fɪɢ. 3-19. Disassembled view of a front suspension for one wheel. (*Cadillac Motor Car Division of General Motors Corporation*)

support is attached to the upper suspension, or control, arm by a pivot. The inner end of the upper suspension arm is attached, through a pivot, to the frame. On some cars, the upper suspension arm is part of the shock absorber (see Chap. 4), as shown in Fig. 3-21. On many cars, the shock absorber is of the telescoping type, which expands or shortens in operation, and is placed inside the coil spring as shown in Figs. 3-18, 3-19, and 3-22.

[60]

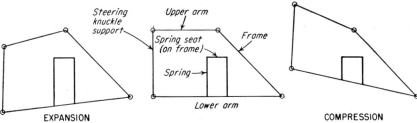

Fig. 3-20. Geometry of front-suspension system. As steering-knuckle support and wheel move up and down, upper and lower arms pivot on frame, causing the spring to expand or compress.

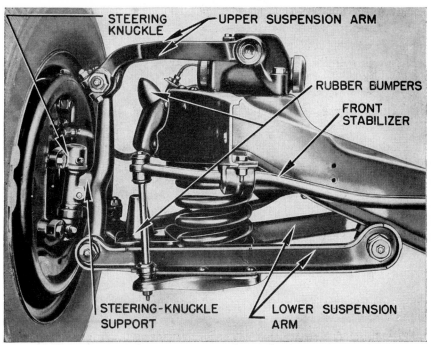

Fig. 3-21. Front view of a passenger-car front-wheel suspension showing the method of connecting the front stabilizer to the lower suspension arm. (*Cadillac Motor Car Division of General Motors Corporation*)

The steering-knuckle support carries the steering knuckle; the two are attached by the kingpin (see Figs. 3-18 and 3-19). The wheel is mounted on, and rotates on, the spindle which is part of the steering knuckle. This arrangement keeps the wheel in vertical alignment with the steering-knuckle support, but permits the wheel to pivot about the kingpin in steering the car (see Chap. 5).

[61]

Figure 3-20 is a simplified line drawing showing the action that takes place as the wheel and steering-knuckle support move up and down. The upper and lower suspension arms swing up or down on the frame pivots, thereby causing the coil spring to compress or expand.

Note that the steering-knuckle support is maintained in nearly vertical alignment as it moves up and down. This keeps the wheel in almost vertical alignment, which is desirable from the standpoint of steering control and tire wear. Such maintenance of alignment is achieved by the relationship between the frame and suspending members.

Rubber bumpers are placed on the frame and lower suspension arm so as to prevent metal-to-metal contact between the frame and arms as the limits of spring compression or expansion are reached.

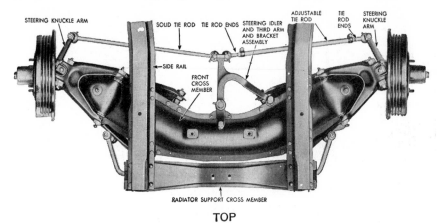

TOP

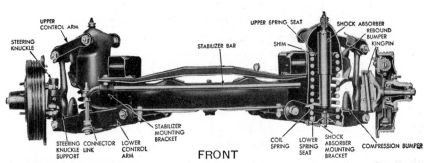

FRONT

Fig. 3-22. Top and front views of a front-suspension system. (*Chevrolet Motor Division of General Motors Corporation*)

[62]

A stabilizer shaft, or sway eliminator, is used on many cars to interconnect the two lower suspension arms. The shaft prevents too great a difference in spring action, thus providing better steering ability and control of body roll. Body roll is the leaning out of the car body caused by centrifugal force as the car rounds a turn; it tends to compress the outer spring and expand the inner spring. When this happens, the stabilizer shaft is twisted. The resistance of the shaft to the twisting effect combats the tendency toward differences in spring length. This, in turn, tends to prevent excessive body roll.

§46. Ball-joint front suspension Figure 3-23 shows a ball-joint type of front suspension. This type of suspension has come into widespread use in recent years. It does not use an intermediate steering-

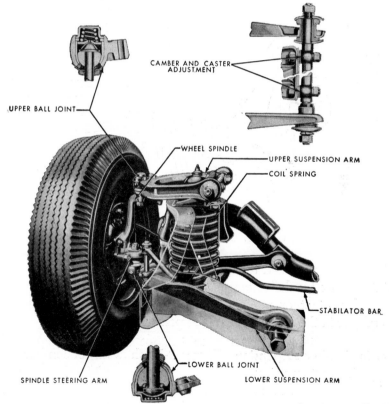

CAMBER AND CASTER ADJUSTMENT

UPPER BALL JOINT

WHEEL SPINDLE

UPPER SUSPENSION ARM

COIL SPRING

STABILATOR BAR

SPINDLE STEERING ARM

LOWER BALL JOINT

LOWER SUSPENSION ARM

Fig. 3-23. Ball joint type of front-suspension system. (*Lincoln-Mercury Division of Ford Motor Company*)

[63]

knuckle support and kingpin. Instead, the wheel spindle is elongated and is attached directly to the upper and lower suspension arms by means of ball joints. Adjustments for wheel camber and caster (see §§58 and 61) are made by installing or removing shims from between the inner shaft, which attaches the upper suspension arm to the frame, and the frame. On this suspension, the inner ends of the suspension arm are attached to the frame through rubber bushings or sleeves which are sandwiched between two steel shells. The inner shells are held stationary on the frame. The

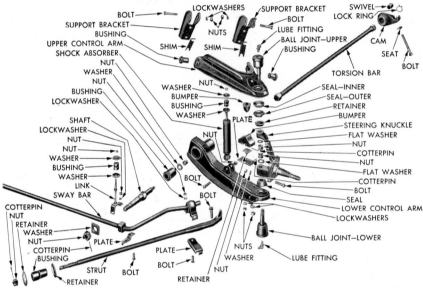

Fig. 3-24. Disassembled view of front suspension which uses torsion bars. (*Chrysler Division of Chrysler Corporation*)

outer shells are locked to the suspension arms. All pivoting at these points occurs by deflection of the rubber. Thus, there is no metal-to-metal contact or movement. As the arms pivot up and down, the rubber in the sleeves deflects to permit the movement.

§47. Torsion-bar suspension   Figure 2-10 shows a torsion-bar front-suspension system using two torsion bars. Figure 3-24 shows this system disassembled. The rear end of each torsion bar is attached to a frame cross member through a car-leveling device. This car-leveling device can be adjusted to level up the car in case any sag occurs in the suspension after long mileage. The rear ends of the torsion bars are kept from turning by this attachment. The front ends of the torsion bars are attached to the lower control arms at the pivot points of the arms. Thus as the lower control arms move up and down in response to up-and-down front-wheel movement, the torsion bars twist. The car weight places an initial twist on the bars, just as it places an initial compression on the coil springs of cars with coil-spring suspension. As already explained (§37, 3), the twisting of the torsion bars provides the springing effect. Figure 3-25 shows the car-leveling device at one rear end of one torsion bar. Turning the height adjusting bolt causes the hub and anchor assembly to turn. This rotates the rear end of the torsion bar so that the front end of the car is raised or lowered.

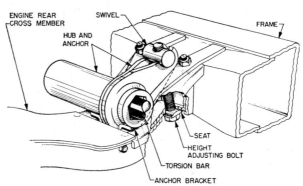

FIG. 3-25. Method of attaching rear of torsion bar to frame. Hub and anchor, swivel, and adjusting bolt are for adjusting height of car. (*Chrysler Division of Chrysler Corporation*)

§48. Air suspension   In air suspension, the four conventional springs are replaced by four air bags or air-spring assemblies. Figure 3-26 is a disassembled view of an air-suspension system at one front wheel. Figure 3-27 shows the components of an air-suspension system at one rear wheel. Figure 3-28 is a schematic diagram of a complete system.

Essentially each air-spring assembly is a flexible bag enclosed in a metal dome or girdle. The bag is filled with compressed air which supports the car's weight. When a wheel encounters a bump in the road, the air is further compressed and absorbs the shock.

An air compressor, or pump, supplies air to the system (Fig. 3-28). On the system shown, the compressor is driven by a belt from the water-pump pulley. Pressure is maintained in the reservoir at about 300 psi (pounds per square inch). The air then passes by two circuits to the four air bags. In one circuit the air pressure is re-

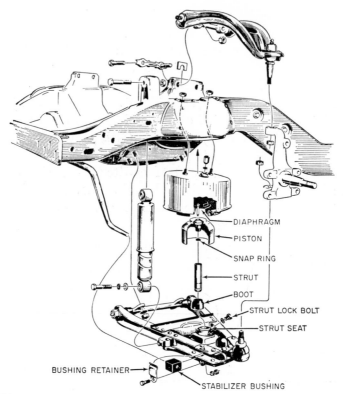

DIAPHRAGM
PISTON
SNAP RING
STRUT
BOOT
STRUT LOCK BOLT
STRUT SEAT
BUSHING RETAINER→
STABILIZER BUSHING

Fig. 3-26. Disassembled view of air-suspension system on front of car. (*Oldsmobile Division of General Motors Corporation*)

duced to 160 psi by a pressure regulator. This pressure is admitted to the four air bags through height control or leveling valves. These valves are attached to the frame and linked to the wheel suspension as shown in Fig. 3-29. When there is insufficient air in an air bag, that side of the car will ride low. This causes the linkage to move the leveling arm so that the valve is opened, admitting more air.

The 300 psi air supply is used to correct for additional loading of the car. This keeps the car level the same regardless of whether there are passengers or not. The action is as follows: When a car door is opened, the door switch closes to turn on the courtesy light. At the same time, the air-suspension solenoid is connected to the battery through the switch, and the solenoid valve opens. Now air at 300 psi is admitted to the leveling valves. If the air bag has been compressed by added weight, as when a passenger climbs in, then

[66]

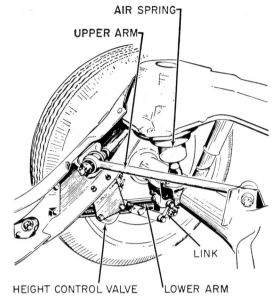

AIR SPRING

UPPER ARM

FIG. 3-27. Air-suspension system on rear of car. (*Oldsmobile Division of General Motors Corporation*)

LINK

HEIGHT CONTROL VALVE   LOWER ARM

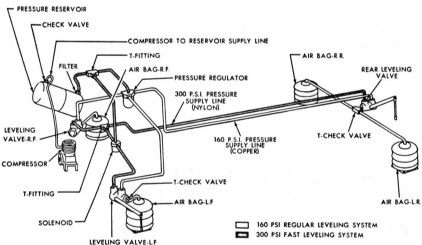

FIG. 3-28. Schematic diagram of an air-suspension system. (*Mercury Division of Ford Motor Company*)

the leveling valve quickly feeds additional air pressure to the low air bag and it is brought up to the proper level. On the other hand, if a passenger has gotten out, then the air bag is high. Now the leveling valve releases air from the air bag to lower it to the proper level.

[67]

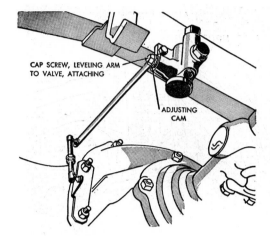

CAP SCREW, LEVELING ARM
TO VALVE, ATTACHING

ADJUSTING
CAM

FIG. 3-29. Rear leveling valve on air-suspension system. (*Mercury Division of Ford Motor Company*)

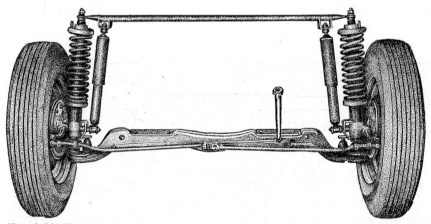

FIG. 3-30. Front-suspension system in which the coil springs are placed around the steering-knuckle pins. (*American Motors Corporation*)

Some systems have a special control that the driver can operate to allow additional pressure to enter the air bags. This raises the car as much as four inches above normal. Such a control would come in handy, for example, when negotiating sharply inclined driveways or rutted roads where the car bottom would drag.

§49. Other types of front suspension A somewhat different type of coil-spring front-suspension system is illustrated in Fig. 3-30. In this system the steering knuckle is permitted to move up and down on a

[68]

FIG. 3-31. Front-suspension system in which the coil springs are located between the upper ends of the steering-knuckle pins and seats in the outer wheelhouse panel. (*American Motors Corporation*)

FIG. 3-32. Front-suspension system using a transverse leaf spring. (*Studebaker-Packard Corporation*)

long steering-knuckle pin that is fastened at its top and bottom to the car body and frame. Hourglass-shaped rollers permit easy relative movement between the steering knuckle and the knuckle pin. The coil spring surrounds the knuckle-pin outer bearing, providing the spring action between the wheel and the car body. The spring is normally covered by a rubber boot (not shown in illustration) to protect the mechanism from moisture and dirt. Direct-acting, or telescoping, shock absorbers are mounted parallel to the coil springs. Rubber bumpers or cushions provide stops for the two extreme coil-spring positions.

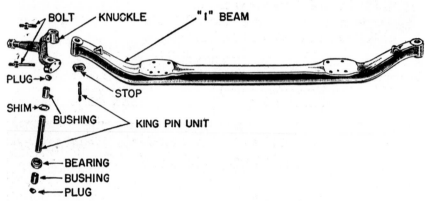

FIG. 3-33. Beam-type front axle showing method of supporting steering knuckle on end of beam. (*Chevrolet Motor Division of General Motors Corporation*)

A variation of this type of suspension is shown in Fig. 3-31. The coil springs are located between the upper ends of the steering-knuckle pins and seats in the outer wheelhouse panel. Direct-acting shock absorbers are used in this system, also.

A type of front-suspension system using a single leaf spring is shown in Fig. 3-32. The leaf is the transverse type; that is, it is installed in the vehicle in a crosswise position, instead of parallel to the sides of the frame. The center of the leaf spring is nested in, and attached to, a channel section of the frame. The ends of the leaf spring are attached to the lower ends of the steering-knuckle yokes by threaded spring bolts. The upper ends of the steering-knuckle supports are attached to the upper suspension arms which are part of the shock absorbers.

Many trucks and other heavy-duty vehicles use a solid, one-piece

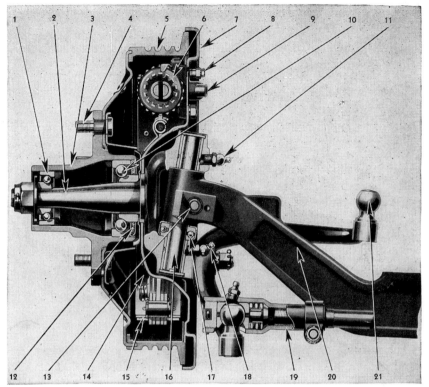

FIG. 3-34. Beam-type front-axle assembly, partly cut away. (*Chevrolet Motor Division of General Motors Corporation*)

1. Outer wheel bearing
2. Wheel spindle
3. Wheel hub
4. Wheel-hub bolt
5. Brake drum
6. Brake-wheel cylinder
7. Brake-flange plate
8. Brake bleeder valve and screw
9. Brake-wheel–cylinder hose connection
10. Inner wheel bearing
11. Lubrication fitting
12. Inner-bearing oil seal
13. Kingpin lock pin
14. Brake shoe
15. Brake lining
16. Kingpin
17. Kingpin thrust bearing
18. Lubrication fitting
19. Tie-rod end
20. Axle I beam
21. Steering and third arm

axle beam at the front instead of an independent wheel suspension. As a rule, this arrangement makes use of leaf springs, one at each wheel. Figure 3-33 shows the manner in which the steering knuckle is supported on the end of the axle beam. Figure 3-34 is a sectional view of an actual suspension; the arrangement of the actual parts can be seen in this illustration. On heavy-duty vehicles using a solid

[71]

front axle and two leaf springs—one at each wheel—the axle is normally underneath the center of the spring; and the two spring ends are attached to the vehicle frame by means of a shackle and a hanger (Fig. 3-16).

CHAPTER CHECKUP

NOTE: Since the following is a chapter review test, you should review the chapter before taking it.

Once more, you will want to test your knowledge of the subjects covered in the chapter you have just completed. The questions that follow have two purposes: (1) to test your knowledge and (2) to help you review the chapter and fix more firmly in your mind the facts discussed. It may be that you will not be able to answer, offhand, all of the questions. If this happens, don't worry. Few people can remember everything they read the first time they read it. Just turn back into the chapter and reread the pages that will give you the answers. The questions require written answers. Write them down in your notebook.

Correcting the Parts Lists

The purpose of this exercise is to give you practice in spotting unrelated parts in a list. In each list below, one item is named that does not belong. Write down each list in your notebook, but do not write down the item that does not belong.

1. Parts in the leaf spring include master leaf, rebound clips or cover, spring eyes, center bolt, frame.
2. Parts that may be found in a spring shackle include bolts, links, bushings, levers, nuts.
3. Parts that may be found in a front-suspension system include spring, steering-knuckle support, suspension arms, suspension gears, shock absorber, stabilizer.
4. Parts that may be found in a rear-suspension system include springs, frame, axle housing, shackles, spring hangers, shock absorbers, snugger, rubber bumpers.

Completing the Sentences

The sentences below are incomplete. After each sentence there are several words or phrases, only one of which will correctly complete the sentence. Write down each sentence in your notebook, selecting the proper word or phrase to complete it correctly.

Automotive Springs and Suspension

1. One end of the semielliptical spring is usually attached to the frame through a   *chain   lever   shackle   brace*

2. The clips placed at intervals along some leaf springs to prevent spring-leaf separation on rebound are called   *separation clips   interval clips   relief clips   rebound clips*

3. The two types of springs used in automotive suspension systems are   *coil and leaf   coil and lever   leaf and suspension   lever and leaf*

4. The device that permits variation in the distance between the spring eyes of a leaf spring as the spring flexes is called the   *spring hanger   spring shackle   spring leaf   spring U bolt*

5. The weight or pressure required to deflect a spring 1 inch is called the   *spring rate   spring weight   spring deflection   spring rebound*

6. The rear-end-suspension arrangement in which rear-end torque is absorbed by the springs is called the   *torque-tube drive   differential drive   Hotchkiss drive   Hooke's drive*

7. The rear-end-suspension arrangement in which rear-end torque is absorbed by a tube connected between the transmission and the differential housing is called a   *torque-tube drive   differential drive   Hotchkiss drive   Hooke's drive*

8. In rear-suspension systems using coil springs, the two devices connected between the axle housing and frame to prevent forward or backward movement of the housing are called   *axle arms   support arms   stabilizers*

9. In the typical front-suspension system, the lower suspension arm is connected between the car frame and the   *upper suspension arm   shock-absorber arm   steering-knuckle support*

10. In the typical front-suspension system, the upper suspension arm is connected between the steering-knuckle support and the   *car frame   shock-absorber arm   lower suspension arm*

Purpose, Construction, and Operation of Components

In the following, you are asked to write down the purpose, construction, or operation of various suspension components discussed in the chapter. If you have any difficulty in writing down your explanations, turn back to the chapter and reread the pages that cover the components you want to write about. Then write your explanation. Don't copy, tell it in your own words. This is a good way of fixing the explanation in your mind. Write in your notebook.

[73]

1. Describe the construction of a semielliptical spring.
2. Describe the construction of a typical spring shackle.
3. What is the purpose of the shackle?
4. What would happen if no spring shackle were used on a leaf spring?
5. What is the basic difference between the Hotchkiss drive and the torque-tube drive?
6. Describe a typical coil-spring rear-suspension system.
7. Describe a typical coil-spring front-suspension system.
8. Describe the construction and operation of a torsion-bar suspension system.
9. Describe the construction and operation of an air-suspension system.

SUGGESTIONS FOR FURTHER STUDY

Study the various front- and rear-suspension systems on different cars. Try to identify the various parts in them and study their purposes. You can see many different makes and models of cars in any automobile garage or filling station, as well as in your school automotive shop. Many school shops also have cutaway parts and automotive chassis which make it easy to see how the suspension parts are related. In addition, study whatever automotive shop manuals you can find. Notice the illustrations and descriptions of the different suspension systems. Write down in your notebook any important facts you come across.

4: Shock absorbers

§50. **Purpose of this chapter** This chapter describes the construction, operation, and servicing of the various types of shock absorber in use on automotive vehicles.

§51. **Purpose of shock absorbers** Springs alone are not satisfactory for a car suspension system. As was already mentioned (in §40), the spring must be a compromise between flexibility and stiffness. It must be flexible so it can absorb road shocks. But if it is too flexible it will flex and rebound excessively and repeatedly, giving

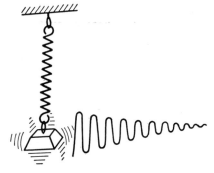

FIG. 4-1. If a weight hanging from a coil spring is set into up-and-down motion, it will oscillate for some time, with the distance it moves up and down gradually shortening as indicated by the curve. Finally, the motion will die out.

a rough ride. A stiff spring will not flex and rebound so much after a bump has been passed. On the other hand, it will also give a hard ride because it will transmit too much of the road shock to the car. By using a relatively flexible or soft spring and a shock absorber, a satisfactorily smooth ride will be achieved.

You can demonstrate to yourself why a spring alone would be unsatisfactory for a vehicle suspension. Hang a weight on a coil spring as shown in Fig. 4-1. Then lift the weight and let it drop. It will expand the spring as it drops. Then it will rebound, or move up. The spring, as it expands and contracts, will keep the weight moving up and down, or oscillating, for some time.

On the car, a very similar action will take place with a flexible

[75]

spring. The spring is under an initial compression because of the car weight. As the wheel passes over a bump, the spring is further compressed. After the bump is passed, the spring attempts to return to its original position, but it overrides this position and expands too much, causing the car frame to be thrown upward. Now, having overexpanded, the spring compresses. Again it overrides and compresses too much. As this happens, the wheel may be raised clear of the road and the frame may drop. Now the spring expands again, and so the oscillations continue, gradually dying out. But every time the wheel encounters a bump or hole in the road, the same series of oscillations will take place.

Such spring action on a vehicle produces a rough and unsatisfactory ride. On a bumpy road, and especially on a curve, the oscillations might become serious enough to cause the driver to lose control of the car. Therefore it is necessary to use some device to quickly dampen out the spring oscillations once the wheel has passed the hole or bump in the road. The shock absorber is the device universally used today. There have been many types of shock absorber, operating on friction, compressed air, and hydraulically. The hydraulic shock absorber is the only type in common use at the present. It contains a fluid that is forced through restricting orifices as the shock absorber is operated by spring flexure. The resistance to the movement of the fluid through the restricting orifices imposes a drag on spring movement, thus quickly dampening out spring oscillations (see §31). Several designs of shock absorbers are discussed below.

§52. Direct-acting shock absorber The direct-acting, or telescope, shock absorber, is the most widely used shock absorber and is found on both front- and rear-suspension systems. Several of the illustrations in the previous chapter show methods of mounting the shock absorber at front and rear wheels (Figs. 3-1, 3-5, 3-18, and so on). Figures 4-2 and 4-3 show the details of front- and rear-mounting direct-acting shock absorbers. Notice that in the mounting methods shown, the two ends of the shock absorber, which are the studs or eyes by which they are attached, are encased in rubber grommets or bushings. This provides a reasonably flexible mounting and at the same time the rubber absorbs vibration and noise.

Regardless of the method of mounting, the shock absorber is

[76]

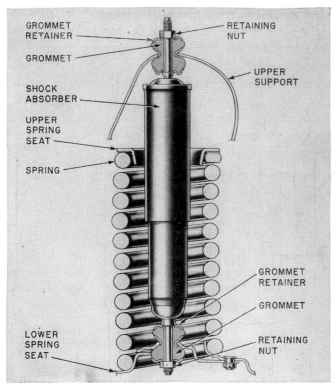

FIG. 4-2. Method of attaching direct-acting shock absorber in front-suspension system. (*Chevrolet Motor Division of General Motors Corporation*)

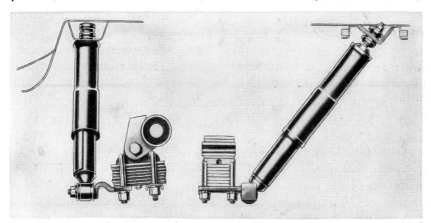

FIG. 4-3. Front and side views showing method of attaching direct-acting shock absorber in rear-suspension system using leaf spring. (*Chevrolet Motor Division of General Motors Corporation*)

[77]

attached in such a way that, as the wheel moves up and down, the shock absorber shortens and lengthens, or telescopes and extends. Since the shock absorber imposes a restraint on this movement (in the manner explained below), excessive wheel and spring movements as well as spring oscillations are prevented.

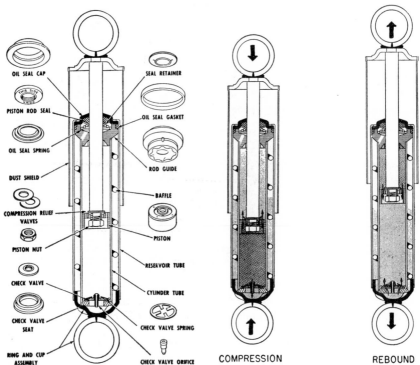

COMPRESSION   REBOUND

Fig. 4-4. Direct-acting shock absorber in sectional view, with internal parts illustrated and their positions in the assembly shown. (*Plymouth Division of Chrysler Corporation*)

Fig. 4-5. Operation of direct-acting shock absorber during compression (left) and extension, or rebound (right). Fluid movement is shown by arrows. (*Plymouth Division of Chrysler Corporation*)

A direct-acting shock absorber is shown in sectional view in Fig. 4-4, with the internal parts illustrated. Figure 4-5 shows the operation of the shock absorber during compression and extension, or rebound. The shock absorber consists of three concentric tubes and a piston, together with valves, gaskets, and so on, as shown in Fig. 4-4. The outer tube is a dust shield, while the two inner tubes are sealed from each other except for a valve at the bottom of the shock absorber. The space between the two inner tubes is the fluid reservoir. The piston, which is attached through a heavy piston rod to the upper shock-absorber mounting eye, moves up and down as the length of the shock absorber changes. As it does this, the fluid in the shock absorber moves one way or the other through small passages in the piston. Let us see how such action takes place and what effect it has on spring movement.

Figure 4-5 shows the actions taking place in the shock absorber when the wheel is moving up, compressing the spring and shock absorber, and the actions taking place when the wheel is moving down, expanding the spring and shock absorber. When the wheel encounters a bump causing it to move up toward the frame, the spring compresses. At the same time, the shock absorber is tele-scoped, or shortened: this causes the piston to move downward in the inside cylinder, or tube. Downward movement of the piston puts pressure on the fluid below the piston. At the same time, it creates a vacuum in the cylinder above the piston. The fluid is forced through the small openings—orifices—in the piston and passes into the upper part of the cylinder. Meanwhile, fluid in the lower end of the cylinder can flow out through the check-valve orifice and into the reservoir that surrounds the inner cylinder.

If the spring movement is very rapid—as it might be if a heavy bump in the road is encountered—then the relief valves flex away from the upper face of the piston to permit the opening of addi-tional passages. Regardless of this, however, the orifices in the piston tend to restrict the movement of the liquid and thus to slow the movement of the piston. This, in turn, places a restriction on the spring action. In other words, the *shock* of the wheel meeting the bump *is absorbed.*

On rebound, when the wheel moves downward after passing a bump, or when it encounters a hole in the road, the shock absorber is extended (Fig. 4-5). As this happens, the piston moves into the upper part of the cylinder and the fluid above it is forced to pass to the lower part of the cylinder through the small orifices in the piston. At the same time, the check valve in the bottom of the cylinder is lifted off its seat, permitting fluid to flow from the reservoir into the lower end of the cylinder.

In both compression and rebound, the spring valves open varying amounts to allow varying speeds of liquid movement through the

[79]

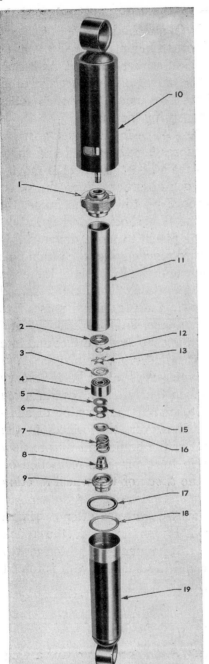

orifices. This permits rapid spring movements, while still imposing a restraining action, and prevents the excessive pressure rise in the fluid that might otherwise occur when large bumps in the road are encountered.

§53. Shock-absorber   service
Some of the earlier-model shock absorbers could be disassembled and reassembled in the shop. However, the direct-acting shock absorbers, now in general use, are usually serviced by complete replacement, although some of these, too, can be disassembled as described in §54.

1. Piston-rod guide and seal
2. Piston washer
3. Piston-intake-valve plate
4. Piston
5. Rebound-valve orifice plate
6. Rebound-valve back plate
7. Rebound-valve spring
8. Piston-rod nut
9. Compression valve
10. Dust-shield tube and piston rod
11. Cylinder tube
12. Piston-washer spacer
13. Piston-intake-valve-plate spider spring
15. Rebound-valve spring disk
16. Rebound-valve spring seat
17. Gasket—upper (rubber)
18. Gasket retainer
19. Reservoir tube and cylinder-base assembly

Fig. 4-6. Disassembled view of direct-acting shock absorber. (*Plymouth Division of Chrysler Corporation*)

§**54. Direct-acting shock ab sorber service** With shock absorber removed from car, clamp lower eye on flat sides in a vise. Pull it to fully extended position, clean it, and insert special wrench through holes in the dust sleeve, so that the wrench lugs engage in the slots in the top guide. Unscrew the guide and lift off the top of the unit. Remove the compression-valve and cage assembly by tapping it lightly. Clamp the top eye in a vise and disassemble the piston and rebound-valve assembly by removing the nut, spring, spring seat, and plates. Note the relationship of parts so that they can be re-assembled in the same relative positions. Before removing the piston, mark the rod and piston location with respect to each other, so they can be assembled in the same relationship. Then remove the piston, intake valve, valve-plate spider spring, and spacing and piston washers. Next remove the cylinder from the piston rod.

After disassembly, wash all parts in cleaner. Do not use thinner or paint remover as either would damage the piston-rod seal. Always install a new rubber gasket and, if necessary, a new gasket retainer. Dip the gasket in shock-absorber fluid before installation. When assembling the top guide and seal assembly, use a shock-absorber rod-guide pilot to avoid damaging the seal when sliding it under the piston-rod shoulder. In reassembly, be sure all parts are replaced in the proper order and in correct relationship to each other. In particular, make sure the piston and rod markings are aligned. Stake the nut in place on the piston rod to avoid loosening in service. Replace the compression-valve and cage assembly and tap it into place. Fill the shock absorber with the exact amount of fluid specified for the type being repaired. Pour fluid into the pressure tube until the tube is filled. Replace the compression valve in the end of the pressure tube, keeping the pressure tube extended. Pour the remaining fluid into the reservoir tube with the tube in upright position. Place the reservoir tube in a vise and assemble the dust shield and reservoir tube. Use a new rod-guide retainer gasket. Insert a special wrench through slots in the dust tube and tighten the rod-guide assembly securely.

CHAPTER CHECKUP

You have been making good progress in the book and have a right to feel that you have made a fine start in your studies of automotive suspension systems and shock absorbers. You may not have much to do with shock absorbers in your automotive work. Nevertheless, you will want to know how they are constructed and how they work so you can talk intelligently about them to anyone. To check up on yourself and find out how well you remember what you have just read, take the following test. If any of the questions stump you, just reread the chapter. As we have said before, there are few people who can remember everything they read, even though they read it more than once. Write your answers in your notebook. Writing down the answers helps you remember them. Also, you make your notebook a valuable source of information you can refer to whenever some fact becomes hazy in your mind.

Correcting Parts Lists

The purpose of this exercise is to give you practice in spotting unrelated parts in a list. In each of the lists below, one item is named that does not belong. Write down each list in your notebook, but do not write down the item that does not belong.

1. Parts in the direct-acting shock absorber include piston, check valve, compression relief valve, dust shield, connecting rod, piston rod.
2. Parts in the direct-acting shock absorber that are in contact with fluid include sealing gaskets, valves, piston, dust shield, piston nut, cylinder tube.

Completing the Sentences

The sentences below are incomplete. After each sentence there are several words or phrases, only one of which will correctly complete the sentence. Write down each sentence in your notebook, selecting the proper word or phrase to complete it correctly.

1. In a coil-spring suspension system, as the wheel passes over a bump the spring is   *expanded*   *extended*   *compressed*
2. When the direct-acting shock absorber is compressed or telescoped, fluid passes through the piston orifices into the upper part of the cylinder and also   *out of the reservoir*   *into the reservoir*   *into the dust shield*   *out of the dust shield*
3. On rebound, in the direct-acting shock absorber, fluid flows out of the upper part of the cylinder and also   *out of the reservoir*   *into the reservoir*   *into the dust shield*   *out of the dust shield*

Shock Absorbers

Purpose and Operation of Shock Absorbers

In the following, you are asked to write down the purpose and operation of the various shock absorbers. If you have any difficulty in your explanations, turn back and reread the pages in the chapter that will clarify the matter for you. But don't copy; try to tell it in your own words. This is a good way of fixing the explanation in your mind. Write in your notebook. Numbers 3, 4, and 5 refer to shock absorbers that are no longer in common use although they may be found on older cars. They are mentioned here in case you want to do a little research on earlier-model shock absorbers.

1. Explain why shock absorbers are needed.
2. Explain how a direct-acting shock absorber is constructed and how it operates.
3. Explain how a single-acting shock absorber operates.
4. Explain how a double-acting, parallel-cylinder shock absorber operates.
5. Explain how a rotating-vane shock absorber operates.

Servicing Procedures

Some of the items mentioned below refer to shock absorbers that are no longer widely used. However, they are included here in case you would like to do a little research on some of the older-model shock absorbers.

1. What is the basic test of a shock absorber?
2. How can leakage of fluid from the shock absorber be detected?
3. How is the single-acting shock absorber filled?
4. How is the double-acting shock absorber filled?
5. How is the vane type of shock absorber filled?
6. How is the direct-acting shock absorber filled?
7. Describe the procedure for changing relief valves on the single-acting shock absorber; on the double-acting, parallel-cylinder shock absorber; on the double-acting, opposed-cylinder shock absorber with external valves; on the double-acting, opposed-cylinder shock absorber with internal valves.
8. Describe the procedure for disassembling the single-acting shock absorber; the double-acting, parallel-cylinder shock absorber; the double-acting, opposed-cylinder, internal-valve shock absorber; the double-acting, opposed-cylinder, external-valve shock absorber; the direct-acting shock absorber.
9. How is the vane type of shock absorber adjusted?

[83]

SUGGESTIONS FOR FURTHER STUDY

If you are especially interested in shock absorbers, you might be able to obtain, from a local service shop, discarded and defective shock absorbers which you can disassemble and study in detail. Some automotive shop manuals also cover the operation and servicing of the shock absorbers used on their cars. Study these manuals if you have a chance. Write down in your notebook any important facts you come across.

5: Steering systems

§55. Purpose of this chapter This chapter covers the various types of steering systems used in automotive vehicles. The requirements of a steering system, as well as types of steering gears and linkages, are described. The discussion of steering gears takes up most of the chapter since there are many varieties of steering gears, both manually- and hydraulically-operated. The latter type is known as *power steering*.

§56. Function of the steering system A simplified drawing of a steering system is shown in Fig. 2-12. We have already described the various methods of supporting the front-wheel spindles (Chap. 3) so the wheels can be swung to the left or right for steering. This movement is produced by gearing and linkage between the steering wheel in front of the driver and the steering knuckle or wheel. The complete arrangement is called the steering system. Actually, the steering system is composed of two elements: a steering gear at the lower end of the steering column, and the linkage between the gear and the wheel steering knuckle. Before we discuss linkages and steering gears in detail, let us take a look at the steering system from the standpoint of geometry, or of the angles involved.

§57. Front-end geometry The term "front-end geometry" refers to the angular relationship between the front wheels, the front-wheel attaching parts, and the car frame. The angle of the kingpin away from vertical, the pointing in or toe-in of the front wheels, the tilt of the front wheels from vertical, all these are involved in front-end geometry. Every one of them influences the steering ease, steering stability, and the riding qualities of the car, and has a direct effect on tire wear. The various factors that enter into front-end geometry are classified under the following terms: *camber, kingpin inclination, caster, toe-in,* and *toe-out on turns.* These are discussed in detail below.

[85]

NOTE: Even though many late-model cars do not use kingpins (see §46), they are treated as though they have kingpins during the front-alignment checks and adjustments. On these cars, reference is made to the "apparent" or theoretical kingpin inclination angle. This is discussed further in §124.

§58. Camber Camber is the tilting of the front wheels from the vertical (Fig. 5-1). When the tilt is outward, so the wheels are farther apart at the top than at the bottom, the camber is positive. Positive camber is shown in Fig. 5-1. When the tilt is inward, so the wheels are closer together at the top than at the bottom, the camber

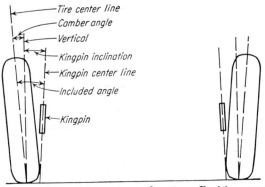

FIG. 5-1. Camber angle and kingpin inclination. Positive camber is shown. (*Plymouth Division of Chrysler Corporation*)

is negative. The amount of tilt is measured in degrees from the vertical, and this measurement is called the camber angle. The wheels are given a slight outward tilt to start with so that when the vehicle is loaded and rolling along on the road, the load will just about bring the wheels to a vertical position. If you started with no camber angle—wheels vertical—then loading the car might give them a negative camber. Any amount of camber—positive or negative—tends to cause uneven or more rapid tire wear, since the tilt puts more of the load on one side of the tread than on the other.

§59. Kingpin inclination Kingpin inclination (or KPI) is the inward tilt of the kingpin from the vertical (Fig. 5-1). Kingpin inclination is desirable for several reasons. First, it helps provide steering stability by tending to return the wheels to the straight-ahead position after any turn; second, it reduces steering effort, particularly when the car is stationary; and third, it reduces tire wear.

The inward tilt, or inclination, of the kingpin tends to keep the wheels straight ahead. It helps recovery, or the return of the wheels to the straight-ahead position after a turn has been made. You can make a table-top demonstration of why this is so with a pencil, a

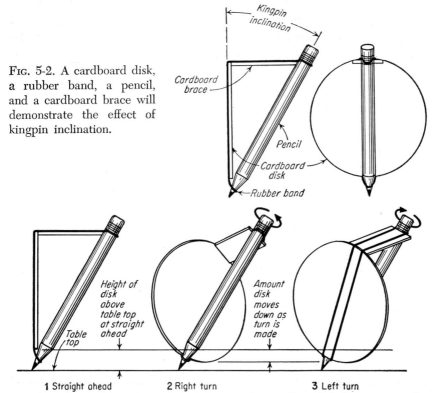

Fig. 5-2. A cardboard disk, a rubber band, a pencil, and a cardboard brace will demonstrate the effect of kingpin inclination.

Fig. 5-3. The effect of kingpin inclination. The cardboard disk represents the left front wheel as viewed from the driver's seat: 1, straight-ahead position; 2, right turn; 3, left turn.

rubber band, a cardboard disk, and a piece of cardboard (Fig. 5-2). Put them together as shown in Fig. 5-2. The cardboard disk represents the wheel, the pencil the kingpin; the cardboard brace at the top holds the two apart there so as to give "kingpin inclination." Needless to say, the angle is greatly exaggerated in the illustration. Now, hold the pencil at an angle with the table top so the wheel is vertical as shown in Fig. 5-3. Then rotate the pencil but do not

[87]

change its angle with the table top. Notice that as you turn the pencil, the wheel is carried around and down toward the table top (Fig. 5-3). If the wheel could not move down, what would happen? As you turned the pencil, the pencil would have to be moved up, always maintaining the same angle with the table top.

This last movement is what actually takes place in the automobile. The wheel is in contact with the ground. It cannot move down. Therefore, as it is swung away from straight ahead, the kingpin and supporting parts are moved upward. This means that the car body is actually lifted. In other words, kingpin inclination causes the car to be raised every time the front wheels are swung away from straight ahead. Then the weight of the car brings the wheels back to straight ahead after the turn is completed and the steering wheel is released.

§**60. Included angle** The included, or combined, angle is the camber angle plus the kingpin inclination (or KPI) angle (Fig. 5-1). The included angle is important because it determines the point of intersection of the wheel and the kingpin center lines (Fig. 5-4).

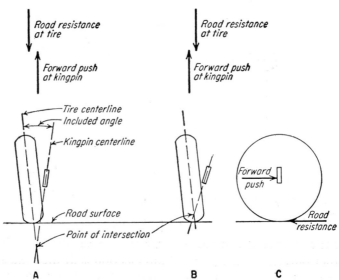

FIG. 5-4. Effect when point of intersection is below road surface (*A*), and above road surface (*B*). Left front wheel as viewed from driver's seat shown in *A* and *B*. *C* is a side view of the wheel to show two forces acting on wheel and kingpin.

[88]

This, in turn, determines whether the wheel will tend to toe out or toe in. "Toe-out" is a term used to describe the tendency for the wheel to point outward. A soldier standing at attention has his feet "toed out." Toe-in is just the opposite; a pigeon-toed person turns the toes of his feet inward. Likewise, a wheel that toes in tries to point inward as it rolls. Figure 5-9 shows what toe-in is on a vehicle. The tire on a wheel that is toed in or toed out will wear more rapidly. The tire has to go in the direction that the car is moving. But, since it is not pointed in that direction—it is toed out or toed in—it is dragged sideways as it rolls forward. The more toe-out or toe-in, the more it is dragged sideways and the faster the tire wears.

When the point of intersection (Fig. 5-4) is below the road surface, then the wheel will tend to toe out. This is because the forward push, which is through the kingpin, is inside the tire center line at the road surface. In the right-hand picture in Fig. 5-4, the two opposing forces working on the wheel are shown. One is the forward push through the kingpin, the other is the road resistance to the tire. If these two forces are exactly in line, then the wheel will have

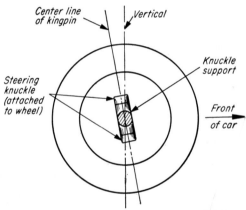

FIG. 5-5. Left front wheel shown from inside so that backward tilt of kingpin from vertical can be seen. This backward tilt is called *positive caster*.

no tendency to toe out or toe in. The two forces will be in line with each other only when the point of intersection is at the road surface. When it is below the road level as shown at *A* in Fig. 5-4, then the wheel attempts to swing outward, or toe out. When the point of intersection is above the road level as shown at *B* in Fig. 5-4, then the wheel attempts to swing inward, or toe in.

[89]

§61. Caster   In addition to being tilted inward toward the center of the car for kingpin inclination, the kingpin may be tiled forward or backward from the vertical (Fig. 5-5). Backward tilt from the vertical is called positive caster. Positive caster aids directional stability since the center line of the kingpin passes through the road surface ahead of the center line of the wheel. Thus, the push on the kingpin is ahead of the road resistance to the tire. The tire is trailing behind, just as the caster on a table leg "trails behind" when the table is pushed (Fig. 5-6).

Caster has another effect that is important. When both front wheels have positive caster, the car tends to roll out or lean out on turns. But if the front wheels have negative caster, then the car

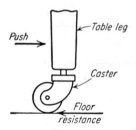

Fig. 5-6. The wheel of the caster trails behind and follows in the direction of the push when the table leg is moved.

tends to bank, or lean in, on turns. Let us use a pencil, rubber band, and cardboard disk to demonstrate why this is so (Fig. 5-7). Fasten the cardboard disk and the pencil together as shown. The disk represents the left-front wheel. Note that we do not include any kingpin inclination here; we want to show only the effect of positive caster. Hold the disk vertical with the pencil at an angle so that both the pencil point and the edge of the disk rest on the table top. Now, rotate the pencil as shown. Note that the disk is lifted from the table top. Actually, in the car, the wheel (the disk) would not be lifted. Instead, the kingpin (the pencil) would move down. In other words, on a right turn, the left side of the car would drop.

Now, let us see what happens at the right-front wheel (Fig. 5-8). As the right turn is made, the wheel pivots on the road surface, causing the kingpin (the pencil) to be lifted. The right side of the car is lifted.

When the left side of the car is lowered, and the right side of the car is lifted as a right turn is made (as described above), then the car rolls, or leans out, on the turn. This is just the opposite of what would be most desirable since it adds to the effect of centrifugal

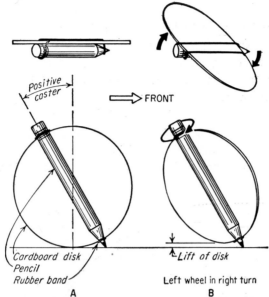

Fig. 5-7. Using a cardboard disk, a pencil, and a rubber band to show the effects of positive caster in a right turn. The disk represents the left-front wheel.

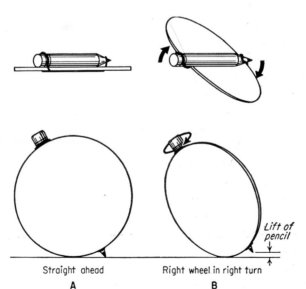

Fig. 5-8. The effect of positive caster on the right-front wheel during a right turn.

force on the turn. By using negative caster—tilting kingpins forward —the car can be made to lean in on a turn and thus decrease the effect of centrifugal force. For instance, with negative caster, the left side of the car would lift during a right turn while the right side of the car would drop. This would combat the roll-out effect of centrifugal force.

Caster has another important effect. Positive caster tries to make the front wheels toe in. With positive caster, the car is lowered as the wheel pivots inward. Thus, the weight of the car is always trying to make the wheel toe in. With negative caster, the wheels would try to toe out.

Note that positive caster increases the effort required to steer. Positive caster tries to keep the wheels straight ahead. In order to make a turn, this tendency must be overcome. Note that kingpin inclination also tries to keep the wheels straight ahead. Thus, to make a turn, the effects of both caster—when positive—and kingpin inclination must be overcome. Later-model vehicles, particularly heavy-duty trucks, tend to have a negative caster. This makes steering easier and there is still sufficient tendency toward recovery, or the return of the wheels to straight ahead, provided by kingpin inclination.

§**62. Toe-in**   As we have already mentioned, toe-in is the turning in of the front wheels; they attempt to roll inward instead of straight ahead. On a car with toe-in (Fig. 5-9), the distance between the front wheels is less at the front (*A*) than at the rear (*B*). The actual amount of toe-in is normally only a fraction of an inch. The purpose of toe-in is to ensure parallel rolling of the front wheels, to stabilize steering, and to prevent sideslipping and excessive wear of tires. The toe-in on the front wheels of a car serves to offset the small deflections in the wheel-support system which come about when the car is moving forward. These deflections are due to the rolling resistance of the tires on the road. In other words, even though the wheels are set to toe in slightly when the car is standing still, they tend to roll parallel on the road when the car is moving forward.

§**63. Toe-out during turns**   Toe-out during turns, also called *steering geometry,* refers to the difference in angles between the two front wheels and the car frame during turns. Since the inner wheel is

[92]

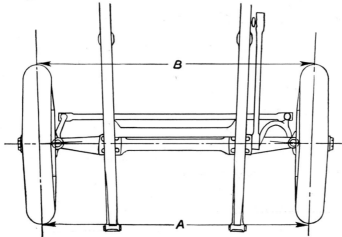

FIG. 5-9. Toe-in. The wheels are viewed from the top with front of car at lower edge of illustration. *A* is less than *B*. (*Chevrolet Motor Division of General Motors Corporation*)

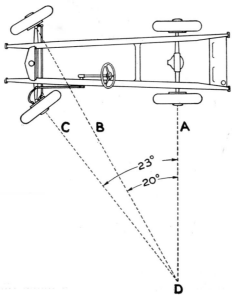

FIG. 5-10. Toe-out on turns. (*Chevrolet Motor Division of General Motors Corporation*)

[93]

rotating on or following a smaller radius than the outer wheel when the car is rounding a curve, its axle must be at a sharper angle with the car frame; that is, it must toe out more. This condition is shown in Fig. 5-10. When the front wheels are steered to make the turn illustrated, the inner wheel turns at an angle of 23 degrees with the car frame, while the outer wheel turns at an angle of only 20 degrees with the car frame. This permits the inner wheel to follow a shorter radius than the outer wheel, and the circles on which the two front wheels turn are concentric—that is, their centers are at the same place (*D*). Toe-out is secured by providing the proper relationship between the steering-knuckle arms, tie rods,

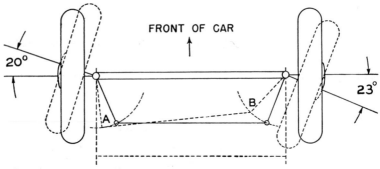

FRONT OF CAR

20°

B

A

23°

FIG. 5-11. Manner in which toe-out on turns is obtained. (*Chevrolet Motor Division of General Motors Corporation*)

and pitman arm. This relationship is such that the inner wheel on a curve always toes out more than the outer wheel. Figure 5-11 illustrates the manner of securing this condition. When the tie rod is moved to the left during a right turn, it pushes at almost a right angle against the left steering-knuckle arm. The right end of the tie rod, however, not only moves to the left but also swings forward (as shown by the dotted line), so that the right wheel is turned an additional amount. When a left turn is made, the left wheel will be turned an additional amount over that which the right wheel turns. Figure 5-11 shows a parallelogram type of linkage (see §64). Other types of linkage give a similar effect and provide a similar toe-out on turns.

§**64. Steering linkages**   Many types of steering linkages have been made to connect the steering knuckles of the front wheels and the pitman arm of the steering gear. You will recall that the pitman arm swings from one side to the other—or forward and backward on some cars—as the steering wheel is turned. This movement must be carried to the steering knuckles at the wheels by some form of linkage. Figure 5-12 shows several types of linkages diagrammatically. All of these have some means of adjusting the lengths of the tie rods or links so that proper alignment of the front wheels can be established. This alignment gives the front wheels a slight toe-in when the car is at rest. When the car begins to move forward, the toe-in practically disappears as all looseness or "sloppage" in the steering system is taken up.

Figure 5-13 shows one form of parallelogram linkage with the connecting-rod assembly connected at one end to the pitman arm and at the other end to the steering idler arm. The steering-knuckle, or spindle, arms are connected to the connecting-rod assembly by two secondary connecting-rod assemblies.

Figure 5-14 shows a center-arm steering linkage with a traverse drag link. The traverse drag link is connected between the pitman arm and the center arm. The center arm is attached through a bushing to the car frame so it can swing back and forth. As the pitman arm swings back and forth, it causes the traverse link to swing the center arm back and forth. This motion is carried through the two tie rods to the steering-knuckle arms.

Figure 5-15 illustrates the details of a connecting-rod assembly used in a parallelogram steering linkage. Note that the pitman arm, idler arm, and tie rods are attached to the connecting rod by means of ball sockets. This type of joint offers very low friction and a minimum of free play in the system so that steering is easier.

§**65. Steering gears** The steering gear is a device for converting the rotary motion of the steering wheel into straight-line motion of the linkage. Essentially, the steering gear consists of two parts: a worm on the end of the steering shaft, and a pitman-arm shaft on which there is a gear sector, toothed roller, or stud. The gear sector, toothed roller, or stud meshes with the worm as shown in Figs. 5-16 and 5-17. In these two illustrations, the steering gear uses a toothed roller. The roller and worm teeth mesh. When the worm is rotated (by rotation of the steering wheel), the roller teeth must follow along and this action causes the pitman-arm shaft to rotate. The other end of the pitman-arm shaft carries the pitman arm;

[95]

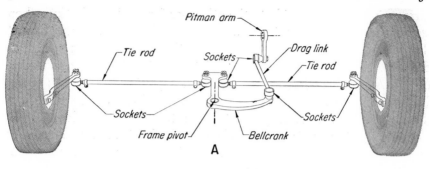

A

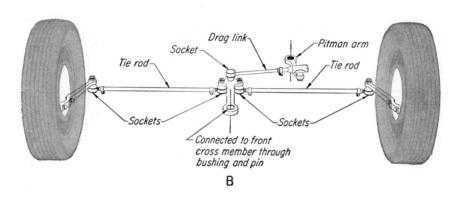

B

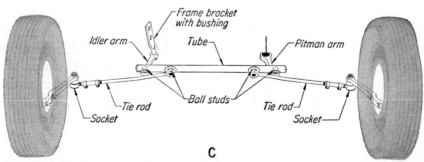

C

FIG. 5-12. Various types of steering linkage. *A*, center arm steering with bell crank intermediate arm; *B*, center-arm steering with traverse drag link; *C*, parallelogram linkage with tubular center link; *D*, parallelogram linkage with

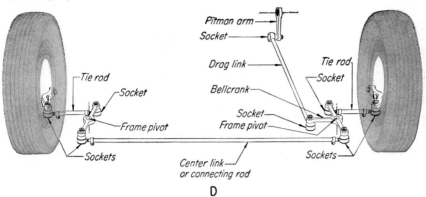

Pitman arm

Socket

Drag link

Tie rod

Socket

Bellcrank

Tie rod

Socket

Socket

Frame pivot

Frame pivot

Sockets

Sockets

Center link
or connecting rod

D

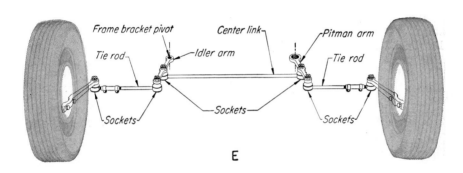

Frame bracket pivot

Center link

Pitman arm

Tie rod

Idler arm

Tie rod

Sockets

Sockets

Sockets

Sockets

E

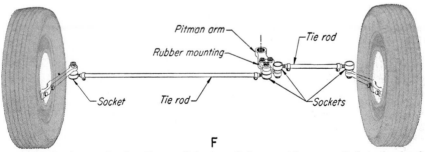

Pitman arm

Tie rod

Rubber mounting

Tie rod

Socket

Tie rod

Sockets

F

center link ahead of axle; *E*, parallelogram linkage with center link in back of axle; *F*, long-arm, short-arm linkage. (*Thompson Products, Inc.*)

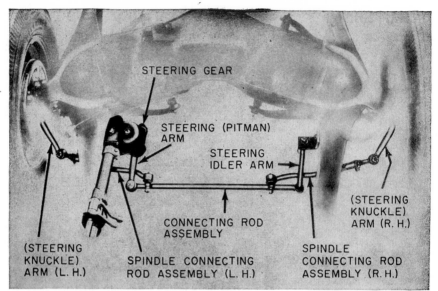

Fig. 5-13. One form of parallelogram steering linkage. (*Ford Motor Company*)

Fig. 5-14. Steering system with center-arm steering and traverse drag link. (*Kaiser Motors Corporation*)

[98]

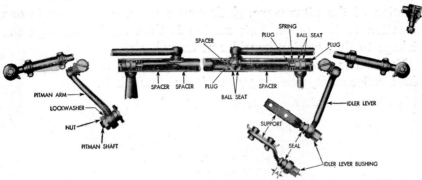

FIG. 5-15. Steering connecting-rod assembly of type used in parallelogram steering linkage, showing details of ball sockets by which it is attached to pitman arm, idler lever, and tie rods. (*Pontiac Motor Division of General Motors Corporation*)

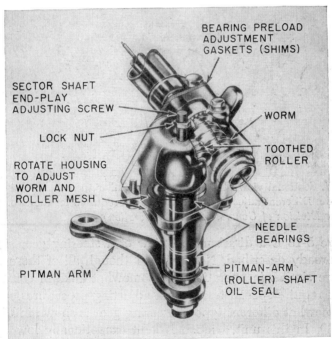

FIG. 5-16. Phantom view of a steering gear using a toothed roller attached to the pitman-arm shaft. Worm and roller teeth mesh. (*Ford Motor Company*)

[99]

rotation of the pitman-arm shaft causes the arm to swing in one direction or the other. This motion is then carried through the linkage to the steering knuckles at the wheels.

NOTE: The pitman-arm shaft is also called the cross shaft, pitman shaft, roller shaft, steering-arm shaft, or sector shaft.

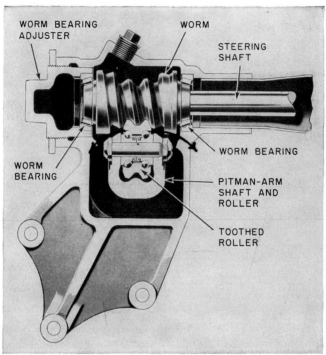

FIG. 5-17. Sectional view of a steering gear similar to one shown in previous illustration. Different adjustment procedures are required for the two. (*Chevrolet Motor Division of General Motors Corporation*)

Figure 5-18 is a disassembled view of a steering gear similar to those already described. Notice that although all of these steering gears are similar in operation and somewhat alike in construction, they all require special testing and adjusting procedures.

A somewhat different type of steering gear is shown in Figs. 5-19 and 5-20. In this unit, friction is kept exceptionally low by interposing balls between the major moving parts, or between the worm teeth and grooves cut in the inner face of a ball nut. The rotation of the worm gear causes the balls to roll in the worm teeth. The balls also roll in grooves cut in the inner face of the nut. Thus, as the worm rotates, the balls causes the nut to move up or down along the worm. The up-or-down motion is carried to the gear sector by teeth on the side of the ball nut. This then forces the gear sector to move along with the ball nut so that the pitman-arm shaft rotates.

The balls are called *recirculating balls* because they can continuously recirculate from one end of the ball nut to the other through a pair of ball return guides. For example, suppose that the driver makes a right turn. The worm gear is rotated in a clockwise direction—viewed from driver's seat—and this causes the ball nut to move upward. The balls roll between the worm and ball nut, and as they reach the upper end of the nut, they enter the return guide and then roll back to a lower point where they reenter the groove between the worm and ball nut.

Still other types of steering gears are in use. All are very similar in operation. A later chapter describes the servicing procedures required on the most popular makes of steering gear in use today.

CHECK YOUR PROGRESS

Progress Quiz 3

Here is your chance to check up on yourself again and find out how well you are remembering what you are reading. As we have mentioned before, there are two good reasons for the quizzes. One is to help you review and remember the important points covered in the book. The other is to let you check yourself on the progress you are making.

Completing the Sentences

The sentences below are incomplete. After each sentence there are several words or phrases, only one of which will correctly complete the sentence. Write down each sentence in your notebook, selecting the proper word or phrase to complete it correctly.

1. The tilting of the front wheels away from the vertical is called
   camber   *caster*   *toe-in*   *toe-out*
2. The inward tilt of the kingpin is called   *caster*   *camber*
   kingpin inclination   *included angle*
3. Camber angle plus kingpin inclination angle is called the
   caster   *included angle*   *point of intersection*   *toe-out*

[101]

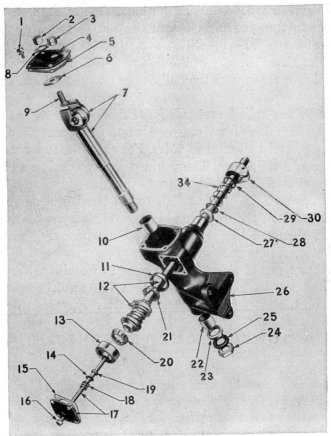

Fig. 5-18. Exploded view of steering mechanism. (*Plymouth Division of Chrysler Corporation*)

1. Shaft-cover screw and lock washer
2. Shaft-adjusting-screw lock nut
3. Housing-lubricant filler plug
4. Shaft cover
5. Shaft-cover gasket
6. Shaft-thrust washer
7. Shaft-and-roller-tooth assembly
8. Shaft-adjusting-screw lock plate
9. Shaft-adjusting screw
10. Shaft bushing (upper)
11. Worm-thrust bearing cup (upper)
12. Steering-tube-and-worm assembly
13. Worm-thrust bearing cup (lower)

14. Steering-tube oil-seal washer
15. Housing-cover shims (worm-adjusting shims)
16. Housing-cover screw and lock washer
17. Housing-cover-and-grease-retaining-tube assembly
18. Steering-tube oil-seal spring
19. Steering-tube oil seal
20. Worm-thrust bearing cage and rollers
21. Worm-thrust bearing cage and rollers
22. Shaft bushing (lower)

[102]

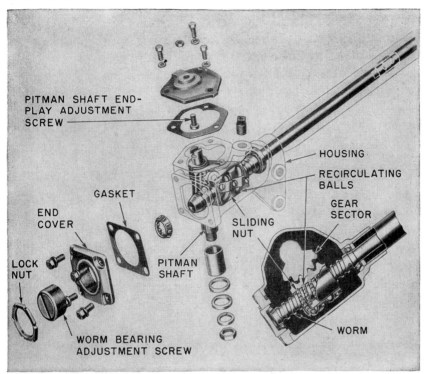

FIG. 5-19. Sectional and phantom views of a recirculating ball-and-nut type of steering gear. (*Cadillac Motor Car Division of General Motors Corporation*)

4. The point at which the center line of the wheel and the center line of the kingpin cross is called the   *included angle*   *point of departure*   *point of intersection*   *point of included angle*

5. When the point of intersection is below the road surface, then the front wheel will tend to   *toe out*   *toe in*   *roll straight*

6. The backward tilt of the kingpin from the vertical is called *positive caster*   *negative caster*   *positive camber*   *negative camber*

7. Positive caster will tend to cause the car to   *roll out on turns* *bank on turns*   *lean in on turns*

23. Shaft oil seal
24. Arm nut
25. Arm-nut lock washer
26. Housing
27. Column-jacket oil seal

28. Column-jacket oil-seal washer
29. Column-jacket oil-seal spring washer
30. Column-jacket clamp
34. Column-jacket oil-seal spring

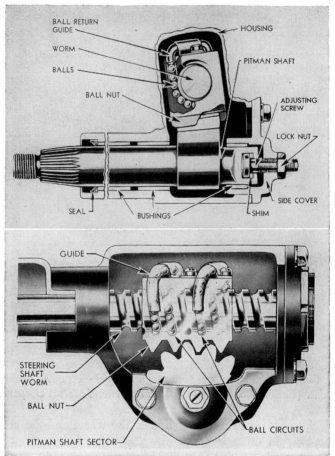

Fig. 5-20. Sectional views of a recirculating ball-and-nut type of steering gear. (*Buick Motor Division of General Motors Corporation*)

 8. Positive caster tends to make front wheels   *toe in*   *toe out*
 9. Toe-out on turns means that the right wheel, in a right-hand turn, would turn out, or away from straight ahead,   *more than the left wheel*   *less than the left wheel*   *same as the left wheel*
10. In the steering gear, a gear sector, stud, or toothed roller is meshed with   *a worm*   *a ball bearing*   *a roller bearing* *a steering wheel*

§66. Power steering   Power steering has been used for a number of years on heavy-duty applications, but it is only in recent years that power steering has been applied to any extent on passenger cars.

[104]

The principle of power steering is very simple; a booster arrangement is provided which is set into operation when the steering-wheel shaft is turned. The booster then takes over and does most of the work of steering. Power steering has used compressed air, electrical mechanisms, and hydraulic pressure. Hydraulic pressure is used on the vast majority of power-steering mechanisms today. You will recall that we discussed hydraulic pressure in some detail (§§12 to 15) and learned that pressure and movement can be transferred from one part of a hydraulic system to another.

In the hydraulic power-steering system, a continuously operating pump provides hydraulic pressure when needed. As the steering wheel is turned, valves are operated that admit this hydraulic pressure to a cylinder. Then the pressure causes a piston to move and the piston does most of the steering work. Specific power-steering systems are described in the sections that follow. There are actually two general types of power-steering systems. In one, the integral type, the power operating assembly is part of the steering gear. In the other, the linkage type, the power operating assembly is part of the linkage.

§67. Saginaw power steering   Two models are in passenger car use, the offset and the in-line (which is the later model).

A. Offset. This unit mounts on the lower end of the steering shaft (Fig. 5-21). The steering unit consists of a recirculating ball-and-nut steering gear (such as is illustrated in Figs. 5-19 and 5-20) to which has been added a hydraulic booster cylinder. Before we discuss the tie-in between the two, let us first talk about the hydraulic part of the system.

1. Hydraulic system. Figure 5-22 shows the hydraulic circuits in the system. The oil pump is mounted on the front part of the engine and is driven by a V belt from the engine crankshaft pulley. Whenever the engine is running, the oil pump supplies oil to the system. The position of the valve spool then determines where the oil will be directed in the system and what effect, if any, it will have on the steering of the car. The valve spool is shown by itself —removed from the housing—at the bottom of Fig. 5-22. Essentially, it is a solid cylinder in which two grooves have been cut, or you could say it is a shaft with three collars on it. The valve spool is a close sliding fit within the hole in the valve housing. The housing

FIG. 5-21. Hydraulic power-steering system. Oil pump is driven by a V belt from the engine crankshaft pulley. (*Cadillac Motor Car Division of General Motors Corporation*)

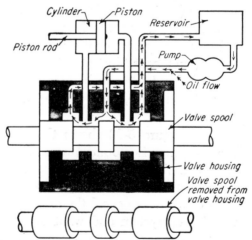

FIG. 5-22. Hydraulic circuits in hydraulic power-steering system. In the position shown, the valve spool directs the oil flow from the pump into the two return passages to the pump reservoir, as indicated by the arrows. Thus, oil pressure is the same on both sides of the piston. (*Saginaw Steering Gear Division of General Motors Corporation*)

[106]

has three internal grooves which are concentric. The two internal grooves at the two ends of the valve housing are connected to the reservoir. The center internal groove is connected to the pump. There are two additional openings from the two internal collars in the housing to the two sides of the cylinder (as shown).

When the valve spool is in the position shown in Fig. 5-22, the oil flows from the pump into the center part of the valve housing and then splits evenly and flows back to the reservoir (as shown by the arrows). Oil pressure is not built up, and the same pressure—

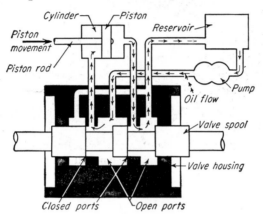

FIG. 5-23. When the valve spool is moved to the right, ports are closed so that oil can no longer flow from the oil pump, past the valve spool, and into the return passages to the pump reservoir. Instead, it flows to the cylinder as shown by the arrows, forcing the piston to move to the right. (*Saginaw Steering Gear Division of General Motors Corporation*)

very low—is applied to both sides of the piston in the cylinder. Thus, there is no tendency for the piston to move one way or the other in the cylinder.

However, if the valve spool is moved in the valve body, oil pressure will build up and the piston will move in the cylinder. When the valve spool is moved (for instance, to the right as in Fig. 5-23), the collars on the valve spool close off the openings, or ports, connecting the pressure line from the oil pump to the return line to the pump reservoir. When these ports are closed, the oil can no longer return to the pump reservoir. It must now flow into the cylinder as shown by the arrows in Fig. 5-23. Thus, the full hydraulic pressure developed by the oil pump is applied to one side of the piston in the cylinder. The piston must move (to the right in Fig.

[107]

5-23). Oil on the other side of the piston is free to discharge from the cylinder and pass through the valve housing and into the pump reservoir as shown by the arrows.

If the valve spool were moved in the opposite direction (to the left in Fig. 5-23), then the oil flow to the cylinder would be reversed. Oil pressure would be applied to the right-hand side of

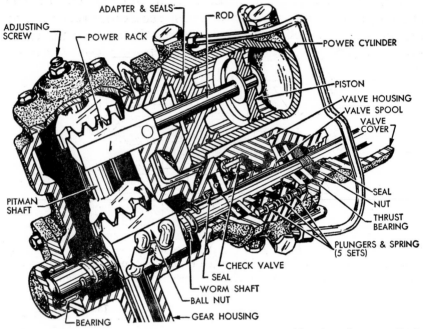

Fig. 5-24. Cutaway view of power-steering gear assembly. (*Buick Motor Division of General Motors Corporation*)

the piston, forcing it to the left. At the same time, the circuit would be open to permit the oil in the left-hand side of the cylinder to return to the pump reservoir.

2. Power cylinder. Figure 5-24 shows a cutaway view of the power-steering gear assembly. Note that the piston rod has a toothed rack on its end, called the *power rack*. This rack is meshed with a gear sector on the end of the pitman shaft. There is another gear sector on the pitman shaft that is meshed with the ball nut. Compare this illustration with Figs. 5-19 and 5-20. Note that the power cylinder and its power rack are simply additions to the circulating ball-and-nut steering gear. The piston moves as hydrau-

[108]

lic oil pressure is applied to it and this movement then provides most of the steering effort. On some models, the two gear sectors are on the same side of the pitman shaft as shown in Fig. 5-24. On other models the two gear sectors are on opposite sides of the pitman shaft. Operation is identical, however.

3. *Valve action.* We have noted that the valve spool movement from the centered position causes oil to be directed into one side of the cylinder or the other. This, in turn, causes the piston to move and thereby turn the pitman shaft in one direction or the other. The valve spool is forced to move as the steering wheel is turned.

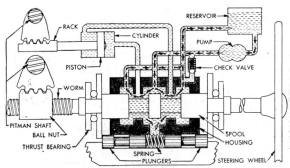

Fig. 5-25. Schematic drawing of the power-steering gear assembly, showing hydraulic circuits with steering wheel in the straight-ahead position. (*Buick Motor Division of General Motors Corporation*)

In Figure 5-25, note that turning the steering wheel to make a left turn would cause the worm to turn in the ball nut and would, in effect, tend to back the worm up and out of the nut. You would get the same effect if you backed a screw out of a nut and at the same time held the nut stationary. The screw would rise upward as it is backed out. There is resistance to ball-nut movement from the ball nut to the front wheels. This tends to hold the ball nut stationary. If the ball nut is held stationary, then the worm and steering shaft will move upward. The upward movement will also carry the valve spool upward so that the valve spool is moved into the position shown in Fig. 5-26. In this position, oil pressure is directed to one side of the piston cylinder, and the other side of the cylinder is connected to the pump reservoir. The piston is moved to the left (in Fig. 5-26) and this assists in turning the pitman shaft so that a left turn is made.

The valve spool is maintained in its centered position during straight-ahead driving by five sets of plungers and springs. These plungers and springs are evenly spaced around the valve housing, and the plunger ends are in contact with two thrust bearings. You can see one set of plungers with its spring in the lower part of Fig. 5-25. Note how the spring must be compressed as the valve spool moves (Fig. 5-26). Actually, the five springs provide a considerable pressure tending to hold the valve spool in its centered position. In one model, for example, the five springs will not compress unless 300 pounds or more are applied. The 300 pounds of end thrust will result if about a 4-pound pull is exerted on the rim of the steering

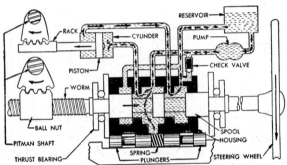

Fig. 5-26. Schematic drawing of the power-steering gear assembly, showing hydraulic circuits with the steering wheel being turned to make a left turn. (*Buick Motor Division of General Motors Corporation*)

wheel. Because of the mechanical advantage of the worm and nut, the comparatively light twisting effort on the steering wheel produces a heavy end thrust on the worm. This causes the valve spool to overcome the pressure of the five plunger springs and to move so that the power piston is brought into action.

Note that under easy steering conditions, when steering can be accomplished with less than 4 pounds of pull at the rim of the steering wheel, there will be no power-steering action. It is only when steering requires more than 4 pounds of pull at the rim that enough end thrust is developed to move the valve spool. When this happens, the power cylinder supplies any effort above the 4-pound pull needed for steering.

4. Check valve. The check valve shown in Figs. 5-25 and 5-26 (close to the pump) is provided to prevent excessive pressures in the system. Since movement of the valve spool shuts off all return passages so that oil cannot return to the pump reservoir, there is a good chance that excessive oil pressures will develop. If this happens, the check valve opens and relieves the excessive pressure by bypassing some of the oil from the pump into the return line to the pump reservoir.

5. *Oil pump.* Figure 5-27 shows two types of pump used with the Saginaw power-steering gear. In the Eaton pump, an inner drive rotor causes the driven rotor to rotate with it. As they rotate, the pockets between the rotors increase and then decrease in size. During increase, oil flows into the pockets through an inlet port

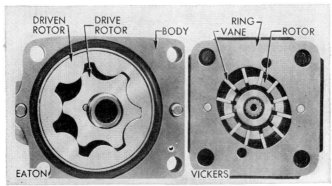

Fig. 5-27. End views, with covers removed, of two types of pump used with the Saginaw power-steering gear. Left, Eaton pump. Right, Vickers pump. (*Buick Motor Division of General Motors Corporation*)

from the pump reservoir. During decrease, this oil is forced out of the pump through an exit port. In the Vickers pump, there is a slotted driving rotor in which 12 vanes are assembled. These vanes slide outward to contact the inner face of the pump body. The inner face is so shaped—oval—as to provide two pumping chambers. As the rotor rotates, the vanes slide out and in to increase and then decrease the pockets between the vanes. During increase, oil enters the pockets from the pump reservoir. During decrease, the oil is forced from the pockets through exit ports. Both pumps have an overload relief valve set to open when the pressure goes above about 750 pounds per square inch.

B. *Saginaw in-line power steering.* This power-steering unit has been used in late-model General Motors cars, among others. It is much like the Saginaw offset power-steering unit. The major differences are that, in the in-line unit, the positions of the power piston

[111]

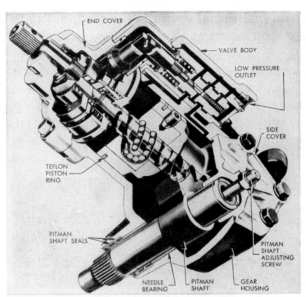

Fig. 5-28a. Cutaway view of Saginaw in-line power-steering unit. (*Buick Motor Division of General Motors Corporation*)

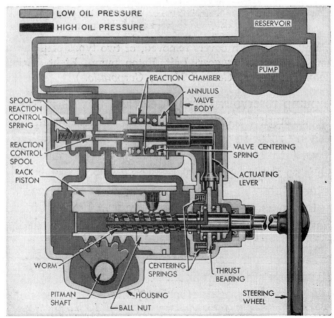

Fig. 5-28b. Circulation of oil through power-steering unit in straight-ahead position. (*Buick Motor Division of General Motors Corporation*)

[112]

and the control valve have been reversed. In the in-line unit, the power piston is in line with the steering shaft while the valve is off to one side. Figure 5-28*a* is a cutaway view of the unit. The piston has a rack on it as shown in Fig. 5-28*b*. The rack meshes with the sector on the pitman shaft. When the steering wheel is turned, the worm at the lower end of the steering shaft turns. This action causes the ball nut and the piston to move endwise. The sector therefore turns the pitman shaft for steering.

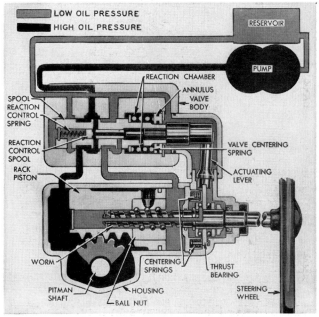

Fɪɢ. 5-28*c*. Circulation of oil when car is making a right turn. (*Buick Motor Division of General Motors Corporation*)

The assisting action of the unit comes into effect whenever more than about three pounds is required to turn the wheel. When this occurs, because of the resistance of the wheels to turning, the worm shifts endwise slightly to cause the valve to operate. This admits oil at high pressure from the pump to one side or the other of the piston, and the piston is moved to assist in the turning effort.

For instance, on a right turn (Fig. 5-28*c*), the worm moves downward a small amount. This movement carries the thrust bearing

[113]

downward, also. As the thrust bearing moves downward (to left in Fig. 5-28c), it causes the actuating lever to tilt, as shown. This brings the spool valve to the right. Now oil at high pressure is admitted to the left side of the piston. The piston is moved to the right. The higher the turning resistance, the more the valve spool is

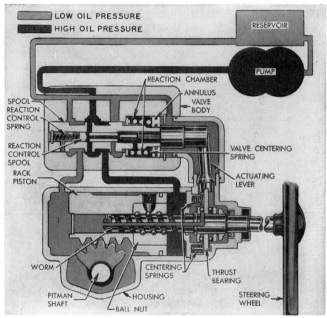

Fig. 5-28d. Circulation of oil when car is making a left turn. (*Buick Motor Division of General Motors Corporation*)

moved, and the higher the oil pressure on the piston. Thus a proportional effect is at work. Most of the turning effort is supplied by the oil pressure on the piston.

Figure 5-28d shows the conditions when a left turn is made. Here the valve spool is moved to the left and oil under pressure is admitted to the right side of the piston.

§68. **Gemmer power steering** The Gemmer Hydraguide power-steering unit is used on Chrysler Corporation cars, including Chrysler and De Soto. Its steering-assist action is very similar to the Saginaw action although the construction and operation of the two units are quite different. Figure 5-29*a* shows the location of the power-steering unit and the hydraulic oil pump. Note that the power-steering unit is part of the steering gear, as in the Saginaw unit. The oil pump is mounted on the back end of the generator; it is driven by a coupling from the generator shaft. The generator, of course, is driven by a V belt from the engine-crankshaft pulley.

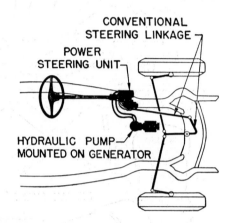

Fig. 5-29*a*. Gemmer Hydraguide power-steering installation, showing location of power-steering unit and the pump. (*De Soto Division of Chrysler Corporation*)

1. Power-steering operation. The Gemmer power-steering unit contains a valve body with valves that are operated when the steering wheel is turned. Valve operation directs hydraulic oil pressure into either of two power cylinders. The oil pressure then moves a piston assembly; movement of the piston assembly supplies the major effort in turning the steering wheel and in steering the car.

Figure 5-29*b* shows the complete layout of the system. Note that the steering shaft (on which the steering wheel is mounted) consists of two parts. The upper part, which is several feet long, carries the steering wheel at the upper end and a flexible rubber coupling at the lower end. It is so mounted that it can rotate only. It does not move up or down. The lower part of the steering shaft is only about one foot long; its upper end is attached to the upper steering shaft by the flexible rubber coupling. There is a spur gear on its lower end. At an intermediate point a single spherical bearing supports it. With this arrangement, the spur gear can move up and down several thousandths of an inch. When a turn is made, the steering shafts rotate, causing the two spur gears to rotate; thus the worm is made to rotate. The worm then starts the roller, pitman shaft, and pitman

[115]

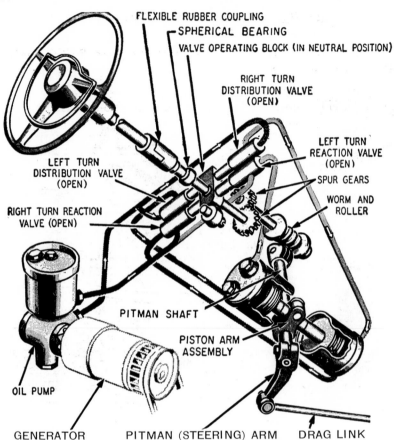

FLEXIBLE RUBBER COUPLING
SPHERICAL BEARING
VALVE OPERATING BLOCK (IN NEUTRAL POSITION)

RIGHT TURN
DISTRIBUTION VALVE
(OPEN)

LEFT TURN
REACTION VALVE
(OPEN)

LEFT TURN
DISTRIBUTION VALVE
(OPEN)

SPUR GEARS

WORM AND
ROLLER

RIGHT TURN REACTION
VALVE (OPEN)

PITMAN SHAFT

PISTON ARM
ASSEMBLY

OIL PUMP

GENERATOR   PITMAN (STEERING) ARM   DRAG LINK

Fig. 5-29*b*. Layout of Gemmer power steering. The neutral, or straight-ahead, position is shown. In this position, the four valves in the valve body are open. Oil from the oil pump flows through the system as shown by the arrows but, since there is no restriction, high oil pressure does not build up. The piston assembly remains centered. (*De Soto Division of Chrysler Corporation*)

arm moving, and this, in turn, causes the steering arm to swing. The drag link then moves to actuate the steering linkage.

Meanwhile, the hydraulic system has gone to work. When the steering shaft is turned, the two spur gears are rotated. Side thrust on the steering-shaft spur gear, or driving gear, attempts to move the spur gear up or down. Since the shaft on which this gear is mounted is carried in a spherical bearing, the gear can move up or down a few thousandths of an inch. This movement causes the valve-operating block in the valve body to move up or down. Valve

[116]

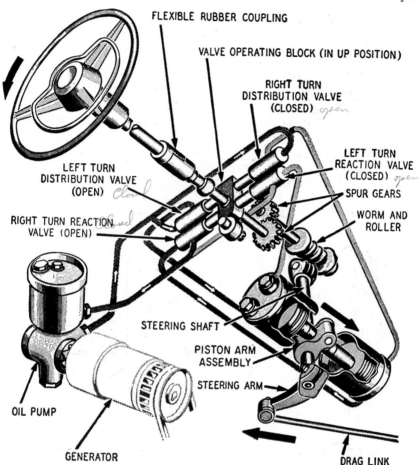

FLEXIBLE RUBBER COUPLING

VALVE OPERATING BLOCK (IN UP POSITION)

RIGHT TURN
DISTRIBUTION VALVE
(CLOSED) *open*

LEFT TURN
DISTRIBUTION VALVE
(OPEN) *Closed*

LEFT TURN
REACTION VALVE
(CLOSED) *open*

SPUR GEARS

WORM AND
ROLLER

RIGHT TURN REACTION *closed*
VALVE (OPEN)

STEERING SHAFT

PISTON ARM
ASSEMBLY

STEERING ARM

OIL PUMP

GENERATOR

DRAG LINK

Fɪɢ. 5-30. Left turn being made with Gemmer power-steering unit. The spur gear on the short steering shaft climbs the spur gear on the worm. This moves the valve-operating block upward, closing the two upper valves as shown and opening wide the two lower valves. Oil now flows to and from the two cylinders as shown by the arrows to cause the power pistons to move and assist the steering. (*De Soto Division of Chrysler Corporation*)

block movement, in turn, actuates the valves. The valves then direct hydraulic oil pressure to the power cylinders so that the piston assembly is moved.

2. *Operation during left turn.* Figure 5-30 shows the actions in the system during a left turn. Reaction between the two spur gears causes the steering-shaft spur gear to climb upward; this lifts the valve-operating block. Movement of the block closes the right-turn

[117]

distribution valve and the left-turn reaction valve. Thus, flow of oil to the right cylinder is halted. At the same time, closing of the left-turn reaction valve halts the flow of oil *from* the left cylinder. Upward movement of the valve-operating block also moves the left-turn distribution valve and the right-turn reaction valve to wide-open position. This means that the oil can now flow freely *into* the left cylinder, but not out. And it can also flow freely from the right cylinder.

Now see what we have. Closing of the right-turn distribution valve halts flow of oil to the right cylinder. Opening of the right-

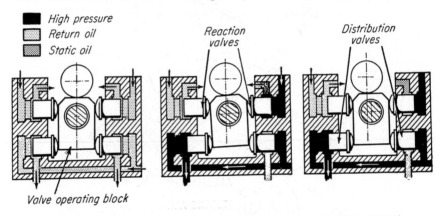

NEUTRAL   PART POWER   FULL POWER

Fig. 5-31. Positions of valve-operating block and valves in neutral or straight ahead, when a turn is made that calls for only part power—a light turn—and when a turn is made that calls for full power—when parking with engine running. (*Gemmer Manufacturing Company*)

turn reaction valve permits oil in the right cylinder to flow freely out of the cylinder. At the same time, opening of the left-turn distribution valve permits oil to flow *into* the left cylinder. And closing of the left-turn reaction valve halts the flow of oil *from* the left cylinder. Oil pressure therefore builds up in the left cylinder, and the left piston causes the piston assembly to move as shown by the large arrow. Since there is no oil pressure in the right cylinder, no resistance to this motion is offered by the right piston. The piston assembly works against an arm fastened to the pitman shaft, thus helping to turn the pitman shaft and swing the steering, or pitman arm.

Figure 5-31 gives you another picture of how the valves are

moved by the operating block. The left illustration shows the block centered and all valves partly opened; this is the neutral, or straight-ahead driving, position. The center illustration shows the action during a turn that does not call for much assistance; since the front wheels are turning rather easily, there is not much steering reaction through the linkage to the worm in the steering gear. The steering-

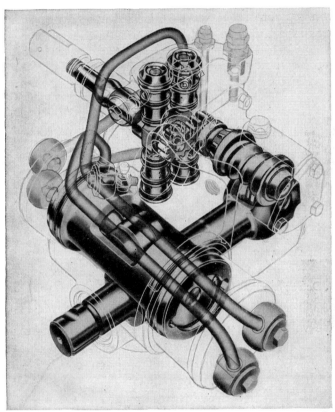

FIG. 5-32. Phantom view of power-steering gear assembly, showing the internal working parts. Compare this with previous illustrations to identify the parts. (*Gemmer Manufacturing Company*)

shaft spur gear therefore climbs the worm spur gear only a little. The valve-operating block does not shift very far; but when full power is called for (right illustration), the block shifts all the way so that the valves are either fully opened or closed.

See Fig. 5-32 for a good phantom view showing the relationship of all the working parts in the assembly. Study this illustration carefully and compare it to Figs. 5-29 to 5-31 so you can identify the various parts and see how they function in the assembly.

3. Oil pump. The oil pump is the inner-outer rotor type such as shown on the left in Fig. 5-27. As the two rotors rotate, the pockets between them increase and then decrease in size. During increase, oil flows into the pockets from the reservoir. Then, during decrease, the oil is forced out of the pump through an exit port. The oil pump contains a pressure relief valve which opens as excessive pressures are approached to prevent high pressures in the system. The open-

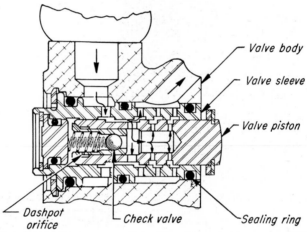

Fig. 5-33. Details of valve construction. (*De Soto Division of Chrysler Corporation*)

ing of the valve bypasses some of the oil from the pump so that it returns to the oil reservoir.

4. Valves. The valves are all alike. Each consists of a valve piston with a spring-loaded ball-check valve plus a valve sleeve (Fig. 5-33). The valve sleeve is assembled into a bore in the valve body and provides a close fit with the valve piston. The valve piston is the part that actually moves in the valve assembly. As it moves, holes in the valve piston and valve sleeve either index or move apart. When they index, oil can flow through. When they move apart, oil flow is stopped. The check valve and dashpot orifice in the valve piston are provided to prevent valve movement, or chattering, when road shocks are encountered. Oil is admitted behind the check valve when the piston moves to the right (in the illustration); pressure opens the check valve to permit this. Then,

[120]

during the return, some restraint on the valve piston is imposed because the oil must flow out through the small dashpot orifice. This small restraint is sufficient to prevent chattering of the valve when road shocks are encountered.

§**69. Linkage-type power steering** In the linkage-type power-steering system, the power cylinder is not part of the steering gear. Instead, the power cylinder, or *booster cylinder* as it is also called,

Fig. 5-34. Linkage-type power-steering system with separate valve assembly and power (booster) cylinder. Top, mounting of the oil pump. Bottom, linkage, valve assembly, and power (booster) cylinder arrangement as viewed from under car looking forward. (*Studebaker-Packard Corporation*)

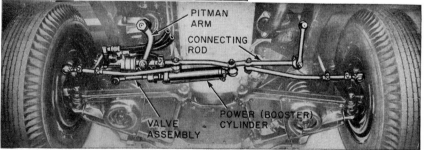

is connected into the steering linkage. In addition, the valve assembly is included in the steering linkage, either as a separate assembly or united with the power cylinder. Figure 5-34 shows one linkage-type power-steering system in which the booster cylinder and valve assembly are separate units. Figure 5-35 is another view of a similar system. In operation, the steering gear works in exactly the same way as the mechanical types described in §65. However, the swinging end of the pitman arm is not directly connected to the steering linkage; instead, it is connected to a valve assembly. As the end of the pitman arm swings when a turn is made, it actuates the valve assembly. The valve assembly then directs hydraulic oil pressure from the oil pump to the booster cylinder. Inside the booster cylinder, pressure is applied to one or the other side of a piston. Movement then takes place—actually, in this unit, the cylinder moves instead of the piston—and this movement is transferred to the connecting rod in the steering linkage. Thus, most of the effort required to move the connecting rod and steer the car is furnished by the booster cylinder.

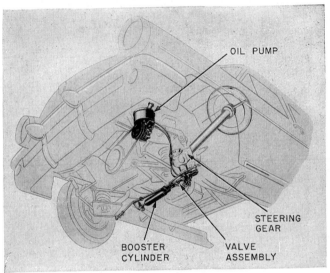

OIL PUMP

STEERING
GEAR

BOOSTER
CYLINDER

VALVE
ASSEMBLY

Fig. 5-35. Phantom view of car from underneath showing arrangement of a linkage-type power-steering system which has separate valve assembly and power (booster) cylinder. (*Lincoln-Mercury Division of Ford Motor Company*)

1. Valve assembly operation. In many ways, the valve assembly is very similar to that used in the Saginaw power-steering unit (Figs. 5-21 to 5-27). The operating part consists of a valve spool that looks much like the valve spool shown at the bottom of Fig. 5-22. The valve spool is assembled into the valve body as shown in Fig. 5-36. The ball on the end of the pitman arm fits a socket in the stem of the valve spool. During neutral, or straight-ahead operation, the valve spool is centered in the valve assembly by one or more centering springs. In this position, the oil circuits through the valve body will impose equal pressure on both sides of the piston in the booster cylinder. Thus, there is no tendency for the booster cylinder to exercise any action.

Figure 5-37 is a cutaway view of the valve assembly showing the centering springs for holding the valve spool in the centered position during straight-ahead driving.

When a turn is made, the pitman arm swings in one direction or the other, thus causing valve action (as already mentioned). Figure 5-36 shows what happens when a left turn is made. Turning the steering wheel to the left (as shown) makes the pitman arm swing

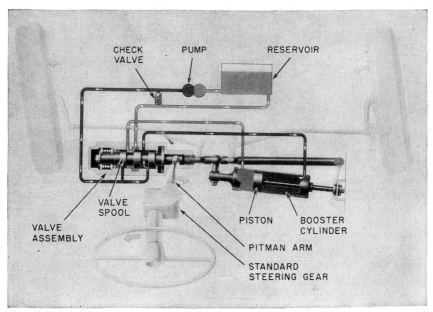

FIG. 5-36. Schematic view of linkage-type power steering shown in previous illustration. Arrows show direction of oil flow when a left turn is being made. Large arrows show direction steering wheel, pitman arm, and front wheels turn. (*Lincoln-Mercury Division of Ford Motor Company*)

to the right. The ball on the end of the pitman arm moves the valve spool to the right. Now, oil under pressure from the pump can flow through the valve body only to one side of the piston in the booster cylinder. In the illustration, oil flows into the cylinder on the right side of the piston as shown by the arrows. Since the piston is fastened to the car frame by the piston rod, it cannot move. Therefore, the hydraulic pressure in the cylinder causes the cylinder itself to move. The cylinder is fastened to the connecting rod. Thus, the major effort of steering is supplied by the booster cylinder. As the cylinder moves to the right (in the illustration), the oil in

[123]

the left-hand side flows back to the reservoir through the valve body (as shown by the arrows). Note that movement of the valve spool to the right has connected the left-hand side of the cylinder to the reservoir.

2. *Booster cylinder.* Figure 5-38 is a cutaway view of the booster cylinder. The cylinder is made up of two concentric shells. Oil

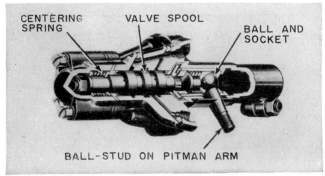

Fɪɢ. 5-37. Cutaway view of valve assembly showing valve spool, centering springs, and ball-and-socket attachment of pitman arm to valve-spool stem. (*Lincoln-Mercury Division of Ford Motor Company*)

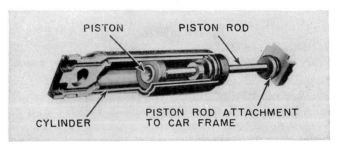

Fɪɢ. 5-38. Cutaway view of booster cylinder showing relationship of piston, rod, cylinder and rod attachment. (*Lincoln-Mercury Division of Ford Motor Company*)

flows between the two shells to enter the piston-rod end of the cylinder. The end of the piston rod is attached to the car frame by a flexible connection so that some movement of the rod can take place to permit its alignment with the cylinder as the cylinder moves back and forth during steering.

§70. Linkage-type power steering (integral valve and power cylinder)
Figure 5-39 shows two methods of attaching the linkage-type power-

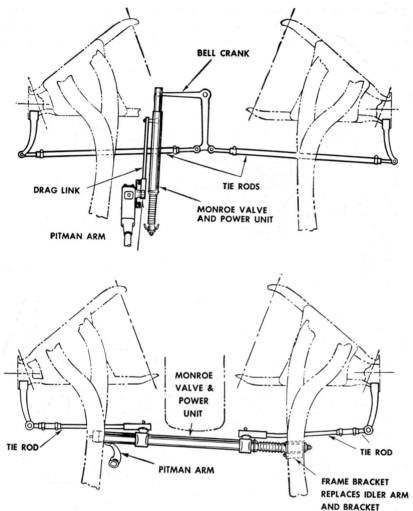

FIG. 5-39. Two methods of attaching the one-unit type (valve an power cylinder in a single unit) of linkage power steering. Top, in center-point steering. Bottom, in relay type of steering. (*Monroe Auto Equipment Company*)

steering unit in which the valve assembly and power cylinder are one unit. In either case, the piston rod of the power cylinder is attached to the car frame. The cylinder is linked to the steering linkage and forms a part of it. Note that this assembly is called the *power link* since it is a part of the linkage and, at the same time, supplies steering power.

[125]

Figure 5-40 is a cutaway view of the power-steering assembly, while Fig. 5-41 is a schematic view of the assembly installed in a linkage system. Figure 5-41 shows the actions during a left turn. When the steering wheel is turned, the ball on the end of the pitman

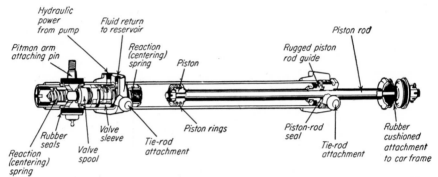

Fig. 5-40. Cutaway view of one-unit type of linkage power-steering assembly. (*Monroe Auto Equipment Company*)

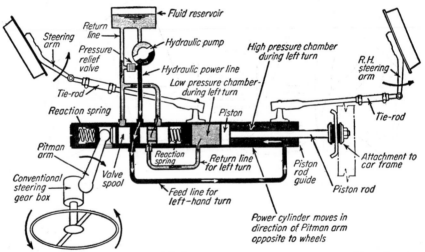

Fig. 5-41. Schematic view of linkage-type power-steering assembly, showing oil flow and movement of parts when a left turn is made. (*Monroe Auto Equipment Company*)

arm shifts the valve spool to the right. This permits oil to flow from the pump under pressure, through the ports in the valve section of the assembly, and into the right-hand side of the power cylinder. The high-pressure oil then forces the cylinder to move to the right and the movement of the cylinder provides the major steering effort.

[126]

§**71. Chrysler power steering** Two models are discussed here, the coaxial and the constant control (the later model).

A. Coaxial power steering. In this unit all the major working parts lie along a common axis (or are *coaxial*). The operating piston, spool valve, and steering shaft are all in a line. Figure 5-42 is a cutaway view of the steering gear. The following paragraphs describe the operation of the unit.

1. Construction. Oil pressure is provided by an oil pump mounted on the generator. This is the arrangement used with the Gemmer

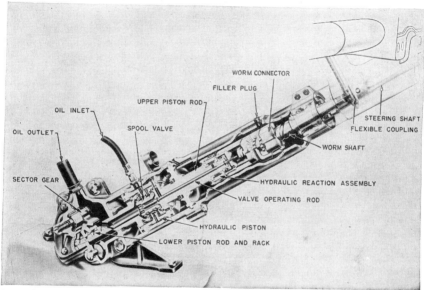

Fig. 5-42. Cutaway view of coaxial power-steering gear. (*De Soto Division of Chrysler Corporation*)

power-steering system (§68). The oil is directed, under pressure, to a spool valve centered in the piston (Fig. 5-43). This spool valve is similar to the one used in the Saginaw power-steering unit. The spool valve is mechanically linked to the steering wheel through a valve-operating rod, the worm connector, and worm shaft (see Fig. 5-42). The worm connector is a recirculating ball nut similar to the recirculating ball nut used on several other steering gears (see Figs. 5-19, 5-20, and 5-24). It is assembled on the worm shaft and moves up or down as the steering and worm shafts are turned. This movement causes the spool valve to move up or down since

[127]

the spool valve is linked to the worm connector by the valve-operating rod.

The valve movement causes oil passages to be opened and closed so oil at high pressure is directed against one end of the piston. The piston therefore moves. This movement, in turn, is carried through the rack on the end of the lower piston rod to the sector gear on the pitman arm.

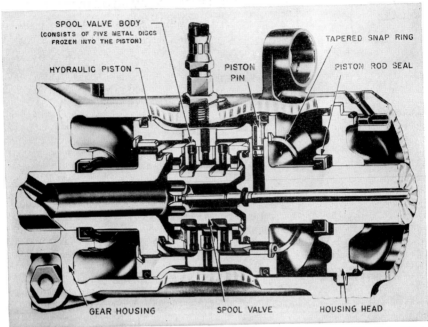

Fig. 5-43. Piston and spool valve in coaxial power-steering gear. (*De Soto Division of Chrysler Corporation*)

2. *Operation.* During straight-ahead driving, the valve spool is centered inside the piston and the same pressure is directed against both ends of the piston (Fig. 5-44). Since the oil passages between the valve and the piston lands are open, there is little restriction of the oil. The pressure is low and there is no tendency for the piston to move.

However, when the driver turns the steering wheel away from straight ahead, the hydraulic system goes into operation to provide steering assistance. Let us consider, for example, what happens when a left turn is made. As the driver turns the steering wheel to

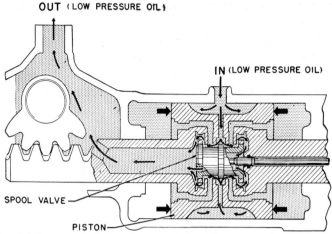

Fig. 5-44. Oil flow with spool valve centered in the piston. (*De Soto Division of Chrysler Corporation*)

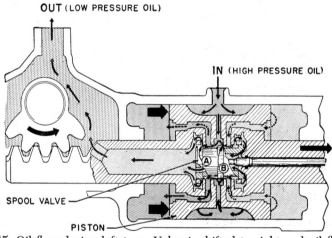

Fig. 5-45. Oil flow during left turn. Valve is shifted to right and oil flows and builds up pressure against the left end of the piston so piston is moved to right as shown by heavy arrows. (*De Soto Division of Chrysler Corporation*)

the left, the worm threads down into the worm connector (or recirculating ball nut) since it has a left-hand thread. This causes the nut to move upward. The first effect of the upward movement is that the valve-operating rod moves upward, carrying the valve spool with it. This displaces the valve spool slightly with respect to the piston as shown in Fig. 5-45. Now, note that oil flow is restricted at points *A* and *B*. Oil pressure therefore builds up on

[129]

one end of the piston. At the same time, the oil ahead of the other end of the piston is released to the low-pressure side of the hydraulic system. This means that the piston and rack assembly is moved (to the right, as shown by the heavy arrows in Fig. 5-45). The rack causes the sector and pitman shaft to rotate so that the front wheels are turned as in a left turn. As long as the driver continues to rotate the steering wheel, he keeps the valve moving slightly ahead of the piston so that hydraulic pressure continues to assist him.

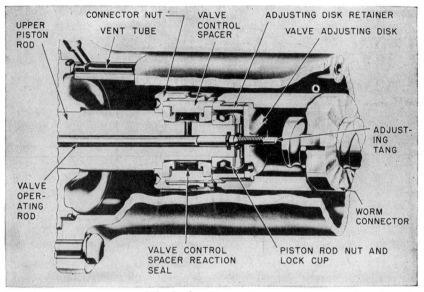

Fig. 5-46. Cutaway view of the hydraulic reaction assembly. (*De Soto Division of Chrysler Corporation*)

If the driver should stop turning the wheel and hold it stationary, then the valve is also held stationary. The piston moves up slightly so it is approximately centered with respect to the valve as shown in Fig. 5-44.

3. *Steering feel.* "Steering feel" is produced by the reaction seal which is located in the hydraulic reaction assembly (Fig. 5-42). This device applies a reaction to the steering wheel that is proportional to steering effort. Thus, when steering is hard, it causes a stronger reaction at the wheel than when steering is easy. This gives the driver full steering feel at all times. However, most of the actual steering effort is provided hydraulically.

To see how this feel is achieved, let us review the manner in which the spool valve and the piston are attached to the worm connector. The spool valve is mechanically linked by the valve-operating rod. The piston is attached through the upper piston rod and the reaction seal. Figures 5-46 and 5-47 show the details of these attachments. The reaction seal is rubber. Oil under operating pressure flows into the undercut part of the seal. The oil pressure forces the seal to expand outward and endwise (in both directions) against the two seal retainers. This endwise force tends to hold the two seal retainers in their outer positions (as shown in Fig. 5-47). But with the seal retainers in the outer positions, the piston is cen-

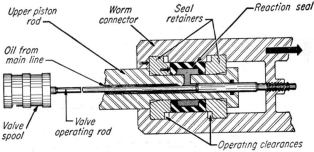

Fig. 5-47. Simplified sectional view of hydraulic reaction assembly. Main-line oil pressure applied inside reaction seal attempts to push both seal retainers out so piston is moved to centered position on valve spool. (*De Soto Division of Chrysler Corporation*)

tered on the valve. You will remember that steering assistance results when the valve moves away from the centered position (see Fig. 5-45); this allows oil pressure to be built up against one end of the piston. The same oil pressure passes along the valve-operating rod and enters the reaction-seal chamber, where it tends to expand the reaction seal and force the two seal retainers out so that the piston centers on the valve. Thus, increasing the oil pressure—due to hard steering—causes an increased reaction through the reaction seal to the steering wheel. With relatively low oil pressure—light steering—the reaction seal offers relatively little resistance when the valve is off center from the piston. However, harder steering requirements (as in parking, for example) cause a higher oil pressure and a greater reaction feel. This is a proportional relationship. Most of the steering effort is taken care of hydraulically.

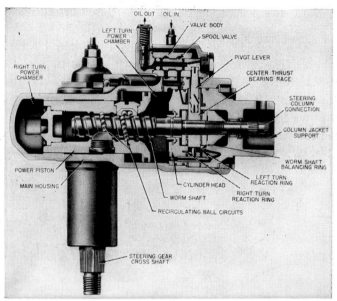

FIG. 5-48. Cutaway view of constant-control power-steering unit. (*Chrysler Division of Chrysler Corporation*)

If the hydraulic system should fail for any reason, mechanical steering results. The worm connector operates directly through the seal retainers against the upper piston rod, causing the rod and piston to move up or down as the steering wheel is turned. This moves the lower piston rod and rack. The sector and pitman arm are therefore rotated. Steering under these circumstances naturally requires a greater effort on the part of the driver, since he is receiving no hydraulic assistance.

B. *Chrysler constant-control power steering.* This power unit is used on late-model automobiles made by the Chrysler Corporation. In many ways it is similar to the Saginaw in-line power-steering unit (§67, *B*). Figure 5-48 is a cutaway view of the unit. Note that it has a pivot lever which forms a linkage between the thrust bearing and the spool valve. The operation of the unit is similar to others already described. When the steering wheel is turned, a slight endwise movement of the worm shaft occurs. This is due to end thrust through the worm. The endwise movement moves the thrust bearing, causing the pivot lever to pivot. Figure 5-49 shows the position of the pivot lever and spool valve when the car is moving straight forward. Figure 5-50 shows their positions when a left turn is made.

[132]

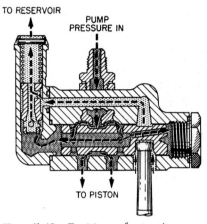

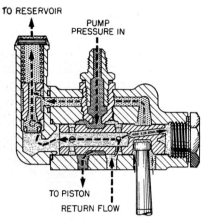

Fig. 5-49. Position of steering-gear valve in straight-ahead driving. (*Chrysler Division of Chrysler Corporation*)

Fig. 5-50. Position of steering-gear valve when car is making a left turn. (*Chrysler Division of Chrysler Corporation*)

Here the worm shaft has been thrust upward (to right in Fig. 5-48) so that the upper end of the pivot lever moves downward (to left in Fig. 5-50). This moves the spool valve as shown so that high-pressure oil is directed to the lower side of the power piston (left in Fig. 5-48) while the return line from the upper side of the power piston is opened. The oil pressure therefore assists the turn.

§**72. Other steering systems**   In addition to hydraulic pressure, other systems use mechanical assistance from the engine or air pressure to help in steering. To increase maneuverability, some applications use four-wheel steering (with or without power steering).

1. Full mechanical power steering. One power-steering system employs mechanical power directly from the engine. It does not use hydraulic pressure as in the power-steering systems previously described. Power is supplied by an input shaft driven from the engine-crankshaft pulley through a V belt. The input shaft, through a ratchet arrangement, drives a pinion gear in the steering assembly. Rotary motion from this pinion is carried through a pair of pinion gears to a pair of ring gears. Each ring gear carries within it a multiple-disk clutch. The upper clutch assists in a left turn, while the lower clutch assists in a right turn. Their respective ring gears are turning in opposite directions; the upper ring gear turns to the left, the lower to the right.

[133]

In operation, when the steering wheel is turned and a pull of more than 2 pounds is required at the wheel rim, the clutch actuating plate moves up or down to actuate one or the other clutch. For example, when a left turn is made, the actuating plate moves upward. This compresses the upper clutch; that is, the disks in the clutch are moved together so that power is transmitted through the clutch. This power is applied, through the clutch hub, to the steering shaft so the driver is assisted in his steering effort. When

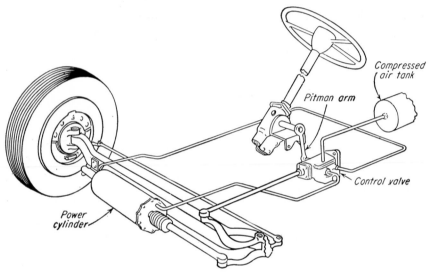

Fig. 5-51. Schematic layout of air power-steering system. (*Bendix-Westinghouse Automotive Air Brake Company*)

he makes a right turn, the lower clutch—which applies turning effort in the opposite direction to the upper clutch—acts to assist.

2. *Air power-steering system.* Figure 5-51 is a schematic diagram of a power-steering system that uses compressed air. Compressed air is supplied by an engine-driven air compressor. Note that the system is the linkage type with a control-valve assembly that is actuated by the pitman arm. The control valve is moved one way or the other by the pitman arm as the steering wheel is turned. This causes compressed air to be admitted to one or the other end of the power cylinder. The compressed air then forces a piston to move in the cylinder. This movement is carried by the piston rod to the steering linkage, and major steering assistance is thereby furnished. The system is balanced to provide steering feel.

[134]

3. *Four-wheel steering.* On some vehicles, all four wheels are steered as the steering wheel is turned. This makes for greater maneuverability of the vehicle. The rear, or driving, axles have universal joints that permit the rear wheels to turn at various angles with the frame of the vehicle. The driving axles continue to deliver power to the wheel through the universal joints, regardless of the angle at which the wheels are turned. The steering-knuckle arms on the rear wheels are linked by tie rods to the same pitman arm to which the front-wheel steering-knuckle arms are linked. Quite often, a vehicle with four-wheel steering also has provision for four-wheel driving—that is, all four wheels are linked by propeller shafts or driving shafts to the engine.

CHECK YOUR PROGRESS

Progress Quiz 4

Once more we pause to give you a chance to check up on yourself and find out what progress you are making in your studies of automotive steering systems. Remember, these quizzes are included for your benefit; they are designed to help you. They not only let you review the material you have just covered, but they also help your memory by laying out before you the important points that you should remember. The more times you think of a fact, the easier it will be for you to remember it. Then too, if you write down the answers to the questions, your memory will be further fortified. Writing down a fact is a fine way to remember it.

Completing the Sentences

The sentences below are incomplete. After each sentence there are several words or phrases, only one of which will correctly complete the sentence. Write down each sentence in your notebook, selecting the proper word or phrase to complete it correctly.

1. Two basic types of power-steering systems are the _____ *integral and valve   booster and power   integral and linkage*
2. The maker of the power-steering system (used in General Motors cars) that has a valve spool in the steering shaft line is *Gemmer   Saginaw   Monroe*
3. The valve spool in the Saginaw power-steering unit is centered, in neutral, by _____ *two centering springs   oil pressure five spring and plunger sets   two disk clutches*

4. In the Saginaw unit, endwise movement of the valve spool is caused by reaction between the   *worm and ball nut*   *piston and valve*   *pitman arm and ball socket*

5. In the Saginaw unit, movement of the valve spool from the neutral position results in application of hydraulic oil pressure from the oil pump to one or the other side of the   *pitman arm*   *connecting rod*   *power cylinder*   *disk clutch*

6. The maker of the power-steering system (used in Chrysler Corporation cars) that has a valve-operating block which actuates four valves is   *Gemmer*   *Saginaw*   *Monroe*

7. The valve-operating block is moved due to side thrust between *cylinder and valve*   *two spur gears*   *steering wheel and shaft*

8. In the power-steering assembly having four valves—two distribution and two reaction—during neutral, or straight-ahead driving, all four valves are   *fully closed*   *partly open*   *fully open*

9. In the linkage type of power-steering system, the swinging end of the pitman arm actuates   *a spool valve*   *a tie rod* *an oil pump*   *an idler lever*

10. In the linkage type of power-steering system, the piston rod is attached at one end to   *a tie rod*   *a connecting rod* *the car frame*

CHAPTER CHECKUP

NOTE: Since the following is a chapter review test, you should review the chapter before taking it.

You have now completed your studies of the construction and operation of automotive suspension and steering systems. The next few chapters describe trouble shooting, maintenance, and repair procedures on these systems. Before you start on them, you should have a good understanding of how the units operate. The checkup that follows tests your knowledge of steering systems as discussed in the chapter you have just finished. If you have any trouble answering the questions, it means you should reread the chapter. If that happens, don't worry; most good students make it a habit to reread their lessons several times. Few people can remember everything they read, especially when they read it only once or twice. Write your answers to the test below in your notebook. Writing down the answers helps you remember them. Also, it makes your notebook an increasingly valuable reference you can go to when you need some information in a hurry.

[136]

Correcting Parts Lists

The purpose of this exercise is to give you practice in spotting unrelated parts in a list. In each list below, there is one item that does not belong. Write down each list in your notebook, but do not write down the item that does not belong.

1. In front-end geometry, factors that are involved include camber, caster, kingpin inclination, toe-in, toe-up, toe-out on turns.
2. The included angle, in front-end geometry, includes camber angle, caster angle, and kingpin-inclination angle.
3. Included in the various types of steering linkage are pitman arm, tie rods, drag link, idler arm, connecting rod, steering-knuckle arms, propeller shaft.
4. Parts to be found in all the steering gears described in the chapter include worm, pitman-arm shaft, oil pump, housing.
5. Parts included in the Saginaw power-steering gear include ball nut, valve spool, piston, power cylinder, plungers and springs, valve-centering block.
6. Parts to be found in the Gemmer power-steering unit include spur gears, valve spool, valve-operating block, distribution valves, reaction valves, valve body.
7. Parts included in the linkage-type power-steering system include valve spool, power cylinder, centering spring, piston, friction clutch.
8. Parts included in the fully mechanical power-steering system are input shaft, multiple-disk clutches, pinion gears, ring gears, valve spool.

Unscrambling the Lists (Front-end Geometry)

When the two lists below are unscrambled and combined, they will form a list of the factors involved in front-end geometry and the conditions that produce them. To unscramble the lists, take one item at a time from the list to the left, and then find the item from the list to the right that goes with it. Write down the results in your notebook.

1 camber	5 turning in of front wheels
2 kingpin inclination	4 forward or backward tilt of kingpin
3 included angle	1 tilting of wheel from vertical
4 caster	2 inward tilt of kingpin from vertical
5 toe-in	3 camber plus kingpin inclination angle

Purpose and Operation of Components

In the following, you are asked to write down the purpose of certain factors, or the operation of various components in the steering systems described in the chapter. If you have any difficulty in writing down your explanations, turn back to the chapter and reread the pages that will give you the answer. Don't copy, try to tell it in your own words. This is an excellent way to fix the explanation firmly in your mind. Write in your notebook.

1. What is the purpose of camber?
2. How does kingpin inclination tend to return the front wheels to straight-ahead when the steering wheel is released?
3. What is the point of intersection?
4. Which will the wheel attempt to do, toe in or toe out, when the point of intersection is below the road surface? Why?
5. What is the relation between caster and the tendency for the car to roll out, or bank, on turns?
6. Does positive caster make the car tend to roll out, or bank, on turns?
7. What is toe-in?
8. Describe the action of a typical steering gear when the steering wheel is turned.
9. Describe the action of the Saginaw power-steering unit when a right turn is made.
10. Describe the action of the Gemmer power-steering unit when a right turn is made.
11. Describe the action of the linkage-type power-steering system when a right turn is made.

SUGGESTIONS FOR FURTHER STUDY

You will have a good chance to study various types of steering linkages at any service station where automobiles are raised on lifts for chassis lubrication. Note the different ways in which the pitman arm is linked to the steering knuckles at the front wheels. Automotive repair shops that handle steering-gear servicing will usually have steering-gear parts that you may be able to examine. Note especially that different methods employed in the various steering gears for changing the rotary motion of the steering wheel into a swinging motion of the pitman arm. If you have a chance, examine the internal mechanisms in power-steering units. The automotive manufacturers describe these mechanisms in their shop manuals. If you can study these manuals, you will learn a great deal about how such units are constructed and serviced. Be sure you write down in your notebook any important facts you run across. This helps you remember the facts, and also gives you a permanent record of them.

6: Diagnosing steering and suspension troubles

THIS CHAPTER discusses various steering and suspension troubles and relates them to possible causes and corrections; that is, it describes trouble-shooting procedures on steering and suspension systems. It is not an easy chapter to study, but at the same time it is an important chapter. It gives you the information you need to understand the various effects produced by different kinds of trouble in the steering and suspension. In addition, it tells you what corrections should be made. Later chapters explain how these corrections are made.

§73. How to study this chapter   There are different ways to study this chapter. One way is to go through it page by page, just as you have studied the previous chapters. Perhaps a better way would be to take one complaint at a time (as listed in the trouble-shooting chart), read through the possible causes and checks or corrections, and then study the section later in the chapter that discusses the complaint. For example, you could take Complaint 1. Excessive play in steering system, and after reading the causes and checks or corrections listed in the second and third columns in the chart, you could turn to §76 referred to under the complaint and study it.

Since a knowledge of trouble causes and corrections is so helpful, you will probably be referring to the trouble-shooting chart many times. One way to help yourself remember the complaints, causes and corrections is to write each complaint, with its list of causes and corrections, on a separate 3- by 5-inch card. Then carry the cards around with you. Every time you get a chance—for instance when you are riding a bus, eating your lunch, or getting ready for bed— take out a card and read it over. Soon you will know the complaints, and their causes and corrections, from "A to Z."

§74. Need for logical procedure   If you are able to relate various complaints with the conditions that cause them, you are much better off than the fellow who seeks blindly to find what is causing a trouble. You will know what items to check and correct to eliminate the trouble. You can save a great deal of time and effort when you know where to look.

The chart that follows tells you where to look when various complaints are made regarding the steering or suspension. Following the chart are detailed explanations of the checking procedures to use with each of the trouble complaints. Then, the next few chapters describe the servicing or repair procedures required to correct the trouble.

§75. The trouble-shooting chart   A variety of steering and suspension troubles will bring the driver to the mechanic, but it is rare that the driver will have a clear idea of what causes his trouble. He can detect an increase in steering difficulty, hard steering, or excessive play in the steering system. But he probably would not have a very good idea of what would cause those conditions. The chart that follows lists possible causes of these, as well as other steering and suspension troubles, and then refers to numbered sections after the chart for fuller explanations of the way to locate and eliminate the troubles.

NOTE: The troubles and possible causes are not listed in the chart in the order of frequency of occurrence; that is, item 1 does not necessarily occur more frequently than item 2, nor does item *a* under Possible Cause necessarily occur more frequently than item *b.*

STEERING AND SUSPENSION TROUBLE-SHOOTING CHART

(See §§76 to 90 for detailed explanation of trouble causes and corrections listed below.)

Complaint	Possible Cause	Check or Correction
1. Excessive play in steering system (§76)	a. Looseness in steering gear	Readjust, replace worn parts
	b. Looseness in linkage	Readjust, replace worn parts
	c. Worn steering-knuckle parts	Replace worn parts

Complaint	Possible Cause	Check or Correction
	d. Loose wheel bearing	Readjust
2. Hard steering (§77)	a. Power steering inoperative	See Chaps. 10 to 13
	b. Low or uneven tire pressure	Inflate to correct pressure
	c. Friction in steering gear	Lubricate, readjust, replace worn parts
	d. Friction in linkage	Lubricate, readjust, replace worn parts
	e. Friction at kingpin	Lubricate, replace worn parts
	f. Alignment off (caster, camber, toe-in, kingpin inclination)	Check alignment and readjust as necessary
	g. Frame misaligned	Straighten
	h. Front spring sagging	Replace
3. Car wander (§78)	a. Low or uneven tire pressure	Inflate to correct pressure
	b. Linkage binding	Readjust, lubricate, replace worn parts
	c. Steering gear binding	Readjust, lubricate, replace worn parts
	d. Front alignment off (caster, camber, toe-in, kingpin inclination)	Check alignment and readjust as necessary
	e. Looseness in linkage	Readjust, replace worn parts
	f. Looseness in steering gear	Readjust, replace worn parts
	g. Looseness at kingpin	Replace worn parts
	h. Loose rear springs	Tighten
	i. Unequal load in car	Readjust load
	j. Stabilizer bar ineffective	Tighten attachment, replace if damaged

[141]

Complaint	Possible Cause	Check or Correction
4. Car pulls to one side during normal driving (§79)	a. Uneven tire pressure	Inflate to correct pressure
	b. Uneven caster or camber	Check alignment, adjust as necessary
	c. Tight wheel bearing	Readjust, replace parts if damaged
	d. Uneven springs (sagging, broken, loose attachment)	Tighten, replace defective parts
	e. Wheels not tracking	Check tracking, straighten frame, tighten loose parts, replace defective parts
5. Car pulls to one side when braking (§80)	a. Brakes grab	Readjust, replace brake lining, etc. See Chap. 15
	b. Uneven tire inflation	Inflate to correct pressure
	c. Incorrect or uneven caster	Readjust
	d. Causes listed under item 4, car pulls to one side during normal driving, above	
6. Front-wheel shimmy at low speeds (§81)	a. Uneven or low tire pressure	Inflate to correct pressure
	b. Loose linkage	Readjust, replace worn parts
	c. Loose kingpin	Replace worn parts
	d. Looseness in steering gear	Readjust, replace worn parts
	e. Front springs too flexible	Replace, tighten attachment
	f. Incorrect or unequal camber	Readjust
	g. Irregular tire tread	Replace worn tires, match treads
7. Front-wheel tramp (high-speed shimmy) (§82)	a. Wheels out of balance	Rebalance
	b. Too much wheel run-out	Balance, remount tire, straighten or replace wheel

Complaint	Possible Cause	Check or Correction
	c. Defective shock absorbers	Repair or replace
	d. Causes listed under item 6, front-wheel shimmy at low speeds, above	
8. Steering kickback (§83)	*a.* Tire pressure low or uneven	Inflate to correct pressure
	b. Springs sagging	Tighten attachment, replace
	c. Shock absorbers defective	Repair or replace
	d. Looseness in linkage	Readjust, replace worn parts
	e. Looseness in steering gear	Readjust, replace worn parts
9. Tires squeal on turns (§84)	*a.* Excessive speed	Take curves at slower speed
	b. Low or uneven tire pressure	Inflate to correct pressure
	c. Wheel alignment incorrect	Check and adjust
10. Improper tire wear (§85)	*a.* Wear at tread sides from underinflation	Inflate to correct pressure
	b. Wear at tread center from overinflation	Inflate to correct pressure
	c. Wear at one tread side from excessive camber	Adjust camber
	d. Feather-edge wear from excessive toe-in or toe-out on turns	Correct toe-in or toe-out on turns
	e. Cornering wear from excessive speeds on turns	Take turns at slower speed
	f. Uneven or spotty wear from mechanical causes	Adjust brakes, align wheels, balance wheels, adjust linkage, etc.
	g. Rapid wear from speed	Drive more slowly for longer tire life

[143]

Complaint	Possible Cause	Check or Correction
11. Hard or rough ride (§86)	a. Excessive tire pressure	Reduce to correct pressure
	b. Defective shock absorbers	Repair or replace
	c. Excessive friction in spring suspension	Lubricate, realign parts
12. Sway on turns (§87)	a. Loose stabilizer bar	Tighten
	b. Weak or sagging springs	Repair or replace
	c. Caster incorrect	Adjust
13. Spring breakage (§88)	a. Overloading	Avoid overloading
	b. Loose center or U bolts	Keep bolts tight
	c. Defective shock absorber	Repair or replace
	d. Tight spring shackle	Loosen, replace
14. Sagging spring (§89)	a. Broken leaf	Replace
	b. Spring weak	Replace
	c. Coil spring short	Install shim
	d. Defective shock absorber	Repair or replace
15. Noises (§90)	Could come from any loose, worn, or unlubricated part in the suspension or steering system. See §90.	

§76. Excessive play in steering system Excessive play or looseness in the steering system means that there will be excessive free movement of the steering wheel without corresponding movement of the front wheels. A small amount of steering-wheel play is desirable in order to provide easy steering. But when the play becomes excessive, it is considered objectionable by most drivers. Excessive play can be due to wear or improper adjustment of the steering gear, to wear or improper adjustments in the steering linkage, to worn steering-knuckle parts, or to loose wheel bearings.

The tie rods and linkage may be checked for looseness by jacking up the front end of the car, grasping both front wheels, pushing out on both at the same time, and then pulling in on both at the same time, (Fig. 6-1). Excessive relative movement between the two wheels means that the linkage connections are worn or out of adjustment. Service on these items is covered in Chap. 7.

Worn steering-knuckle parts and loose wheel bearings may be detected by jacking up the front end of the car, grasping the wheel top and bottom, and checking it for side play (Fig. 6-2). Try to see how much you can wobble the wheel. Excessive looseness indicates worn or loose parts, either in the steering knuckle or in the wheel bearing. The bearing should be readjusted (§§96, 108,

Fig. 6-1. Checking tie rods and linkage for looseness. (*Bear Manufacturing Company*)

and 114) to see whether the looseness is in the bearing or in the knuckle.

A rough check for looseness in the steering gear can be made by watching the pitman arm while an assistant turns the steering wheel one way and then the other with the front wheels on the floor. If, after reversal of steering-wheel rotation, considerable initial movement of the steering wheel is required to set the pitman arm in motion, then the steering gear is worn or in need of adjustment (Chap. 9).

§**77. Hard steering** If hard steering occurs just after the steering system has been worked on, chances are it is due to excessively tight

[145]

adjustments in the steering gear or linkages. If hard steering develops at other times, it could be due to low or uneven tire pressure, abnormal friction in the steering gear, in the linkage, or at the kingpin, or to improper wheel or frame alignment.

On a car equipped with power steering, failure of the power-steering mechanism will cause the steering system to revert back to straight mechanical operation and a considerably greater steering

FIG. 6-2. Checking for wear in steering knuckle and wheel bearing. (*Bear Manufacturing Company*)

effort. In such a case, the power-steering unit and the hydraulic pump should be checked as outlined in Chaps. 10 to 13.

The steering system may be checked for excessive friction by jacking up the front end of the car, turning the steering wheel, and observing the steering-system components to locate the source of excessive friction. Disconnect the linkage at the pitman arm. If this eliminates the frictional drag that makes it hard to turn the steering wheel, then the friction is either in the linkage itself or at the steering knuckles. If the friction is not eliminated when the linkage is disconnected at the pitman arm, then the steering gear is probably at fault. Steering gear service is discussed in Chap. 9, while linkage service is described in Chap. 7.

If the trouble does not seem to be due to excessive friction in the steering system, chances are it is due to incorrect front-wheel alignment or to a misaligned frame or sagging springs. Excessive caster, especially, will cause hard steering (see Chap. 8 on front-end alignment).

§78. Car wander   Car wander is experienced as difficulty in keeping the car moving straight ahead, so that frequent steering-wheel movements are necessary to prevent the car from wandering from one side to the other of the road. An inexperienced driver may sometimes complain of car wander because he tends to oversteer; he has to keep moving the wheel back and forth unnecessarily to stay on his side of the road.

A considerable variety of conditions can cause car wander. Low or uneven tire pressure, binding or excessive play in the linkage or steering gear, or improper front-wheel alignment will cause car wander. Any condition that causes tightness in the steering system will keep the wheels from automatically seeking the straight-ahead position and the driver has to correct the wheels constantly. This condition would probably also cause hard steering (§77). Looseness or excessive play in the steering system might cause car wander, too, since this would tend to allow the wheels to waver somewhat and would permit the car to wander.

Excessively low caster, uneven caster, or a point of intersection too far above or below the road surface (due to the wrong camber angle) will tend to cause the wheels to swing away from straight ahead so the driver must steer continually. Excessive toe-in will cause the same condition. Front-end alignment is covered in Chap. 8.

§79. Car pulls to one side (normal driving)   If the car persistently pulls to one side so that pressure must more or less constantly be applied to the steering wheel to maintain forward movement, the trouble could be due to uneven tire pressure, uneven caster or camber, a tight wheel bearing, uneven springs, or to the wheels not tracking (rear wheels not following in the tracks of the front wheels). Anything that would tend to make one wheel drag, or toe in or toe out more than the other will make the car pull to that

[147]

side. The methods used to check tracking and front-wheel alignment are covered in Chap. 8.

§80. Car pulls to one side (when braking) The most likely cause
of this condition is grabbing brakes. Such brakes could be due to
the brake linings' becoming soaked with oil or brake fluid, to brake
shoes unevenly or improperly adjusted, to a brake backing plate
loose or out of line, or to other causes that would cause the brake
at one wheel to apply harder than the brake at the corresponding
wheel on the other side. Chapter 15 covers brake service. The other
conditions listed in §79 could also cause pulling to one side when
braking since the condition, from whatever cause, tends to become
more noticeable when the car is braked.

§81. Front wheel shimmy (low speed) Front-wheel shimmy and
front-wheel tramp (§82) are sometimes confused. Low-speed shimmy is the rapid oscillation of the wheel on the knuckle pin. The
wheel tries to turn in and out alternately. This action causes the
front end of the car to shake from side to side. On the other hand,
front-wheel tramp, or high-speed shimmy, is the tendency for the
wheel and tire assembly to move up and down and, under severe
conditions, to actually leave the pavement. Even when the tire does
not leave the pavement, tramp can be observed as a rapid flexing-
unflexing action of the part of the tire in contact with the pavement.
That is, the bottom of the tire first appears deflated (as the wheel
moves down) and then inflated (as the wheel moves up).

Low-speed shimmy can result from low or uneven tire pressure,
loose linkage, excessively soft springs, incorrect or uneven wheel
camber, or from irregularities in the tire treads.

§82. Front-wheel tramp As explained in the previous section, front-
wheel tramp is often called high-speed shimmy. This condition
causes the front wheels to move up and down alternately. One of
the most common causes of front-wheel tramp is unbalanced wheels,
or wheels that have too much runout. An unbalanced wheel is
heavy at one part; as it rotates, the heavy part sets up a circulating
outward thrust that tends to make the wheel hop up and down.
A similar action occurs if the wheel has too much runout. Runout
is the amount the wheel is out of line with the axle so that one part
of the wheel "runs out" or moves to the side more than other parts

of the wheel. Defective shock absorbers, which fail to control natural spring oscillations, will also cause wheel tramp. Any of the causes described in the previous section may also cause wheel tramp. Later sections describe the servicing of the wheel and tire so they can be restored to proper balance and alignment.

§83. Steering kickback   Steering shock, or kickback, consists of sharp and rapid movements of the steering wheel that occur when the front wheels encounter obstructions in the road. Normally, some kickback to the steering wheel will always occur; but when it becomes excessive, an investigation should be made. This condition could result from incorrect or uneven tire inflation, sagging springs, defective shock absorbers, or looseness in the linkage or steering gear. Any of these defects could permit road shock to carry back excessively to the steering wheel.

§84. Tires squeal on turns   If the tires skid or squeal on turns, the cause may be excessive speed on the turns. If this is not the cause, then it is probably low or uneven tire pressure or misalignment of the front wheels—particularly camber and toe-in.

§85. Improper tire wear   Various types of abnormal tire wear can be experienced. The type of tire wear found is often a good indication of a particular defect in the suspension or steering system, or improper operation or abuse. For example, if the tire is operated with insufficient air pressure—underinflated—the sides will bulge over and the center of the tread will be lifted clear of the road. The sides of the tread will take all the wear and the center will hardly be worn (Fig. 6-3). The uneven tread wear shortens tire life. But even more damaging is the excessive flexing of the tire side walls that takes place as the underinflated tire rolls on the pavement. The repeated flexing causes the fabric in the sidewalls to crack or break and the plies to separate (Fig. 6-4). Naturally, this seriously weakens the sidewalls and may soon lead to complete tire failure. Aside from all this, the underinflated tire is unprotected against rim bruises. That is, if the tire should strike a rut or stone on the road, or if it should bump a curb a little too hard, the tire will flex so much under the blow that it will actually be pinched on the rim. This causes plies to break and leads to early tire failure.

Overinflation causes the tire to ride on the center of its tread so that only the center of the tread wears. The uneven tread wear shortens tire life. But more damaging than this is the fact that the overinflated tire does not have normal "give" when it meets a rut or bump in the road. Instead of giving normally, the tire fabric takes the major shock of the encounter. As a result, the fabric may crack or break so that the tire quickly fails.

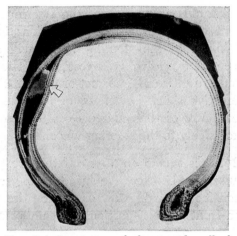

Fig. 6-3. Wear of treads along sides due to underinflation. (*Oldsmobile Division of General Motors Corporation*)

Fig. 6-4. Separation of plies in sidewall of tire resulting from use of tire in underinflated condition. A piece of wood (arrow) has been inserted between the plies to show clearly where separation has occurred. (*Studebaker-Packard Corporation*)

Excessive camber of the wheel causes one side of the tire tread to wear more rapidly than the other, as shown in Fig. 6-5.

Excessive toe-in or toe-out on turns causes the tire to be dragged sideways while it is moving forward. The tire on a front wheel that toes in 1 inch from straight ahead will be dragged sideways about 150 feet every mile. This sideward drag scrapes off rubber as shown in Fig. 6-6. Characteristic of this type of wear are the feather edges of rubber that appear on one side of the tread design. If both front tires show this type of wear, the front system is misaligned. But if only one tire shows this type of wear—and if both tires have been on the car for some time—then a bent steering arm is indicated. This causes one wheel to toe in more than the other.

"Cornering wear," caused by taking curves at excessively high speeds, may be mistaken for camber wear or toe-in or toe-out wear. Cornering wear is due to centrifugal force acting on the car and causing the tires to roll, as well as skid, on the road. This produces a diagonal type of wear, which rounds the outside shoulder of the tire and roughens the tread surface near the outside shoulder. In

  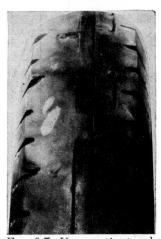

Fig. 6-5. Tire-tread wear resulting from excessive camber. (*Chevrolet Motor Division of General Motors Corporation*)

Fig. 6-6. Tire-tread wear caused by excessive toe-in or toe-out on turns. Arrows point to feather edges which are characteristic of this type of wear. (*Chevrolet Motor Division of General Motors Corporation*)

Fig. 6-7. Uneven tire-tread wear caused by mechanical troubles. (*Chevrolet Motor Division of General Motors Corporation*)

severe cornering wear, fins or sharp edges will be found along the inners edges of the tire treads. There is no adjustment that can be made to correct the steering system for this type of wear. The only preventive is for the driver to slow down on curves.

Uneven tire wear (such as shown in Fig. 6-7) with the tread unevenly or spottily worn, can result from a number of mechanical conditions. These include misaligned wheels, unequal or improperly adjusted brakes, unbalanced wheels, and incorrect linkage adjustments.

High-speed operation causes much more rapid tire wear because of the high temperature and greater amount of scuffing and rapid flexing to which the tires are subjected. The chart (Fig. 6-8) shows just how much tire wear increases with car speed. According to the chart, tires wear more than three times faster at 70 mph (miles per hour) than they do at 30 mph. More careful, slower driving and correct tire inflation will increase tire life greatly.

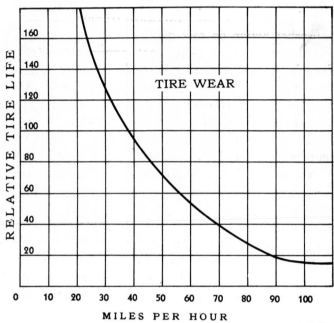

Fig. 6-8. Manner in which tire wear increases with speed. (*Studebaker-Packard Corporation*)

§86. Hard or rough ride A hard or rough ride could be due to excessive tire pressure, improperly operating shock absorbers, or excessive friction in the spring suspension. The spring suspension can be checked easily for excessive friction in leaf-spring suspension systems. Place strips of adhesive tape at the lower edges of the car body, front and back. Lift the front end of the car as high as possible by hand, and very slowly let it down. Carefully measure from the floor to the tape and note the distance. Then push down on the car bumper at the front end, and again slowly release the car. Remeasure the distance from the floor to the tape, and note the difference in measurements. Repeat this action several times to obtain accurate measurements. The difference is caused by the friction in the suspension system and is called *friction lag*. After determining friction lag at the front end, check it at the back end of the car. Make correction by lubricating springs, shackles, and bushings (on types where lubrication is specified), and by loosening the shock-absorber arm linkages, shackle bolts, and U bolts. Then retighten the U bolts, shackle bolts, and shock-absorber linkages in that order. Such a procedure permits realignment of parts that might have slipped and caused excessive friction.

Shock-absorber action on cars giving a hard or uneven ride may be roughly checked by bouncing each corner of the car in turn. This is done by seizing the bumper, pulling up and pushing down on it several times so that the car bounces, and then releasing the bumper.[1] If the shock absorber is operating normally, the car will come to rest immediately. If the car continues to bounce after the bumper is released, the shock absorber is probably defective. A more accurate check can be made by disconnecting the shock-absorber linkage so that the arm is free and then noting the resistance to the arm movement. If the resistance is small or is not uniform through the full arm stroke, or if the movement is very stiff, the shock absorber will require additional attention (Chap. 4).

NOTE: The shock-absorber arm should not be disconnected on front-suspension systems in which the arm forms the upper control or suspension arm unless the wheel alignment is to be adjusted or parts are to be replaced. Disconnecting this arm will change wheel alignment.

§87. Sway on turns Sway of the car body on turns or on rough roads may be due to a loose stabilizer bar or shaft. Their attachments to the frame, axle housing, or suspension arms should be checked. Weak or sagging springs could also cause excessive sway. If the shock absorbers are ineffective, they may permit excessive spring movement which could cause strong body pitching and sway, particularly on rough roads. If the caster is excessively positive, it will cause the car to roll out, or lean out, on turns (see §61). This requires front-wheel realignment.

§88. Spring breakage Breakage of leaf springs can result from (1) excessive overloading; (2) loose U bolts which cause breakage near

---

[1] Some direct-acting shock absorbers, such as those used on Plymouth, cannot be tested in this way since they are valved to permit slow spring oscillations in the interest of smoother riding.

the center bolt; (3) loose center bolt, which causes breakage at the center-bolt holes; (4) improperly operating shock absorber, which causes breakage of the master leaf; or (5) tight spring shackle, which causes breakage of the master leaf near or at the spring eye. Determining the point at which breakage has occurred will make the cause obvious.

§89. Sagging springs Springs will sag if they have become weak—as they might, for example, from habitual overloading. Loss of the shim from the coil spring seat on coil spring suspension—due to failure to return it during overhaul—will also cause the spring to sag, and to seem shorter. Not all coil springs require or use shims (see discussion on shims in following chapter). Defective shock absorbers may tend to restrict spring action and thus make them appear to sag more than normal.

§90. Noises The noises produced by spring or shock-absorber difficulties will usually be either rattles or squeaks. Rattling noises can be produced by looseness of such parts as spring U bolts, metal spring covers, rebound clips, spring shackles, or shock-absorber linkages or springs. These can generally be located by a careful examination of the various suspension parts. Spring squeaks can result from lack of lubrication in the spring shackles, at spring bushings (on the type requiring lubrication), or in the spring itself (leaf type requiring lubrication). Shock-absorber squeak could result from tight or dry bushings. Steering-linkage rattles may develop if linkage components become loose. Under exceptional circumstances, squeaks during turns could develop because of lack of lubrication in steering linkage joints or bearings. This would, of course, also produce hard steering.

CHAPTER CHECKUP

The chapter you have just completed is a hard one. But it is very important to anyone who wants real insight into various kinds of trouble—and their causes—that might occur in steering and suspension systems. The fact that you have come this far in the book shows that you have made a determined start toward becoming an automotive expert. As you increase your fund of knowledge of the automobile, you become better equipped for the future that lies ahead of you. The checkup below will help you check yourself on how well you remember the material you have just completed. If any of the questions seem hard to answer, just review the chapter again. Technical material, such as you are reading, will not "stick with you" the first time you read it. You may have to go over it several times before all the facts will stay in your mind.

Correcting Trouble Lists

The purpose of this exercise is to help you spot related and unrelated troubles on a list. For example, in the list *Hard steering: low tire pressure, friction in linkage, friction in steering gear, front-alignment off, power-steering unit operating, frame misaligned,* you can see that the term *power-steering unit operating* does not belong because that would *not* make steering hard. Any of the other conditions in the list could.

In each list, you will find one item that does not belong. Write down each list in your notebook, but *do not write down* the item that does not belong.

1. Excessive play in steering system: looseness in steering gear, looseness in linkage, excessive caster, worn steering-knuckle parts, loose wheel bearing.
2. Hard steering: low tire pressure, friction in steering system, front-wheel alignment off, tight U bolt, frame misaligned, front spring sagging.
3. Car wander: low or uneven tire pressure, binding in linkage or steering gear, front-wheel alignment off, looseness in linkage or steering gear, engine mounting tight, loose rear springs, unequal load in car, stabilizer bar ineffective.
4. Car pulls to one side during normal driving: uneven tire pressure, uneven caster or camber, tight wheel bearing, wheels out of balance, uneven springs, wheels not tracking.
5. Car pulls to one side when braking: brakes grab, uneven tire inflation, incorrect or uneven caster, defective shock absorbers.
6. Front-wheel shimmy at low speeds: uneven or low tire pressure, looseness in linkage or steering gear, springs too flexible, steering gear binding, incorrect or unequal camber.
7. Front-wheel tramp: wheels out of balance, grabbing brakes, too much wheel run-out, defective shock absorbers.
8. Steering kickback: low or uneven tire pressure, sagging springs, defective shock absorbers, caster too low, looseness in linkage or steering gear.
9. Tires squeal on turns: excessive speed, power steering inoperative, low tire pressure, wheel alignment incorrect.

10. Improper tire wear: underinflation, overinflation, wheel aligned with axle, excessive camber, excessive toe-in or toe-out on turns, excessive speed.
11. Hard or rough ride: excessive tire pressure, underinflation, defective shock absorbers, excessive friction in spring suspension.
12. Sway on turns: loose stabilizer bar, weak or sagging springs, caster incorrect, binding in steering linkage.
13. Spring breakage: overloading, loose center or U bolts, defective shock absorber, underinflation, tight spring shackle.
14. Sagging spring: broken leaf, spring weak, tight wheel bearing, coil spring short, defective shock absorber.
15. Noises in suspension or steering system: caster too low, loose bolts, lack of lubrication, loose rebound clips or spring shackles.

SUGGESTIONS FOR FURTHER STUDY

Careful observation of steering and front-alignment checking procedures in the automotive shop will be of great value to you. If you can watch a good front-alignment man at work, you will be able to learn a great deal about the various factors that go to make up proper wheel alignment. Knowledge of the different troubles that can occur if any of the factors are out of line will help you when you go into the automotive shop or office and have to deal with such matters.

You will want to remember the important trouble-shooting points covered in the chapter. To help you do this, write each trouble and its related causes down on a 3- by 5-inch card, and carry the cards around with you. You can study the cards every chance you get. For example, just before you go to bed, read over one of the cards several times. Or pick up the cards while listening to the radio, and study them. If you do this earnestly, it won't be long before you know the troubles and their causes thoroughly.

7: Servicing steering linkage and front and rear suspension

THIS CHAPTER describes the disassembly and reassembly procedures on various steering linkages and front- and rear-suspension systems. Later chapters describe front-wheel alignment service and steering-gear service (manual and power). It is extremely important to always check and correct front-wheel alignment whenever any work has been done on the front suspension that might disturb alignment. In the pages that follow, steering-linkage and front-suspension servicing procedures for Chevrolet, Ford (two types), and Plymouth are described in detail. Servicing procedures for other cars usually will be found to be similar to one of these four procedures although there may be some variations in individual details. Always refer to the car shop manual covering the specific car model you are working on, when servicing steering linkage and front- and rear-suspension systems.

§91. Chevrolet front-suspension and steering-linkage service   Figure 3-22 illustrates the Chevrolet front-suspension system for which servicing procedures are detailed below. Procedures include:

1. Tie-rod removal, replacement, and adjustment
2. Steering-idler and third-arm-and-bracket-assembly removal and replacement
3. Stabilizer removal and replacement
4. Hub and drum removal and replacement
5. Front-spring removal and replacement
6. Lower control arm (and associated parts) removal and replacement
7. Upper control arm (and associated parts) removal and replacement
8. Kingpin bushing service

[157]

Caution: After most of the above operations, the front-wheel alignment should be checked and adjusted (Chap. 8).

§92. Tie-rod removal and replacement There are two tie rods on Chevrolet to connect the steering idler and the two steering-knuckle arms (see Fig. 3-22). Only the left tie rod (from driver's seat) is adjustable. It has right-hand threads at one end and left-hand threads at the other so it can be easily lengthened or shortened for toe-in adjustment. The tie-rod ends (Fig. 7-1) are self-adjusting for

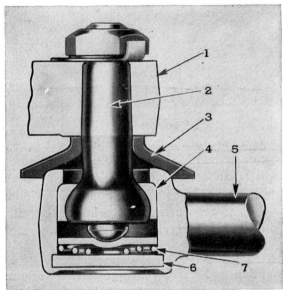

1. Arm
2. Ball stud
3. Seal
4. Ball seat
5. Socket on tie-rod end
6. Plug
7. Spring

Fig. 7-1. Construction of tie-rod ends in steering linkage. (*Chevrolet Motor Division of General Motors Corporation*)

wear and require no attention in service except for periodic lubrication and inspection to make sure they are in good condition. Excessive end play or free up-and-down motion means that parts are worn and that tie-rod ends or the complete tie rod require replacement.

1. Removal. Bend tangs of lock plate down and take off nuts from ball studs. To detach ball stud from steering-knuckle arm, put special remover on threaded end of stud (to protect threads), support steering-knuckle arm, and drive on the remover with a hammer. To detach ball stud from third arm and steering idler, use special ball-stud remover. This remover is like a clamp; the top jaw rests on the threaded end of the ball studs. When the remover screw is turned, the ball studs are forced out of the third arm and steering idler. Tie-rod ends can be removed from left tie rod by loosening clamp bolts.

2. *Replacement.* Install tie-rod ends on left tie rod. Turn both on with the same number of turns. Make sure threads on ball studs are perfectly clean; otherwise, studs may turn in the tie rods when the nuts are turned. Install seals on ball studs. Put ball studs into position in steering-knuckle arms and in third arm and steering idler. Use new stud-nut lock plates, put on ball-stud nuts, and tighten securely. Bend tangs up against flats on nuts to lock nuts in place. Adjust toe-in (§122) and tighten clamp bolts.

1. Bracket
2. Idler and third arm
3. Seal
4. Seal retainer
5. Lock pin
6. Shim
7. Bushing
8. Plug
9. Pivot shaft

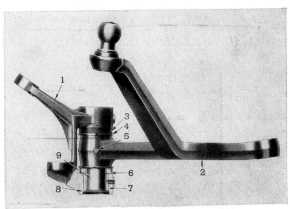

Fig. 7-2. Steering-idler and third-arm-and-bracket assembly. (*Chevrolet Motor Division of General Motors Corporation*)

§93. Steering-idler and third-arm-and-bracket assembly (Fig. 7-2)

1. *Removal.* Raise front of car and put on stand jacks. Detach tie rods as already explained (§92). Remove cotter pin and end plug from the end of the steering connecting rod. Then disconnect rod from ball on steering idler and third arm. Thread plug back into connecting rod to prevent losing parts from rod. Take out three bolts holding steering-idler and third-arm assembly to frame and take off assembly.

2. *Disassembly.* Put assembly in vise, with vise jaws clamped on bracket (Fig. 7-3). Use ⅛-inch punch to drive out lock pin (5 in Fig. 7-2). Remove shaft plugs (8 in Fig. 7-2) by driving with a sharp punch through one plug and into end of pivot shaft. Pivot

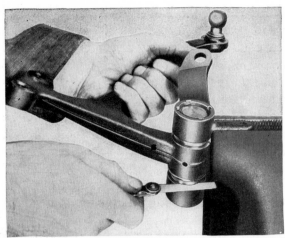

Fig. 7-3. Checking clearance between the steering idler and third arm and the bracket. (*Chevrolet Motor Division of General Motors Corporation*)

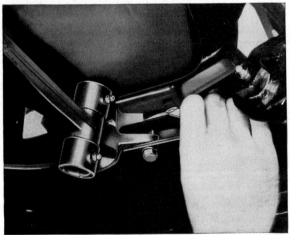

Fig. 7-4. Checking clearance between bracket and frame cross member before installing the upper attaching bolt. (*Chevrolet Motor Division of General Motors Corporation*)

shaft will force other plug out. Remove shaft and take off idler and third arm, with shim. If bushings in bracket are worn, they should be removed with a special bushing driver. Then new bushings should be installed with the same driver. New bushings must be reamed to size (0.9222 to 0.9230 inch). A special, long reamer must be used so that it will pilot in one bushing while reaming the other; this assures good alignment.

[160]

3. *Assembly.* Replace rubber dust seals if necessary. Install shim between lower face of idler and third-arm assembly and the bracket (see Fig. 7-2). Install pivot shaft. Check clearance between idler and third-arm assembly and the bracket (Fig. 7-3). If it exceeds 0.006 inch, install additional shim (this is a special part). Align pin hole in shaft and arm assembly. Drive in new pin. Install pivot-shaft plugs and stake plugs in four places. Install lubrication fittings.

4. *Installation.* Attach assembly to frame cross member with two lower bolts and lock washers. Tighten to 30 lb-ft (pound-feet) minimum torque. Check clearance between cross member at upper mounting hole with feeler gauge (Fig. 7-4). If it exceeds 0.008 inch, add shims as necessary. Then install upper bolt and tighten to 65 lb-ft torque. Attach tie rods (§92). Put rubber dust cover over ball (short end to rear) and attach steering connecting rod to ball. Screw plug into connecting rod until spring is compressed solid. Then back off one complete turn plus amount necessary to insert cotter pin. Install cotter pin. Check and adjust steering connecting rod and the toe-in adjustment.

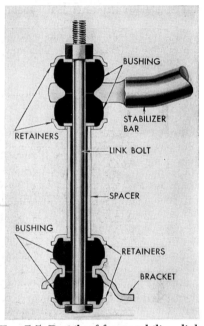

FIG. 7-5. Details of front stabilizer link attachment to lower control-arm bracket. (*Chevrolet Motor Division of General Motors Corporation*)

§94. Stabilizer   The stabilizer bar is attached to brackets on the two lower control arms (Fig. 3-22) through a link bolt. Figure 7-5 shows the details of this link bolt. Rubber bushings insulate the bolt from the stabilizer bar and the brackets. To remove the stabilizer bar, disconnect the links by removing the nuts and pulling the link bolts out through the lower control-arm brackets. Then remove the bolts and nuts that attach the stabilizer brackets to the radiator-support cross member. When reattaching the stabilizer bar, first attach it by the support brackets to the radiator-support cross member, running in the bolts loosely. Next, install link bolts, retainers, bushings, and spacer (Fig. 7-5), and tighten nuts to the limit of the bolt threads. Bounce the front end of the car up and down several times (wheels on floor) so as to settle the parts into alignment. Then tighten the bracket attaching bolts securely.

§95. Hub and brake drum   *1. Removal.* Remove hub caps, loosen wheel-hub nuts, raise vehicle from floor, and take off wheels. Then remove hub grease cap, cotter pin, spindle nut, and washer, and slide drum and hub assembly off (see Fig. 7-6). Take outer

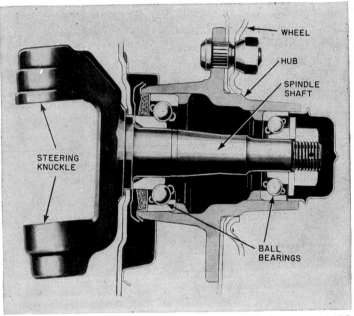

Fig. 7-6. Details of a front-wheel support using ball bearings. (*Oldsmobile Division of General Motors Corporation*)

bearing from hub. Pry out the inner felt seal and remove inner bearing from hub.

   2. Inspecting and replacing parts. Wash all parts in cleaning solvent. Inspect bearings for worn or scored races, worn or pitted balls, or cracked bearing cages. If outer races are damaged or loose in the hub, they should be replaced. This can be done by using special race-removing and replacement tools to tap out the old and drive in the new races. Make sure the race is square and not cocked in the bore when it is driven into place.

If the brake drum is out-of-round, scored, or worn, it must be turned or replaced (see §209). The brake drum can be removed from the hub by cutting off the heads of the three rivets that attach it. Drill the rolled end of rivet first and use sharp cold chisel to avoid enlarging rivet holes in hub or drum. Drive out rivets with pin punch. Clean gasket surface on hub after taking off drum and gasket. Install new drum with new gasket. Rivet together with new rivets, supporting rivet heads when peening over rivet ends.

If the hub or hub bolts are damaged, a new hub and bolt assembly is required. Individual bolts can be replaced. After the brake drum is removed (see previous paragraph), the hub bolts are driven from the hub so that the oil deflector and gasket can be removed. When replacing the oil deflector, use a new gasket, and paint gasket on both sides with heavy shellac or paint to assure a tight seal. Use special tool to peen the shoulder on the hub bolts into the countersink around the bolt holes.

3. *Installation.* Pack inner and outer bearings with a high-melting-point, short-fiber, grease. Put inner bearing in hub; then install a new inner felt seal assembly. Install hub on spindle. Make sure inner oil deflector is in position between inner bearing race and shoulder on spindle. Install outer bearing, pressing it into the hub by hand. Put on spindle washer and nut. Adjust bearings as noted in the following section.

§**96. Adjusting front wheel bearings** It is extremely important to adjust the front wheel bearings properly. Incorrect bearing adjustment will cause the car to have poor steering control. Rapid tire wear and early bearing failure may result.

1. To adjust, tighten spindle nut to specified torque (33 lb-ft on Chevrolet).
2. Check relationship of slots in nut and holes in spindle. If a slot lines up with a hole—either a vertical or horizontal hole—back off nut one-sixth turn until the next slot in the nut lines up with the same hole in the spindle (see *A* and *B* in Fig. 7-7). Then insert and clinch cotter pin.
3. If no slot lines up with a hole when the nut is tightened to specified torque, first note which slot has moved slightly *past* alignment with a hole. Then back off the nut until the next slot in the nut lines up with the *other* hole in the spindle. For

[163]

example, in Fig. 7-7, *C* shows that slot 1 has moved slightly beyond the vertical hole. Thus, the nut should be backed off, as at *D*, until slot 3 lines up with the horizontal hole. This gives a back-off of a little less than one-sixth turn. Backing off more than one-sixth turn will probably give an excessively loose bearing.

4. After adjustments, insert and clinch cotter pin, and install grease cap and wheel. Lower vehicle to floor and retighten wheel nuts. Then install hub caps.

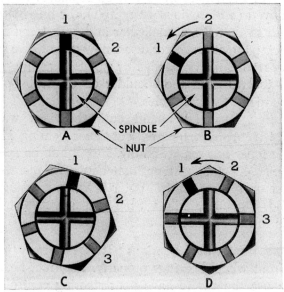

Fig. 7-7. Method of adjusting front-wheel bearings. (*Chevrolet Motor Division of General Motors Corporation*)

§97. Front springs   *1. Checking spring height.* If the car does not seem to be level or if the springs seem to sag, put the car on a level floor and rock it several times. Then measure the distance from the center of the outer pivot bolt and from the center of the inner bushing on the lower control arm to the floor (points *B* and *A* in Fig. 7-8). The difference between the two measurements should be 1⅝ inch, plus or minus ¼ inch. If the difference is less, the spring is sagging and a special ¹⁄₁₆-inch shim can be installed at the top of the coil spring. If more than two shims are required, the spring should be replaced. More than two shims will cause the spring to bottom before the rubber bumper stops the arm movement.

[164]

2. *Spring removal.* Disconnect stabilizer (§94). Remove shock absorber (see Fig. 4-2) by holding upper stem with ¼-inch open-end wrench and removing retaining nut, grommet retainer, and grommet from upper stem. Then remove nut and lock washer which attach shock-absorber lower bracket to the lower control arm. Shock absorber can then be pulled down and out through the opening in the lower control arm.

FIG. 7-8. Maintaining alignment of inner-shaft bracket and frame cross member with long drift punch while lifting bracket with jack. *A*, inner bushing; *B*, outer pivot bolt. (*Chevrolet Motor Division of General Motors Corporation*)

Next, raise front of car and put stand jacks under frame side rails. Put a hydraulic jack under the inner shaft of the lower control arm (Fig. 7-8) and remove nuts and lock washers from the inner-shaft-bracket bolts. Drive out bolts. Lower hydraulic jack slowly to release spring pressure. Remove shims, if present, from upper spring seat.

3. *Spring replacement.* Replacement springs may be supplied with shims; these shims assure correct spring height when installed with a spring. Flat end of spring goes up, with shim (if supplied) above it. Raise lower control arm. Make sure lower end of spring

seats in recess in arm. Put hydraulic jack under inner shaft of lower control arm as shown in Fig. 7-8. Slowly raise arm with jack to compress spring. Use a long drift punch as shown in Fig. 7-8 to maintain alignment between the mounting holes in the inner-shaft bracket and the frame cross member. Attach bracket to frame with bolts, lock washers, and nuts, Remove hydraulic jack and stand jacks, and lower car to floor. Connect stabilizer bar and install shock absorber.

Fig. 7-9. Using special gauge to position arm on shaft. The indexing pin in the gauge enters mounting hole in shaft bracket, and bushing is tightened on shaft until arm touches end of gauge. (*Chevrolet Motor Division of General Motors Corporation*)

§98. Servicing lower control arm   *1. Removal.* Remove and detach the following (as explained in previous sections): wheel, front spring, and tie rod. Then remove lock nut and lubrication fitting from outer pivot bolt (*B* in Fig. 7-8) and take out bolt. Control arm is now free.

2. Disassembly. With inner shaft in a vise (Fig. 7-9), use open-end wrench to loosen the bushing lock nuts (on inside). Remove lubrication fittings from bushings and remove bushings. Take control arm off shaft and then remove the grease seals from the shaft.

3. Assembly. With shaft in a vise (Fig. 7-9), put new grease seals on threaded ends of shaft. Slip them up onto shaft shoulders temporarily where they will be out of the way. Put bushing lock nuts on shaft, with the chamfered sides toward ends of shaft. Position control arm on shaft and then thread bushings onto shaft ends and through control arm. At the same time, thread lock nuts onto bushing. Use special gauge (Chevrolet J-3184) to position arm on shaft. Indexing pin of gauge should be fitted into mounting hole in bracket; then bushing should be turned in, until inner face of arm touches gauge (Fig. 7-9). Hold bushing and tighten lock nut securely. Finally, use torque wrench to tighten bushing (to 150 to 200 lb-ft on Chevrolet). Slip seals off shaft shoulders and into their seats. Install lubrication fittings into ends of bushings.

4. *Outer pivot bolt and bushing.* While the control arm is off, and the outer pivot bolt is out, the bushing in the knuckle support can be removed. Turn the wheel being worked on to the extreme outward position to lock the knuckle support. Bushing can now be backed out of the knuckle support. New bushing should be installed with 150 to 170 lb-ft torque (on Chevrolet).

5. *Installation.* The main point in installing the lower control arm is to make certain that it is centered on the knuckle support. Procedure is as follows. Put new seals over ends of bushing in knuckle support. Then start pivot bolt in lower control arm from rear side. Hold control arm in position at knuckle support with knuckle support centered between two sides of arm. Thread pivot bolt into bushing in knuckle support; be very sure that control arm is centered. Turn pivot bolt in until it contacts the front face of the control arm. If the threads on the bolt and in the control arm index, continue to turn bolt in until its head seats firmly against the rear face of the arm.

If the threads in the bolt and control arm do not index, put a C clamp on the two legs of the control arm and compress them slightly. Keep trying the threads until they index. Then turn in pivot bolt, as mentioned above.

Tighten pivot bolt to 100 to 200 lb-ft, and install lock nut and tighten it to 90 to 120 lb-ft. Use a wire hook to slip seals off ends of knuckle-support bushing and into their seats. Then install spring, attach tie rod, and install wheel and shock absorber. Connect stabilizer bar.

§99. Servicing upper control arm *1. Removal.* Raise front of car and then lower it on a stand jack placed under the outer end of the lower control arm. Remove wheel. Remove front and rear bushings (Nos. 2 and 5 in Fig. 7-10) from upper control arm outer pivot. Remove seals (No. 6) and clamp bolt (No. 3), using a ¼-inch Allen wrench. Pivot pin (No. 4) can now be slid out, and the knuckle support can be swung out of the way of the upper control arm.

Now, the control arm can be detached from the upper spring housing by unscrewing the front and rear bushings from the shaft. After seals are removed, a special upper-control-arm-shaft remover must be used to remove the shaft from the spring housing.

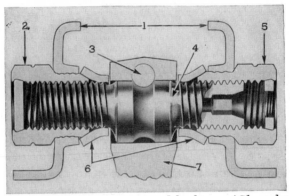

Fig. 7-10. Upper control-arm pivot pin and bushings. (*Chevrolet Motor Division of General Motors Corporation*)

1. Upper control arm	3. Clamp bolt	5. Rear bushing
2. Front bushing	4. Pivot pin	6. Seals
		7. Knuckle support

2. *Installation.* Install shaft from front to rear with special tool used to remove it. Shaft must project out 1⅛ inches in back of spring housing.

NOTE: Replacement shafts are marked *F* at one end to indicate front end.

Caution: Do not drive new shaft in housing too far. Threads on rear end of shaft are tapered. Turning shaft in too far and then backing it out will leave it a loose fit in the spring housing.

Install new seals over ends of shaft and position control arm on shaft. Start both front and rear bushings on shaft. Center arm and start bushings into arm, making sure threads index. Tighten bushings to 45 to 65 lb-ft. Install lubrication fittings, and lubricate bushings. Check arm operation; arm should fall of its own weight.

Refer to Fig. 7-10; attach outer end of upper arm to knuckle support. Put pivot pin through arm and into knuckle support. Hole in pin should be to rear of car. Center pin in knuckle support and install lock bolt, lock washer, and nut. Tighten to 30 to 35 lb-ft. Put new seals over ends of pivot pin.

Start front bushing on pivot pin. Keep knuckle support centered and index bushing threads into control arm. Repeat for rear bushing. Tighten to 45 to 60 lb-ft. Install lubrication fittings, and lubricate. Install wheel, remove stand jack, and lower car to floor.

§**100. Kingpin bushings** *1. Removal.* Raise car with jack under spring seat and remove the wheel, kingpin lockpin, upper bearing plug cover, upper and lower lock rings, and lubrication fittings.

Remove kingpin by first driving upward through the lower bearing plug with a sharp drift punch. This will force kingpin upward so the upper plug is forced out. The kingpin may then be driven out the bottom with a soft steel drift. With the kingpin out, the thrust bearing can be removed from the knuckle bearing and the floating bushings from the knuckle.

Caution: Be extremely careful not to damage the hydraulic-brake hose!

2. Installation. When installing new bushings, make sure the oil grooves line up with the lubrication fitting hole in the steering knuckle. With new bushings in place, put knuckle on knuckle support. Put thrust bearing between the lower yoke of the knuckle and the knuckle support. Shield on bearing should be toward top. Install kingpin from bottom. Be sure to line up the lockpin slot with lockpin hole in the knuckle support. With kingpin installed, check the clearance between the steering knuckle and knuckle support with a feeler gauge. If more than 0.006 inch, put a steel shim between the steering knuckle and top of knuckle support.

To hold the shim in position, use a short pilot (about 1½ inches long) made from an old kingpin. The pilot will hold shim in line as the kingpin is pushed up from the bottom and it will be pushed out as kingpin comes up into place. Install lockpin, bearing plugs, and lock rings; then install upper plug cover. Install lubrication fittings, and lubricate. Install wheel and lower car to floor.

§**101. Ford front-suspension and steering-linkage service** Figure 3-18 illustrates the Ford front-suspension system for which servicing procedures are detailed below. Figure 7-13 is a disassembled view of this same system. Procedures include:

1. Rod-end replacement
2. Rod replacement
3. Steering idler-arm replacement
4. Coil spring and lower supension, or control, arm replacement
5. Upper suspension, or control, arm replacement
6. Spindle support, or knuckle support replacement
7. Bushing replacement

Caution: After most of the above operations, the front-wheel alignment should be checked and adjustments made (Chap. 8).

§102. Rod-end and rod replacement (Fig. 7-11) *1. Rod-end replacement.* Remove cotter pin and nut attaching rod end to spindle arm. Support spindle arm near rod-end stud and drive stud out with a soft metal hammer. Loosen clamp bolt and back rod end from sleeve. Thread new rod end into sleeve. It should be threaded in the same amount as the end of the spindle connecting rod is threaded into sleeve. Tighten clamp bolt, insert rod-end stud into spindle-arm hole and attach with nut and cotter pin.

2. Spindle connecting-rod replacement. Rod is replaced by detaching it from the steering-arm-to-idler-arm rod. Take out cotter pin, turn nut off, support idler-arm rod near stud, and drive stud out with soft hammer. Loosen clamp bolt on connecting-rod sleeve and back rod out. Install new rod, turning it in the same amount as the other rod is turned into its sleeve. Tighten clamp bolt. Then insert rod stud into hole in idler-arm rod and attach with nut and cotter pin.

3. Steering-arm-to-idler-arm-rod replacement. Remove cotter pin and nut attaching rod to steering-gear arm. Support steering-gear arm and drive stud out of arm with a soft metal hammer. Detach spindle connecting rods in same manner. Detach rod from idler arm. Reverse procedure to reinstall rod.

NOTE: Be sure seals are in good condition and installed in proper positions (Fig. 7-11) when replacing rods or rod ends.

§103. Steering idler arm The idler-arm bushings will require replacement if the internal or external threads are worn or damaged. The idler arm or the bracket will also require replacement if the

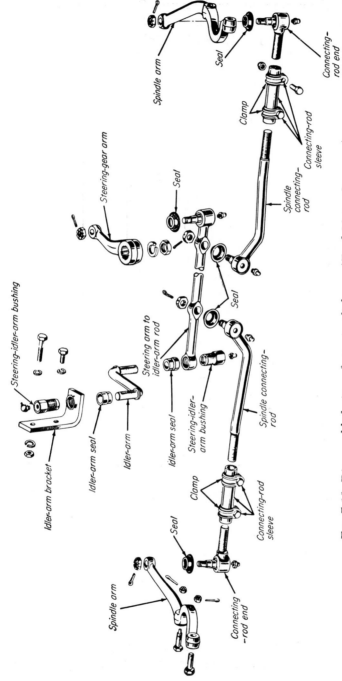

FIG. 7-11. Disassembled view of steering linkage. (*Ford Motor Company*)

Spindle arm

Seal

Connecting-rod end

Clamp

Connecting-rod sleeve

Steering-gear arm

Seal

Spindle connecting-rod

Connecting-rod sleeve

Steering-idler-arm bushing

Seal

Steering arm to idler-arm rod

Idler-arm seal

Idler-arm

Idler-arm bracket

Idler-arm seal

Steering-idler-arm bushing

Spindle connecting-rod

Clamp

Seal

Connecting-rod sleeve

Spindle arm

Connecting-rod end

threads in them are worn or damaged. On the late-model cars, the idler arm should be threaded into the idler-arm-rod bushing until the shoulder on the arm is $^{19}\!/_{32}$ inch, plus or minus $^{3}\!/_{64}$ inch, from the top face of the rod when the arm is in the straight-ahead position (Fig. 7-12). Likewise, the bracket and bushing assembly should be threaded onto the idler arm until the shoulder on the arm is $^{19}\!/_{32}$ inch, plus or minus $^{3}\!/_{64}$ inch, below the bottom side of the bracket (Fig. 7-12). The bracket should then be attached to the car frame.

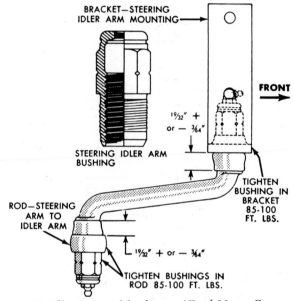

Fig. 7-12. Idler arm and bushings. (*Ford Motor Company*)

Note that prior to installing the idler arm, the bushings are installed in the idler-arm bracket and the steering-arm-to-idler-arm rod. They should be tightened to 85 to 100 lb-ft torque.

§104. Coil spring and suspension arms (Fig. 7-13) Upper suspension arm can be removed without removing the spring. During removal of the lower suspension arm, however, the spring is also removed.

1. Upper suspension-arm removal. Place jack under spring seat in lower arm and raise car. Remove front wheel and wire the spindle support to car frame to avoid excessive movement and damage to

[172]

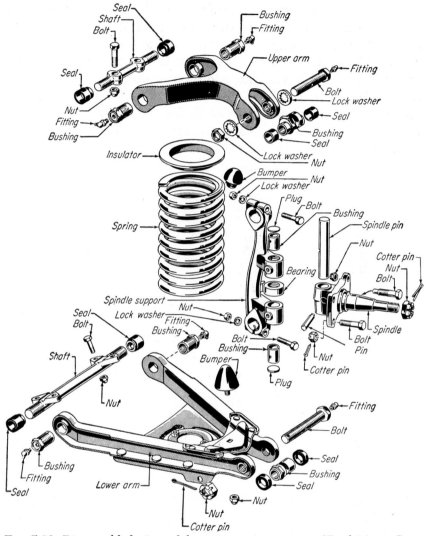

Fig. 7-13. Disassembled view of front-suspension system. (*Ford Motor Company*)

the brake hose. Remove two cap screws that attach upper-arm inner shaft to frame. Take off spindle-support-bolt nut, back out support bolt, and remove upper arm and seals from car. Inner shaft may be removed from upper arm by backing out the bushings.

2. *Upper suspension-arm replacement.* Use new seals if old ones are at all damaged. To install inner bushings, first position inner

[173]

shaft and seals in the arm, then install bushings and tighten to at least 50 lb-ft torque. Position arm on frame cross member and then attach it to the spindle support with the support bolt, with seals and bushings in place. Install and tighten nut to 70 to 80 lb-ft torque. Then attach inner shaft to frame with two bolts, tightened to 60 to 70 lb-ft.

3. *Lower suspension-arm removal.* Support car with stand jacks under frame. Remove shock absorber and detach stabilizer bar from arm. Put hydraulic jack under lower-arm inner shaft and apply enough pressure to keep shaft tight against frame. Remove four bolts holding the shaft to the frame. Lower jack slowly until spring is fully extended. Take out spring. Then detach outer end of lower suspension arm from spindle support by taking off cotter pin and nut and then backing out the support bolt. Take off seals and remove suspension arm. From the suspension arm remove the inner-shaft bushings, inner shaft, and seals.

4. *Lower suspension-arm replacement.* Put the inner shaft and seals in the lower arm, and install the inner-shaft bushings. Tighten bushings to at least 50 lb-ft torque. Attach the lower arm to the spindle support with the support bolt. Tighten bolt to 70 to 80 lb-ft torque; install nut and tighten by like amount. Install cotter pin. Put spring in spring seat of arm, with flat end up. Put insulator on spring. Use hydraulic jack under inner shaft and raise arm. Align bolt holes in inner shaft and frame cross member (see Fig. 7-8). Attach shaft to frame with four bolts, tightened to 45 to 55 lb-ft torque. Install shock absorber and attach stabilizer bar.

§105. Spindle support (Fig. 7-13) 1. *Removal.* Support car with jack under the lower-arm spring seat. Remove wheel and drum assembly. Detach brake backing plate and wire it to the frame to protect the brake hose from damage. Drive out the lock pin locking the spindle pin, or kingpin, to the spindle. Take out upper expansion plug from spindle support so that upper end of spindle pin is exposed. Drive spindle pin down and out. Take off spindle assembly and thrust bearing. Take out the upper and lower support bolts (after removing cotter pins and nuts). Spindle support can now be removed. Upper and lower bushings can be removed from spindle support by loosening the clamp bolts.

NOTE: On later models, the expansion plugs in the spindle support, above and below the spindle pin, are spun into place. This leaves burrs in the countersink when the plugs are removed. The burrs should be removed with a special counterbore tool.

2. *Installation.* Position the upper and lower bushings in the spindle support, aligning the grooves in the bushings with the clamp-bolt holes. Install clamp bolts. Attach spindle support to upper and lower arms with bolts and nuts as mentioned in §104, above. Put spindle and thrust bearing in place on the spindle support and drive spindle pin into place so that groove in pin aligns with locking-pin hole in spindle. Install locking pin. Tap new upper and lower expansion plugs into position and stake them in at least six places.

§**106. Front-suspension bushings** Kits are available that contain all the parts needed to rebush the front suspension. As a rule, it is best to replace all bushings if one bushing is found to be worn. Replacement of the upper and lower arm bushings has already been discussed. When replacing the spindle-support bushings—in which the spindle pin or kingpin turns—the new bushings must be driven into place, burnished, and then reamed to the proper size with special tools. On reassembly, install the spindle assembly and thrust bearing in the yoke of the spindle support, and check the clearance between the upper surface of the thrust bearing and the support. If this is more than 0.018 inch, install shims, as necessary, to reduce the clearance. A minimum clearance of 0.004 inch is best for easy steering.

§**107. Ford ball-joint-suspension service** Figure 3-23 shows the ball-joint suspension for which servicing information is detailed below. Figure 7-14 is an exploded view of this same suspension. Removal and installation of the upper and lower suspension arms (and spring) are covered in the following paragraphs.

1. *Removal of lower suspension arm.* Support car with stand jacks under frame. Remove shock absorber and wheel. Remove cotter pin from nut on the lower ball-joint stud. Unscrew the nut one or two turns. Now use special expanding tool between the two ball-joint studs. Turn hex head on tool to expand it so that the lower ball joint is popped loose. Remove tool. Disconnect stabilizer bar from lower arm. Put a jack under the outer end of the lower arm and raise it until the upper-arm rebound bumper is clear of the

[175]

frame. Now, remove nut from ball-joint stud and lift spindle and brake assembly off the ball-joint stud. Lower the jack until spring is free. Remove spring. Remove nuts and bolts attaching inner end of lower arm to frame and take arm off car. Bolts may have to be tapped out.

2. *Servicing lower suspension arm.* Note that the bushings are pressed into place in the arm. To press old bushings out and new

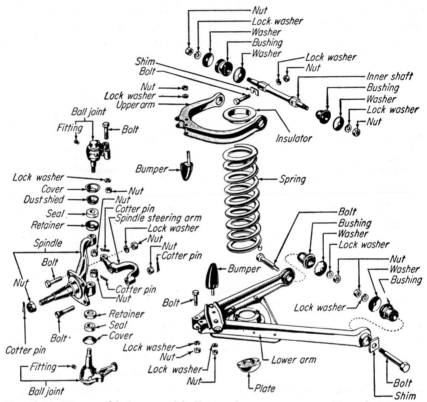

FIG. 7-14. Disassembled view of ball-joint front suspension. (*Lincoln-Mercury Division of Ford Motor Company*)

bushings in, it is necessary to use special bushing tools and an arbor press. When installing a new bushing, press it into place until the shoulder ribs of the bushing bottom on the suspension arm—*but no further.* Replace bushings in pairs. That is, never replace *only one* bushing.

Remove retainer, seal, and cover from ball joint. Examine joint and replace it if it appears defective. But never wash the joint in solvent since this would remove lubricant packed in the joint on original assembly. When replacing sponge-rubber seal, stuff it down into metal retainer cup before pushing it down over the ball-joint stud.

3. *Replacing lower suspension arm.* Attach the rear leg of the arm to the frame cross-member tube and tighten the nut to 80 to 100 lb-ft torque. With the arm thus tight against the tube, install enough shims to fill tightly the space between the bushing in the forward leg of the arm and the front cross member. If more than ½ inch of shimming is required, something is wrong. The bushings

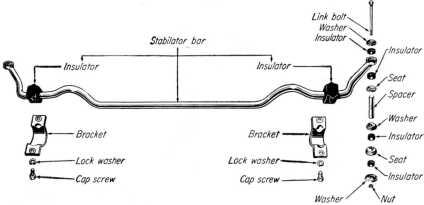

Fig. 7-15. Stabilizer, or Stabilator, bar and attaching parts. (*Lincoln-Mercury Division of Ford Motor Company*)

are not correctly installed, or the arm or frame is bent. Install bolt and washers and run nut on finger tight. Loosen nut on rear bolt. Support the arm at normal curb-load position—about horizontal with outer end slightly lower than inner—and then tighten nuts to 80 to 100 lb-ft torque.

Put coil spring, with insulator, in spring seat. Use jack under lower arm to compress the spring. Make sure both ends of spring are seated. Guide the spindle boss over the ball-joint stud, and install the nut and tighten it to 100 lb-ft. Then tighten further until a cotter-pin hole lines up. Install cotter pin. Remove jack, install shock absorber, and attach stabilizer bar. Figure 7-15 shows the sequence of parts installation when attaching the bar. Install wheel and adjust bearings (§108).

Caution: Do not lubricate rubber bushings since this would cause the rubber to deteriorate.

4. Removal of upper suspension arm. Put jack under lower suspension arm near the ball-joint mounting and raise the lower arm until some of the tension has been removed from the upper bumper. Remove wheel. Wire the spindle to the frame to avoid damage to the brake hose. Remove cotter pin from nut on the upper ball-joint stud. Unscrew nut one or two turns. Use special expanding tool between the two ball-joint studs. Turn hex head on tool to expand it so that the upper ball joint is popped loose. Remove tool and take nut off. Remove the two bolts that attach the inner shaft to the frame. Note carefully the number and location of the shims between the shaft and frame at each of the bolts. When the two bolts are removed, upper suspension arm will come off.

5. Servicing upper suspension arm. Note that the bushings are pressed into place in the arm. To press old bushings out and install new bushings, special bushing tools and an arbor press are required. When removing bushings, the front bushing is removed first (inner shaft still in place). Then inner shaft is removed and the rear, double-shouldered, bushing is removed. On reinstallation, tighten nuts on shaft finger tight, and position shaft so bolt holes are parallel to arm. Then tighten nuts to 80 to 100 lb-ft.

Inspect ball joint as in item 2, above.

6. Replacing upper suspension arm. Position arm on frame cross member and attach with two bolts. Be sure to replace the shims originally used between the shaft and frame bracket. These shims determine wheel alignment (caster and camber—see §124). Tighten bolts to 70 to 80 lb-ft. Put ball-joint stud into spindle boss and attach with nut. Tighten nut to 80 lb-ft and then tighten it further until a cotter-pin hole lines up. Install cotter pin. Install wheel and remove jack. Check front-wheel alignment.

§108. Adjusting Ford front-wheel bearings Figure 7-16 shows the construction, in exploded view, of the Ford front hub and bearings. To check the bearing adjustment, jack up the front of the car, grasp the tire at the sides, and alternately push inward and pull outward. Looseness means the bearing should be readjusted. To readjust, remove the hub cap, grease cap, and cotter pin. Tighten the adjusting nut while rotating the wheel back and forth until a slight drag is felt. This assures proper seating of the bearing cones and rollers. Back off the adjusting nut until the nearest slot in the nut aligns with a hole in the spindle. This is about one-sixth to one-fourth turn, but no more. Lock the adjusting nut with a new cotter pin.

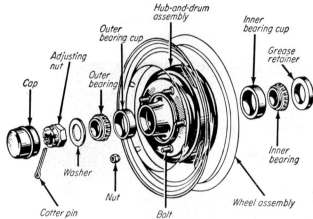

Fig. 7-16. Front hub and bearings in disassembled view. (*Ford Motor Company*)

§109. Plymouth front-suspension and steering-linkage service Figures 7-17 and 7-18 are assembled and disassembled views of the Plymouth front-suspension system for which servicing procedures are detailed below. Procedures include:

1. Tie-rod-end replacement
2. Steering-knuckle-and-support-assembly replacement
3. Upper control-arm replacement
4. Lower control-arm and front-spring replacement
5. Wheel-bearing adjustment

Caution: After most of the above operations, the front-wheel alignment should be checked and adjustments made (Chap. 8).

§110. Tie-rod-end replacement Remove tie-rod end by taking off cotter pin and nut and then driving out stud from steering-knuckle arm. If stud sticks, insert a pry bar between the tie-rod end and the steering-knuckle arm. Then, while prying, tap on the rear end of the steering-knuckle arm with a hammer. Loosen clamp bolt and back tie-rod end off rod. When replacing tie-rod end, be sure to thread it onto the rod an amount equal to the other tie-rod end.

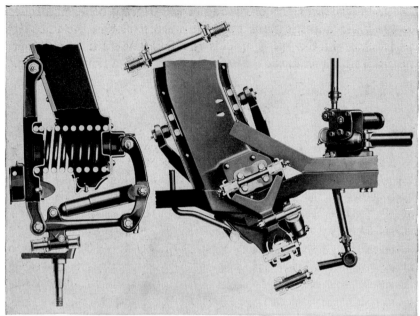

Fig. 7-17. Assembled view of a front-suspension system. (*Plymouth Division of Chrysler Corporation*)

Tighten clamp bolt 10 to 15 lb-ft. Do not overtighten as this may distort clamp and cause it to loosen.

§111. Steering-knuckle-and-support assembly (Fig. 7-18) *1. Removal.* The steering knuckle and support can be removed from the car as an assembly. This is done by detaching the shock absorber, supporting the car weight with a jack under the lower spring seat, and then taking off the wheel and brake backing plate. Handle plate carefully to avoid damaging the brake line. Back out upper and lower support pins from upper and lower arms. Knuckle-and-support assembly is now free and can be taken to the bench for further disassembly and repair. New bushings, seals, and lock pins should always be used when overhauling the assembly.

The old bushings must be removed, and new bushings installed and reamed with special tools. Make sure the slot or identification marks on the bushings face toward the expansion plugs. After the kingpin has been put into place with thrust washer, the knuckle is attached to the support by putting the lock pin and expansion plugs into place and staking them in at least four places.

[180]

2. *Replacement.* Attach the assembly to the upper and lower control arms as explained in later sections describing removal and replacement of these arms. Install brake backing plate and wheel and attach shock absorber.

§112. Control arms and spring (Fig. 7-18) *1. Upper.* The procedure for removing the upper control, or suspension, arm is the same as for Ford (§104) except that the shock absorber must also be detached.

2. *Installation.* No special problems should be encountered when the same control arm and parts are replaced on the car. However, if a new arm is required, then new bushings should be used. This requires the use of a special tool that will maintain the proper spread of the control-arm yoke while the bushings and pivot shaft are installed. The tool is installed and the control-arm yoke spread $\frac{1}{16}$ inch. Then the bushings are started in from both ends. They should be lubricated as they are turned onto the pivot shaft since they must cut their own threads in the control arm. Bushings should be tightened on the control arm to 120 to 140 lb-ft torque.

Before attaching the pivot shaft to the frame cross member, the outer end of the upper control arm must be attached to the steering-knuckle support. To avoid damaging the seals, place one seal on the eccentric bushing at the hex end. Put other seal on the opposite boss of the upper control arm. Then use special tool or a flat strip of metal to hold down the outer lip of the seal in the boss, slide the control arm into position, and remove the tool or metal strip. Attach with pin.

3. *Lower control arm and front spring removal (Fig. 7-18).* Lift car, place a support under the lower control arm, and lower car to take pressure off spring. Then detach outer end of lower arm from knuckle support by removing pin. Raise car to release spring. Remove spring and detach inner shaft from frame by removing four bolts. Control arm is now free.

4. *Installation.* Install new inner shaft bushings and dust seals. A special tool should be used to hold the two sides of the yoke at the proper spread while the shaft and bushings are installed. Bushings should be tightened against the control arm with at least 165 lb-ft torque. Attach the shaft to the frame cross member. Put spring into control arm, flat end up. If spring is equipped with silencers, put above and below spring. Turn spring until it indexes

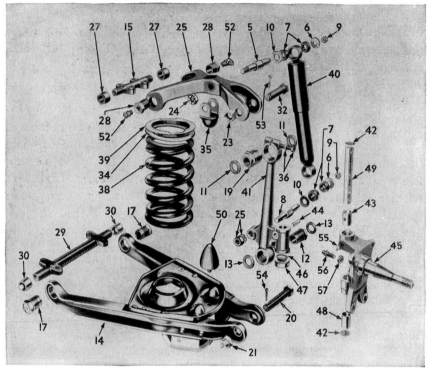

Fig. 7-18. Disassembled view of a front-suspension system. (*Plymouth Division of Chrysler Corporation*)

5. Upper-control-arm shock-absorber stud
6. Front shock-absorber-bushing retainer—outer
7. Front shock-absorber bushings
8. Front shock-absorber lower stud
9. Front shock-absorber mounting nut
10. Front shock-absorber-bushing retainer—inner
11. Upper-control-arm-pin dust seal
12. Lower-control-arm-pin bushing
13. Lower-control-arm-pin dust seal
14. Lower-control-arm assembly
15. Upper-control-arm pivot shaft
16. Upper-control-arm pivot-shaft bolt and lock washer
17. Lower-control-arm-shaft bushing
18. Lower-control-arm-shaft bolt

19. Upper-control-arm-pin bushing
20. Lower-control-arm pin
21. Lower-control-arm-pin nut
22. Upper-control-arm pin
23. Upper-control-arm-pin nut
24. Upper-control-arm shock-absorber-stud nut
25. Upper control arm
26. Sway-eliminator-shaft-and-link assembly
27. Upper-control-arm pivot-shaft dust seal
28. Upper-control-arm pivot-shaft bushing
29. Lower-control-arm pivot-shaft bushing
30. Lower-control-arm-shaft-bushing dust seal
31. Lower-control-arm-shaft-bolt lock

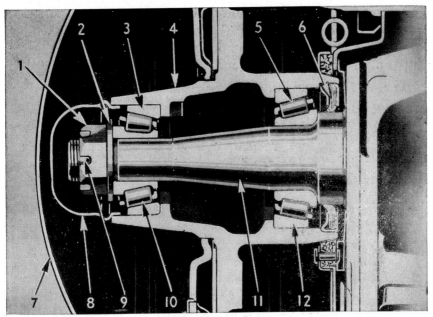

FIG. 7-19. Front-wheel mounting with roller bearings. (*Plymouth Division of Chrysler Corporation*)

1. Bearing nut
2. Bearing thrust washer
3. Outer-bearing cup
4. Hub
5. Inner-bearing cone and rollers
6. Hub dust seal
7. Hub cap
8. Grease cap
9. Bearing-nut cotter pin
10. Outer-bearing cone and rollers
11. Steering knuckle
12. Inner-bearing cup

---

32. Lower-control-arm bolt nut and lock washer
33. Lower-control-arm assembly
34. Front-spring spacer
35. Upper-control-arm bumper
36. Steering-knuckle-support clamp screw and lock washer
37. Frame front cross member
38. Front spring
39. Front-spring silencer—upper
40. Front shock-absorber assembly
41. Steering-knuckle support
42. Steering-knuckle-oil-seal plug
43. Steering-knuckle bushing
44. Steering-knuckle-kingpin lock pin
45. Steering knuckle
46. Steering-knuckle-thrust-bearing shim
47. Steering-knuckle thrust bearing
48. Steering-knuckle bushing
49. Steering-knuckle kingpin (pivot pin)
50. Lower-control-arm bumper
51. Front-spring seat
52. Lubricant nipple
53. Cotter pin
54. Cotter pin
55. Lubricant nipple
56. Stop screw
57. Stop-screw lock nut

with the seat in the lower control arm. Bring arm up until spring enters spring seat in frame. Put jack under lower control arm and lower car to compress spring. Line up knuckle-support bushing and control arm, install pin, and tighten nut to 100 to 110 lb-ft torque.

§113. Wheel-bearing adjustment To adjust the front-wheel bearings (Figs. 7-19 and 7-20), remove hub cap, grease cap, and cotter pin. Rotate wheel and gradually tighten adjusting nut until a slight binding is felt. Back off the adjusting nut to the nearest cotter-pin slot and install cotter pin. Never back off less than half the distance

Fig. 7-20. Disassembled view of front-wheel bearings. See previous illustration for names of numbered parts. (*Plymouth Division of Chrysler Corporation*)

from one slot to the next. In other words, if a slot almost aligns, do not back off to it, but back off until the next slot aligns. This assures sufficient freeness without undue bearing tension, or preload.

§114. Torsion-bar suspension service Figures 2-10 and 3-24 show the torsion-bar front-suspension system used in Chrysler-produced automobiles. Procedures for removal, servicing, and replacement of the components follow.

1. Sway bar. The sway bar is attached to the frame with links as shown in Fig. 7-21. To remove bar, disconnect the two link retaining nuts and concave washers. Then remove the nuts that attach the bar-insulator assembly to the lower control arm. Slide bar out through struts on control arms. If bushings are worn, install new bushings. To replace the sway bar, dip link in water and push it into frame bracket, using a twisting motion. Thread sway bar into position over top of lower-control-arm struts. Engage cushion housings with struts and install lock plates. Insert bolts, lock washers, and nuts. Tighten to 25 lb-ft. Install washers over ends of links (concave side up) and slide links up through bushings. Install washers, concave side down, over ends of links and down on bushings. Install nuts and tighten to 15 lb-ft.

2. *Upper control arm and ball joint.* Lift front wheel off floor with jack under frame cross member. Remove wheel. Take cotter pin, nut, and washer from upper ball-joint stud (Fig. 7-22). Install special tool to place pressure on stud. Hit steering knuckle at ball-joint boss to loosen stud. Remove front and rear pivot bolts from

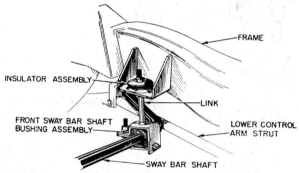

Fig. 7-21. Attachment of front sway bar to frame. (*Chrysler Division of Chrysler Corporation*)

inner ends of control arm and lift out arm. Do not remove support brackets from frame. The ball joint can be unscrewed from the arm after the seals and retainer have been taken off. Note that it is not necessary to remove the arm to remove the ball joint. It can be unscrewed from the arm after the stud has been forced out of the knuckle. When replacing the control arm, tighten nuts on pivot bolts to 60 to 70 lb-ft. Tighten nut on ball stud to 135 lb-ft and install cotter pin.

3. *Lower control arm and ball joint.* Lift front wheel off floor with jack under frame cross member. Remove wheel. Take torsion bar from control arm (see next paragraph). Disconnect shock absorber and strut from arm. Take cotter pin, nut, and washer from ball-joint stud (Fig. 7-22) and use special tool to loosen stud from steering knuckle. Hit knuckle with hammer at stud boss to loosen stud. Take cotter pin, nut, and washer from control-arm shaft. Reinstall nut flush

with end of thread (to protect thread) and use brass drift and hammer to loosen shaft. Remove nut and slide shaft with control arm to the rear out of cross member. Ball joint can be unscrewed from arm after removing seal. To reinstall arm, put shaft and arm into position, install washer and nut, and tighten to 175 to 200 lb-ft. Replace cotter pin. Put ball stud in steering knuckle, install washer, nut (135 lb-ft), and cotter pin. Reattach shock absorber, strut, and torsion bar.

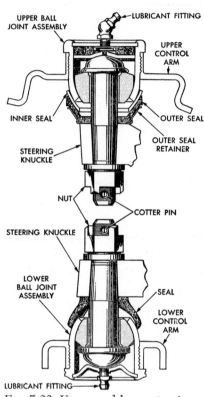

UPPER BALL JOINT ASSEMBLY

LUBRICANT FITTING

UPPER CONTROL ARM

INNER SEAL

OUTER SEAL

OUTER SEAL RETAINER

STEERING KNUCKLE

NUT

COTTER PIN

STEERING KNUCKLE

LOWER BALL JOINT ASSEMBLY

SEAL

LOWER CONTROL ARM

LUBRICANT FITTING

FIG. 7-22. Upper and lower steering-knuckle ball-joint assemblies. (*Chrysler Division of Chrysler Corporation*)

4. *Torsion bar.* Raise vehicle with jack under frame cross member. Back off height adjusting bolt (Fig. 3-25) to release load from torsion bar. Remove lock ring from rear end of bar. Slide bar to rear far enough to disengage front end from lower control arm, then forward to disengage rear end from bracket anchor. When reinstalling bar, turn height adjusting bolt into the swivel bar. Push torsion bar into anchor and turn until anchor is as close as possible to floor pan. Push torsion bar back far enough to permit it to slide forward into the control-arm bracket. Center and install lock ring in rear of anchor housing. Tighten height adjusting bolt until about one inch of threads shows above swivel bar. Adjust suspension height as noted in next paragraph.

5. *Suspension height.* With car on alignment equipment, install special leveling tool to check height. Tires should be properly inflated. If height is not correct, tighten or loosen the height-adjusting bolt (Fig. 3-25).

§115. **Air-suspension service** Figures 3-26 to 3-29 show details of different air-suspension systems. About the only trouble this system might develop would be due to leakage of air or blockage of lines by dirt or condensation. Also, malfunctioning of the compressor or valves could change air pressure so that the car would be too high or too low. Tests for leakage may be made by covering air lines and other parts with soap solution and watching for soap bubbles. Air pressure should be brought up to normal before the test by running the engine for a few minutes. Air pressures may be checked with a pressure gauge. There are special connectors at the valves and compressor to which the gauge may be connected.

1. *Compressor service.* On some cars the compressor and the power-steering pump must be removed as an assembly. On others,

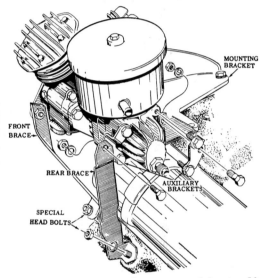

Fig. 7-23. Mounting of compressor for air suspension and hydraulic pump for power steering. (*Oldsmobile Division of General Motors Corporation*)

MOUNTING BRACKET
FRONT BRACE
REAR BRACE
AUXILIARY BRACKETS
SPECIAL HEAD BOLTS

the compressor is separately mounted and can be removed by itself. To remove the separately mounted units, exhaust all air pressure at the reservoir, disconnect oil and air lines, take out mounting bolts, and lift off compressor.

On units mounted with the power-steering pump (Fig. 7-23), loosen compressor pulley nut, remove fan belts, and slip off pulley. Disconnect hoses from compressor and pump. Hold pan under pump to catch oil. Cap pump fittings and hoses to prevent loss of oil. Take out bolts and remove nuts holding assembly to mounting brackets and lift off assembly.

Figure 7-24 is a disassembled view of a single-cylinder compressor. Some cars use a two-cylinder compressor. Before disassembling the unit, clean the outside carefully with a stiff brush and

[187]

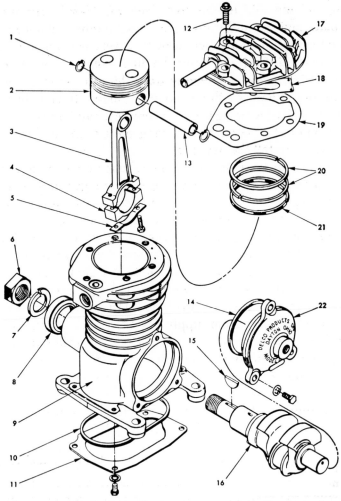

FIG. 7-24. Disassembled view of compressor used in air-suspension system. (*Chevrolet Motor Division of General Motors Corporation*)

1. Piston-pin lock
2. Piston
3. Connecting rod
4. Connecting-rod cap
5. Lock strap
6. Nut
7. Lock washer
8. Seal
9. Cylinder housing

10. Gasket
11. Sump cover plate
12. Cylinder-head attaching bolts
13. Piston pin
14. Bearing housing O-ring seal
15. Woodruff key
16. Crankshaft
17. Cylinder head

18. Valve
19. Cylinder-head gasket
20. Piston rings—compression
21. Piston ring—oil control
22. Bearing housing

cleaning solvent. To disassemble (see Fig. 7-24), remove sump cover plate and gasket by taking out four screws. Remove cylinder head and gasket by taking out six bolts. Invert assembly and take off the rod bolts and rod cap after bending back the lock-strap tabs. Remove piston and rod assembly from the top. Bearing housing is removed by taking out three screws. Crankshaft can then be removed by pulling it straight out. A new seal can be installed in the cylinder housing if required by prying the old one out and using a special tool to install the new one.

If new rings are installed, use a hand hone on the cylinder wall to cut the glaze so they will seat properly. Stagger piston-ring gaps about 120 degrees apart. Use ring compressor when installing piston and rod assembly in cylinder. Attach rod to crankshaft with bolts and secure by bending tabs of lockstrap over boltheads. Use new gasket and attach sump cover. Use new head gasket and attach head. Make sure the flat valve is in place and is undamaged.

On reinstallation, attach compressor in place. Before connecting oil lines, make sure they are free and clean. Run engine briefly to make sure oil will flow from supply line (catch it in a container). Be sure air lines are clean and in good condition. Connect lines. Adjust belt to proper tension and tighten retaining bolts.

2. *Air-spring service.* Figure 3-26 shows one front-suspension system using air springs in disassembled view. Figure 7-25 shows a somewhat different front air spring. To remove a front air spring, raise car frame to take weight off wheel, depressurize the spring, remove connections and attaching bolts, and lift spring out. On some cars it is easier to remove the air spring if the wheel is first taken off. Some specifications call for depressurizing the air spring by loosening the pressure line at the spring. On others the pressure reservoir is first depressurized, and then the leveling valve link is disconnected and the valve arm raised to release the pressure. The installation procedure is the reverse of the above. Be sure air line is clean before connecting it.

Rear air springs are removed and replaced in a similar manner. The weight must be taken off the wheel and, on some cars, the wheel removed. Then the connections and attaching bolts are removed so the air spring can be lifted out. The procedure is reversed to replace the air spring.

3. *Leveling or height control valve.* A variety of leveling valves are used in the different air-suspension systems. Figure 7-26 is a

disassembled view of one type. Figure 7-27 is another. Height can be adjusted by means of the linkage between the valve and the car frame. These adjustments vary with different cars and the car manual should always be consulted.

4. Draining reservoir. The reservoir (or high-pressure accumulator) should be drained every 1,000 miles to eliminate condensation that may have accumulated. If this is not done, sufficient water may accumulate to prevent normal operation of the system. This

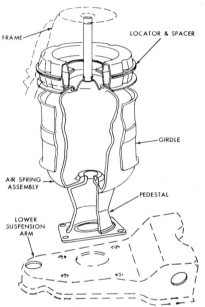

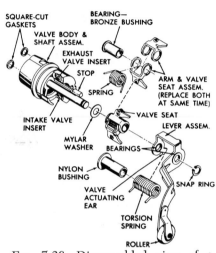

FIG. 7-25. Front air spring on an air-suspension system. (*Mercury Division of Ford Motor Company*)

FIG. 7-26. Disassembled view of a leveling valve used in an air-suspension system. (*Chevrolet Motor Division of General Motors Corporation*)

action is not necessary on closed systems in which the air is recirculated. It is necessary on open systems in which air is drawn into the compressor from the atmosphere.

5. Towing. When towing a car with air suspension, remember that, without air in the system, it has only a few inches of road clearance and that the car is riding on the rubber bumpers. If possible, install special blocks to hold the car up at normal height. Drive slowly and only on smooth roads to avoid damage to the car.

§116. Rear-suspension service

Two basic procedures are required to service rear springs; one applies to leaf springs, the other to coil springs. Chapter 3 described and illustrated various rear-suspension systems.

1. Leaf springs. To remove a rear leaf spring, raise the car with a jack and place supports under the frame rails, just in front of the

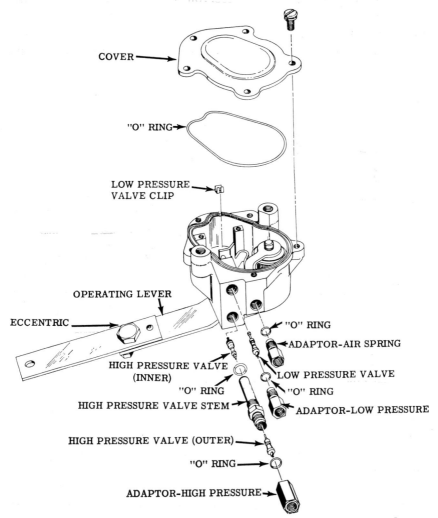

COVER

"O" RING

LOW PRESSURE VALVE CLIP

OPERATING LEVER

ECCENTRIC

"O" RING

ADAPTOR-AIR SPRING

HIGH PRESSURE VALVE (INNER)

LOW PRESSURE VALVE

"O" RING

"O" RING

HIGH PRESSURE VALVE STEM

ADAPTOR-LOW PRESSURE

HIGH PRESSURE VALVE (OUTER)

"O" RING

ADAPTOR-HIGH PRESSURE

Fig. 7-27. Disassembled view of a leveling, or height-control, valve used in an air-suspension system. (*Oldsmobile Division of General Motors Corporation*)

rear springs. With the jack providing pressure under the rear-axle housing, disconnect the shock absorbers and slowly lower the jack until it supports the weight of the rear-axle assembly alone. In this position, the rear springs will be fully extended and free, except for the attaching nuts and bolts. Detach the axle assembly from the springs by removing attaching nuts, clips, washers, and bolts. To free the spring, remove the shackle bolt at one end and the spring-attaching bolt at the other end.

Replacement is the reverse of removal. During replacement the shackle bolts must be tightened the correct amount so as to permit proper shackle operation. On some cars, such as Plymouth, the correct tightening of the bolts is obtained when the two shackle links are the specified distance apart. On other cars, such as Chevrolet, the shackle rubber bushings are installed, the bolts put in place, and the lock nuts turned about halfway on. Then the car is lowered so that the car weight is on the springs, and the car is bounced a few times to assure seating of the bushings. Finally, the nuts are tightened to the specified tension.

Where springs have a metal cover, it may sometimes become necessary to replace the cover when a spring leaf has been broken and requires replacement, or when the cover has been damaged. On some cars, the old spring covers can be removed and new covers installed without removing the spring from the car. On others, the spring must be removed and loaded in a special fixture to straighten it out. The fixture consists of a device for holding the two spring ends while pressure from a jack is applied at the spring center to straighten the spring. In this position the cover can be removed and a new cover installed. A flat-nosed chisel and a hammer are used to remove and replace the cover. The cover edges lock into each other on reassembly, since the edges are hammered into each other to form a locked seam.

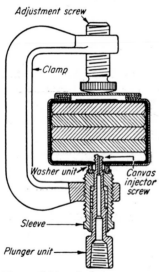

FIG. 7-28. Lubricating a metal-covered leaf spring. (*Chevrolet Motor Division of General Motors Corporation*)

Metal-covered leaf springs may be lubricated—when recommended—by use of a pressure grease gun and a special fitting (Fig. 7-28). The lubricant plug in the cover should be pried out—or a hole drilled one-third of the distance from the spring eye, when no plug is present—and the lubricating fitting screwed into the hole. With the car frame supported so that there is no load on the springs, the spring leaves will separate to permit the entrance of the lubricant when the pressure gun is operated. Apply pressure slowly until grease appears at both ends of the metal cover. Install a new plug in the cover hole.

Interliners, or inserts between spring leafs, can be replaced (if required) by prying the spring leaves apart. There are two general types of interliner, rubber and fabric. The rubber type does not require any lubrication and should not, in fact, be lubricated.

2. *Coil springs.* To remove coil springs from the rear suspension, disconnect the brake hose at the axle, disconnect the propeller shaft at the differential, disconnect both shock absorbers, and remove the upper spring bolt and axle-housing insulator bolt. Take the car weight off the springs with a jack under the frame. Reverse this procedure to reinstall the springs. Always examine the suspension carefully to note individual variations so you can restore the parts in the same order on reassembly.

CHAPTER CHECKUP

You have now finished the first of several chapters in the book that cover the servicing of various chassis components. It is important for you to have a good understanding of how the steering linkage and the front and rear suspension on cars are serviced; thus the information in the chapter you have just completed is of value to you. Here is your chance to check up on how well you remember the important points covered in the chapter. If any of the questions stump you, do not be discouraged. Just reread the chapter so you can get the material in it "down pat." These periodic checkups are included in the book to help you. They tell you whether or not you are ready to go on to the next chapter. When you do well in answering the questions, then you know you are ready to go on. In this way, you get the most out of the book, and you are doing a better job for yourself.

Completing the Sentences

The sentences below are incomplete. After each sentence there are several words or phrases, only one of which will correctly complete the sentence. Write down each sentence in your notebook, selecting the proper word or phrase to complete it correctly.

1. In the Chevrolet steering linkage, one of the tie rods is adjustable; viewed from the driver's seat, this is the   *left tie rod*   *center tie rod*   *right tie rod*

2. In the Chevrolet, three bolts attach the steering-idler and third-arm-and-bracket assembly to the   *tie rods*   *car frame*   *third arm*

3. In the Chevrolet, the stabilizer bar is attached at each end to brackets on the   *lower control arms*   *upper control arms*   *tie rods*   *brake drum*

4. When a front-wheel hub has been removed for any reason, it is very important after reinstallation, to   *readjust spindle shaft*   *readjust bushings*   *readjust wheel bearings*   *readjust tie rods*

5. In installing the lower control arm on Chevrolet, it is important to make sure that the two legs of the control arm are centered on the   *idler arm*   *stabilizer bar*   *wheel hub*   *knuckle support*

6. On Chevrolet, the outer end of the upper control arm is attached to the knuckle support by a   *tie bar*   *stabilizer bar*   *pivot pin*   *spindle*

7. On Ford, the spindle connecting rod is connected between the steering-arm-to-idler-arm rod and a   *connecting rod sleeve*   *spindle arm*   *wheel hub*   *idler arm*

8. On Ford, the idler arm is attached by a bracket to the   *car frame*   *spindle connecting rod*   *rod sleeve*   *spindle arm*

9. On Ford, the lower-arm inner shaft is attached by bolts to the   *spindle*   *upper arm*   *lower arm*   *car frame*

10. On Ford, the upper-arm inner shaft is attached by two bolts to the   *spring seat*   *spindle support*   *lower arm*   *car frame*

11. On many Fords, the outer ends of the upper and lower arms are attached by bolts to the   *spring seat*   *spindle support*   *car frame*   *wheel hub*

12. Whereas the Chevrolet and Plymouth front axles are the reverse-Elliott type, the Ford front axle is of the   *Lemoine type*   *Elliott type*   *solid-axle type*   *reverse-Lemoine type*

13. On Plymouth, the kingpin is locked by a lock pin in the   *knuckle support*   *steering knuckle*   *lower control arm*   *upper control arm*   page 182

14. On Plymouth, the upper control-arm pivot shaft, or inner shaft, is attached by four bolts to the   *car frame*   *lower arm*   *upper arm*   *spindle*

15. To remove a leaf spring from a car, axle assembly must be detached, and then the two ends of the spring must be detached from the car

[194]

frame by removing the spring attaching bolt and the <u>*shackle*</u>
<u>*bolt*</u>   *U bolt*   *center bolt*

Servicing Procedures

In the following, you should write down in your notebook the procedures asked for. Do not copy from the book, but try to write in your own words, the way you would explain it to another person. Give a step-by-step story. This will help you to remember the procedure later when you go into the shop.

1. List the service procedures for Chevrolet front suspension and steering linkage.
2. Describe, step by step, how to perform the service procedures listed in the previous question. (If you do not have time to write out all of the procedures, select one or two of them.)
3. List the service procedures for Ford front suspension (both types) and steering linkage.
4. Describe, step by step, how to perform the service procedures listed in the previous question. (If you do not have time to write out all of them, select one or two.)
5. List the service procedures for Plymouth front suspension and steering linkage.
6. Describe, step by step, how to perform the service procedures listed in the previous question. (If you do not have time to write out all of them, select one or two.)
7. Describe the procedure for removing, servicing, and replacing a rear leaf spring.
8. Describe the procedure for removing and replacing a rear coil spring.

SUGGESTIONS FOR FURTHER STUDY

When you are in the service shop or in a service station, you can learn a great deal about different suspension and steering-linkage systems by studying the different cars as they are put on the lift or jacked up. Study car shop manuals whenever you can get your hands on them. If possible, watch automotive mechanics at work, servicing front suspensions and steering linkages. Keep writing down in your notebook any important facts you come across. This methodical recording of facts will not only give you a valuable reference notebook, it will also help train you in the good habit of noticing and remembering important facts. And writing down these facts will teach you, above all, how to express yourself. In this way, you will learn to think more clearly, to talk more easily, to "get your point across" to the other fellow. All this, of course, equips you for the bigger job ahead of you.

[195]

8: Front-end alignment

THIS CHAPTER discusses the various procedures required to attain proper front-wheel, or front-end, alignment. It explains how caster, camber, toe-in, toe-out on turns, and kingpin inclination are checked and, where possible, adjusted. In addition, the chapter describes those important preliminary checks and adjustments that are made before the front wheels are aligned.

§117. Front-wheel alignment—preliminary Numerous devices are used to check front-wheel alignment, varying from lines marked on the floor to complete wheel-aligner machines, as shown in Fig.

Fig. 8-1. Special equipment for wheel balancing, front-end alignment, and steering service. (*Bear Manufacturing Company*)

8-1. While the different alignment-checking devices vary in complexity and construction, they all check the same fundamental factors on the front end of the car. Three systems of wheel alignment, using three types of alignment-checking devices, are discussed in the following sections.

Several interrelated factors besides wheel alignment influence car-steering control. Before caster, camber, toe-in, toe-out on turns, and kingpin inclination are checked, these other factors should be investigated. They include tire pressure, wheel-bearing condition, wheel balance, wheel run-out, shock-absorber action, frame alignment, and steering-knuckle and support condition. Remember, if

[196]

any of these factors are off, the wheel-alignment checks and adjustments will mean little; they may actually make conditions worse. Even though you adjusted caster and camber exactly "on the nose" in a car with loose wheel bearings or worn kingpin bushings, it would mean little. As soon as the car went out on the road, the looseness or wear would probably throw the adjustments off.

§118. Preliminary checks The first step in wheel alignment is to make sure that all tires are inflated to the proper air pressure. Next, jack up the front end of the car and check the tie rods and linkages for looseness and the steering knuckle and wheel bearings for wear and adjustment as already outlined (§76). Correct wheel alignment cannot be maintained if steering system parts are worn or out of adjustment. A worn wheel bearing can often be detected by spinning the wheel and placing a finger on the car bumper. If the wheel bearing is worn, a slight vibration or grinding may be felt as the wheel is spun.

Wobble, or run-out, of the wheel can be checked by spinning the front wheels and holding a piece of chalk against the rim or side wall of the tire. If the wheel has run-out—that is, if the wheel does not run true—the chalk mark will not be uniform around the circumference of the tire. It will be wide where the wheel runs out or will miss where it runs in. If the run-out exceeds the allowable maximum ($\frac{1}{16}$ to $\frac{1}{8}$ inch, varying with the model), the tire and the wheel must be straightened. An indicator or a pointer, such as that shown in Fig. 8-2, permits accurate measurement of run-out. While the pointer is shown being used to check a demounted wheel, it can also be used to check a wheel on the car. To correct excessive run-out, it may only be necessary to deflate the tire and work it around to another position on the rim. On the other hand, if the excessive run-out is due to a bent wheel, then the wheel must be replaced or straightened.

Wheel balance should be checked and corrected if necessary (see §119). Condition of the shock absorbers should be checked (§86). Another factor that should be considered is tracking. Tracking is the following of the rear wheels directly behind, or in the tracks of, the front wheels. Failure to track usually means that the frame is out of alignment; this causes rapid tire wear and poor steering control. If tracking is bad, it can be readily detected by follow-

FIG. 8-2. Wheel-mounting device and pointer to check wheel run-out. (*Plymouth Division of Chrysler Corporation*)

ing the car on the highway and observing the tracks. Checking and restoring frame alignment is covered in Chap. 19.

§119. Wheel balance If a wheel and tire assembly is out of balance, the car will be hard to steer, riding will be rough, and tire wear will be rapid. Wheel balance can be checked in several ways. One method is to use a so-called "shimmy detector" which drives the wheel after the car has been jacked up (Fig. 8-3). The shimmy detector, consisting of an electric motor and a driving wheel, is placed in contact with the jacked-up car wheel, and drives the wheel at high speed. If the car wheel is out of balance, the end of the car will shake or shimmy as the wheel is spun (Fig. 8-4). This device is a demonstrator and does not accurately indicate what must be done to balance the wheel.

Front wheels can be checked for balance, and balanced, either on or off the car, depending on the type of checking equipment available. Figure 8-5 shows one type of wheel balancer. Correction is made by fastening weights to the wheel rim to balance heavy spots in the tire or wheel.

[198]

FIG. 8-3. Shimmy detector, or dynamic wheel demonstrator, for demonstrating out-of-balance wheel condition. (*Bear Manufacturing Company*)

FIG. 8-4. Shimmy detector in use. As wheel is driven, an out-of-balance condition will cause the front end to shimmy. (*Bear Manufacturing Company*)

Fig. 8-5. Wheel balancer in operation, spinning wheel to check it for dynamic balance. An indicating device in the balancer indicates where and how much the wheel is out of dynamic balance. (*Bear Manufacturing Company*)

Wheels must be checked for balance in two ways, statically and dynamically. A wheel that is statically out of balance is heavier in one section than in another. When it is suspended on a spindle in a vertical plane (as on car), it will rotate until the heaviest section is at the bottom. A dynamically out-of-balance wheel does not have an even distribution of weight in a plane vertical to the wheel axle.

Fig. 8-6. A wheel may be statically in balance but dynamically out of balance. For example, a heavy spot on a tire might be statically balanced by another heavy spot, or a weight, placed on the other side of the tire and 180 degrees around the tire. But such a wheel would be dynamically out of balance and would wobble, or run out, as it rotates.

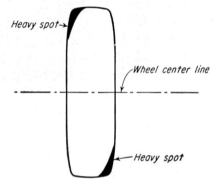

A wheel that is statically in balance can be dynamically out of balance. For example, a wheel with a heavy spot on one side can be balanced, statically, by a heavy spot 180 degrees from it (Fig. 8-6). When this wheel starts to rotate, it will try to wobble, or run out, because the heavy spots have more centrifugal force working on them.

1. Static balance. To check for static balance, the wheel is allowed to rotate and come to rest while it is supported in a vertical position (as on car). The heaviest part of the tire will come to rest at the bottom. Static balance is then corrected by placing weights on the wheel rim. Figure 8-7 shows how a weight can be attached to the wheel rim to balance the wheel. Figure 8-8 shows weights of various sizes. It is unlikely that a single weight will be found to achieve perfect static balance. More likely, two weights of the same size will be found to work best, as follows. Place the

Fig. 8-7. Balancing a wheel by placing a weight on wheel rim. (*Bear Manufacturing Company*)

two weights on the rim exactly opposite—180 degrees apart—the heavy spot (Fig. 8-9). The weights should have a combined weight which is just a little more than needed to balance the wheel. Now, move the two weights slightly away from each other, moving both like amounts, as shown by the arrows (Fig. 8-9). Test static balance again. Move the two weights a little further apart and repeat the test. You will find a place where the two weights will produce adequate static balance of the wheel.

2. *Dynamic balance.* To check dynamic balance, the wheel is spun and the indicating device in the wheel balancer indicates the

place and approximate amount the wheel is dynamically out of balance. Balance is then achieved by putting additional weights on the indicated spots on the rim. It may happen that a weight will be required, for dynamic balance, on a spot on a rim that is near a weight installed for static balance. For example, suppose a weight

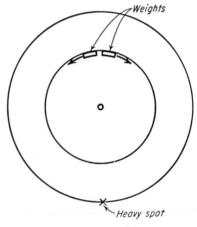

Weights

Heavy spot

Fig. 8-8. Wheel-balancing weights are available in different weights. (*Bear Manufacturing Company*)

Fig. 8-9. Use of two weights to achieve static balance. Weights are moved apart, being moved equal amounts, until static balance is attained.

A is added (as shown in Fig. 8-10) to achieve static balance. For dynamic balance, another weight B is required on the other side of the rim, as shown. Adding the second weight throws the wheel out of static balance. But static balance can be restored by a weight at C (Fig. 8-10). The weight at C does not throw dynamic balance off since it is on the same side as weight B. A better way to take care of the balance is to combine the effect of weights A and B. For instance, if weight A is 4 ounces and weight B is 2 ounces, approximately correct static *and* dynamic balance can be achieved by using only one weight, at B of 2 ounces. In such a case, no weight would be needed at C. Other combining arrangements are possible. The reason they are desirable is that they keep the total amount of weight added to the rim to a minimum. The less weight added the better, so long as static and dynamic balance are achieved. In any event, *no more than 8 ounces should be added to a rim,* according to authorities.

[202]

§**120. Making the alignment checks** After the above preliminary checks have been performed and necessary corrections made, the next step is to place the car in position on the aligner machine in readiness for the alignment checks. Then the frame height should be equalized. This is done by grasping the front bumper and raising

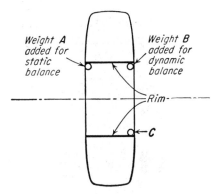

Fɪɢ. 8-10. Method of adding weights to wheel rim to achieve static and dynamic balance.

and lowering the front end of the car several times so that the frame comes to rest in its normal position. If someone then gets into and out of the car, it will be necessary to repeat this operation. On some models, the use of a height gauge is recommended (Fig. 8-11). The height gauge has holes that fit over the lower-support-

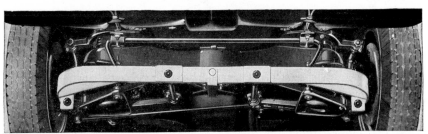

Fɪɢ. 8-11. Height gauge being used to establish correct frame height from floor, before checking wheel alignment. (*Chevrolet Motor Division of General Motors Corporation*)

arm shaft bushings and the lower pivot pins to establish the proper frame height from the floor.

After equalizing the frame height, the caster, camber, toe-in, kingpin inclination, and toe-out on turns are checked. The procedure for performing these checks varies somewhat depending on

[203]

the kind of car, as well as the equipment, that is used. The complete aligning procedures for late-model Chevrolet, Plymouth, and Ford passenger cars are detailed below, with some additional data pertaining to other types of front-suspension systems. It is recommended that the vehicle shop manual be followed when wheel alignment is being checked, since the details of alignment, as well as the specifications to which the different alignment factors should be set, vary somewhat from year to year and from car to car.

Fig. 8-12. Wheel being set out 20 degrees with wheel aligner. (*Chevrolet Motor Division of General Motors Corporation*)

§121. Listing the preliminary steps Let us make a list of the preliminary steps to be taken before the front-end alignment is checked. They are:

1. Check tire inflation
2. Check wheel bearings
3. Check wheel run-out
4. Check steering knuckles

5. Check steering linkages
6. Check wheel balance
7. Check shock absorbers
8. Check tracking

§122. Front-wheel alignment—Chevrolet After performing the preliminary checks as outlined in the previous sections and placing the car in position on the front-end aligner, center the front wheels on the turntables and block the rear wheels to prevent car movement. Be sure frame height is equalized. Then proceed as follows in the order outlined.

1. *Checking caster.* Turn one wheel out 20 degrees. This angle may be obtained by pushing the contact bar of the aligner in so that it touches the tire. The pointer will indicate 20 degrees when the wheel is properly turned (Fig. 8-12). Then turn the contact

FIG. 8-13. Setting caster scale to zero, before measuring the caster angle. (*Chevrolet Motor Division of General Motors Corporation*)

bar to the vertical position and move it in against the tire. Loosen and set the caster scale to zero (Fig. 8-13). This establishes the slant, or tilt, of the wheel due to the caster angle when the wheel is turned out. Now turn the wheel a total of 40 degrees so that the wheel will be pointing in 20 degrees. Use the contact bar in the horizontal position again (as in Fig. 8-14) to establish the 20-degree angle. Finally, turn the contact bar to the vertical position again,

[205]

move it in against the tire, and note the reading on the caster scale. The scale is calibrated so as to read the caster angle when the above procedure is followed. Repeat the procedure for the other wheel and make note of the caster angles for both wheels. Caster and camber are adjusted together after camber has been checked.

2. *Checking camber.* The first step in checking camber is to raise the car on jacks, spin the wheels, and check the run-out with

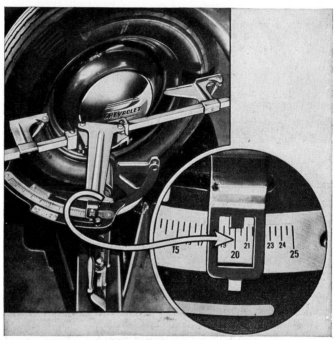

Fig. 8-14. Wheel being set in 20 degrees. (*Chevrolet Motor Division of General Motors Corporation*)

a piece of chalk, as already explained in §118. The mark indicating maximum run-out (maximum thickness of chalk mark) should be placed at top. Then, with wheels straight ahead, move the contact bar—keeping it in the horizontal position—in against the tire, and set the wheel so that the pointer on the toe-in scale reads zero. Rotate the wheel 180 degrees. If the pointer still remains at zero, the maximum run-out point has been accurately determined. Rotate the wheel 90 degrees to place the point of maximum run-out halfway between top and bottom. Then lower the wheel to the turntable. Install the camber-checking contact arm on the contact bar,

[206]

and move the bar in so that it touches the tire in the vertical position as shown in Fig. 8-15. The camber scale on the wheel aligner will indicate the amount of camber.

3. *Adjusting caster and camber.* Caster and camber are adjusted together by turning the upper control-arm pivot pin with an Allen wrench (Fig. 8-16). The pivot pin changes both caster and camber of the wheel when it is turned. Both ends of the pivot pin are

FIG. 8-15. The camber angle being measured. (*Chevrolet Motor Division of General Motors Corporation*)

threaded in the front and rear bushings in the upper control arm. Thus, when the pivot pin is turned with an Allen wrench, the pin and upper end of the steering-knuckle support are shifted backward or forward with respect to the upper control arm. This causes the kingpin to tilt backward or forward to change the caster angle. Change of the camber is effected by an eccentric section of the pivot pin on which the upper end of the steering-knuckle support pivots. As the pivot pin is turned with an Allen wrench, this eccentric center section rotates, moving the upper end of the steering-knuckle

[207]

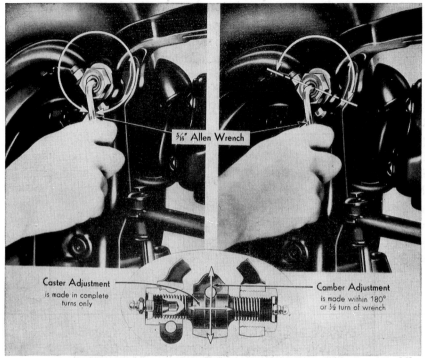

Fig. 8-16. Adjusting caster and camber by turning the pivot pin. (*Cadillac Motor Car Division of General Motors Corporation*)

support in toward, or out away from, the car. This moves the top of the wheel in to decrease, or out to increase, the camber. One rotation of the pivot pin represents the full range of camber adjustment. The adjusting procedure, in detail, follows:

    a. Loosen the clamp bolt at the top of the steering-knuckle support (Fig. 8-16).

    b. Remove the lubricating fitting from the upper front pivot-pin bushing.

    c. Use an Allen wrench and turn the pivot pin clockwise to increase the caster, or counterclockwise to decrease the caster. If the pin is turned one or more full turns, the eccentric will always be brought back to the same position to provide the same camber angle.

    d. To change camber, turn the pivot pin only part of a turn. If the caster angle has been adjusted to the approximately correct value, adjusting the camber by turning the pivot pin a part turn will change the caster angle slightly but not enough to throw the caster angle out of specifications.

e. Recheck caster and camber adjustments and, if they are correct, tighten the clamp bolt and install lubrication fitting.

4. *Checking kingpin inclination.* The kingpin inclination should be checked if the car has been involved in an accident such that the camber adjustment cannot be made to the correct angle. Kingpin inclination is the inward tilt of the top of the kingpin. This inward tilt affects the amount that the wheel will rotate on its bearing as the steering wheel is turned when the car is stationary. Decreasing the kingpin inclination increases the amount the wheel will rotate. Thus the wheel rotation during turning of the steering wheel can be used to measure kingpin inclination.

To measure kingpin inclination, remove the hub cap and install a checking gauge on the wheel spindle (Fig. 8-17). Tighten clamp screws securely. Turn the wheel out 20 degrees, and install a leveling plate on the contact bar as shown in Fig. 8-18. Move the plate

FIG. 8-17. Installing kingpin-inclination gauge. (*Chevrolet Motor Division of General Motors Corporation*)

in until it touches the two pins indicated by arrows on the pointer. Now move the indicator scale one way or the other so that the indicator will point to zero. Remove the leveling plate and turn the wheel a total of 40 degrees, so that it is turned in 20 degrees. Put the leveling plate on the other side of the contact bar and move it in until its edge comes up against both pins (Fig. 8-19). It will strike one pin first, causing the indicator to move. Read the amount

Fig. 8-18. Checking the kingpin inclination with gauge and leveling plate. (*Chevrolet Motor Division of General Motors Corporation*)

the indicator has moved on the scale as it is brought up against both pins. The scale is calibrated to give the kingpin inclination directly in degrees.

Check the kingpin inclination of the other wheel in the same manner. If, although the kingpin inclination is correct, the camber angle cannot be correctly adjusted, the steering knuckle is bent and must be replaced. If the kingpin inclination is incorrect, then the knuckle support is bent and it must be replaced. After any replacement of parts, the caster and camber must be readjusted.

[210]

5. *Toe-in check and adjustment.* Raise the car with a jack and rotate the front wheels 90 degrees to place the maximum run-out point at the top. The point of maximum run-out is indicated by the maximum thickness of the chalk mark when chalk is held against the spinning wheel. Set wheels straight ahead, and turn the contact bars to the horizontal position. Move one contact bar in against one wheel, and set the wheel so that the pointer on the toe-in scale

FIG. 8-19. Leveling plate with wheels set in 20 degrees. (*Chevrolet Motor Division of General Motors Corporation*)

will read zero (Fig. 8-20). Move the second contact bar in against the other wheel. Read the amount of toe-in on the toe-in scale.

Toe-in is adjusted by loosening the clamp bolts at the ends of the left-hand tie rod and turning the tie rod in or out as required. Increasing the tie-rod length increases toe-in; decreasing the tie-rod length decreases the toe-in. Before locking the clamp bolts, be sure the tie-rod ends are in alignment with their ball studs. Figure 8-21 shows a tie-rod end that is in alignment and one that is out of alignment. Failure to secure alignment will cause binding.

[211]

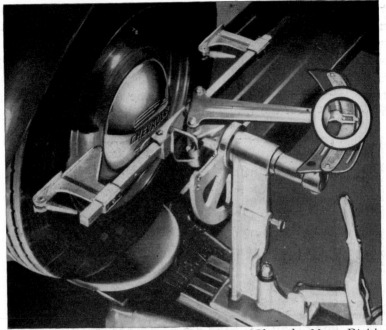

FIG. 8-20. Contact bar being set to read toe-in. (*Chevrolet Motor Division of General Motors Corporation*)

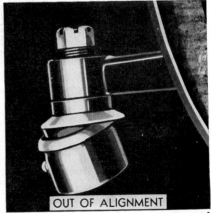

IN ALIGNMENT   OUT OF ALIGNMENT

FIG. 8-21. Alignment of tie-rod ends. (*Chevrolet Motor Division of General Motors Corporation*)

6. *Checking toe-out on turns.* Toe-out on turns is measured by turning the wheels in and out and noting the difference in the turning angles between the inside and the outside wheels. This provides a check on whether or not the steering arms are bent. The inside wheel (or inner wheel on a turn) should turn more than the outside wheel because the inside wheel travels on a smaller radius (Fig. 5-10). To check the right steering arm, turn the left wheel

Fig. 8-22. Wheel turned in 20 degrees to check toe-out on turns. (*Chevrolet Motor Division of General Motors Corporation*)

in 20 degrees as measured with the contact bar on the wheel aligner (Fig. 8-22). Then use the contact bar to determine how much the right wheel is turned in. It should be turned in 2 to 6 degrees more than the left wheel—from 22 to 26 degrees. If it is not within these specifications, the right steering arm should be replaced. To check the left steering arm, turn the right wheel in 20 degrees, and check the amount the left wheel has turned in. It should be turned in 22 to 26 degrees. If either arm is found to be bent, it should be replaced. Any attempt to straighten steering arms by bending them will weaken the metal to a point where failure may occur.

[213]

§123. Front-wheel alignment—Plymouth After performing the preliminary checks as outlined in §§117 to 121, make sure all other steering factors are correct by proceeding as follows in the order outlined:

1. *Kingpin inclination.* Kingpin inclination is the first angle to be checked on the Plymouth. This can be checked by using a plumb-bob device, such as illustrated in Fig. 8-24. With the car on a level

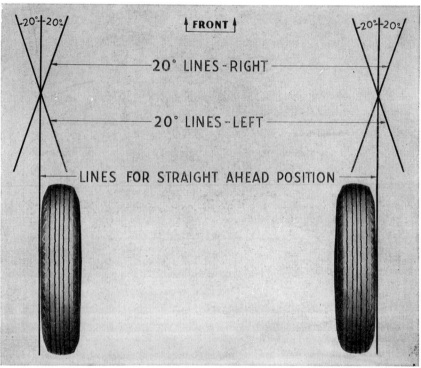

FIG. 8-23. Floor markings to check wheel alignment. (*Plymouth Division of Chrysler Corporation*)

floor, use a straightedge and chalk-mark lines on the floor as shown in Fig. 8-23. A 20-degree angle plate can be used to make the 20-degree lines. Roll the car forward until the front wheels are over the intersections of the lines. Then install the adapter and gauge on one of the front wheels as shown in Fig. 8-24. Adjust the gauge so that the reading is zero with the wheel straight ahead. Then turn in the wheel 20 degrees to align with the 20-degree line on the floor. (Turn the wheel slightly past the 20-degree line and

[214]

then back in order to relieve friction between the tire and the floor.) Note the gauge reading on the 40-degree scale. Then turn the wheel a total of 40 degrees—until it is turned out 20 degrees. Note the reading on the gauge. Add the two readings to obtain the kingpin inclination. Repeat the above process for the other wheel. Incorrect kingpin inclination indicates defective or bent parts, which must be replaced before further checks are made.

Fig. 8-24. Gauge being used to check kingpin inclination. (*Plymouth Division of Chrysler Corporation*)

2. Checking caster. Check caster with the gauge installed on the left wheel, as shown in Fig. 8-25. Turn the wheels to the left (left wheel out) 20 degrees. Turn slightly past 20 degrees and then back to relieve friction between tires and floor. Note the reading on the 40-degree scale of the gauge. Turn the wheels to the right (left wheel in) a total of 40 degrees, or 20 degrees past straight-ahead, and take the reading on the 40-degree scale. Subtract the second reading from the first to secure the caster angle. If the pointer crosses zero, add the two readings.

Repeat the above check for the right wheel. Turn the wheels to the right 20 degrees (right wheel out), and take the reading; then

FIG. 8-25. Caster angle being checked with gauge. (*Plymouth Division of Chrysler Corporation*)

FIG. 8-26. Camber being checked with gauge. (*Plymouth Division of Chrysler Corporation*)

turn the wheels to the left 20 degrees, and take the second reading. Subtract the second from the first reading, or add the two if the pointer crosses zero, as above.

The caster angle is not adjustable, but proper setting is made when the camber eccentric bushing is installed.

3. *Checking camber.* Camber is checked with the wheels straight ahead and with the gauge attached as shown in Fig. 8-26. The

Fig. 8-27. Camber being adjusted by turning the upper-control-arm-pin eccentric bushing. 1, lock screw; 2, upper-control-arm-pin eccentric bushing; 3, steering-knuckle support; 4, adjusting tool. (*Plymouth Division of Chrysler Corporation*)

camber reading is taken on the 60-degree scale. When the pointer is between the wheel and zero, camber is positive; when it is on the opposite side of zero, camber is negative. Camber is adjusted by loosening the lock screw and turning the upper-control-arm-pin eccentric bushing (Fig. 8-27). This tilts the top of the steering-knuckle support in toward, or out away from, the car to change the

[217]

FIG. 8-28. Toe-in gauge for measuring toe-in of front wheels. (*Bear Manufacturing Company*)

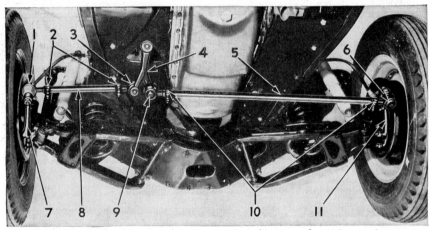

FIG. 8-29. Front-wheel-suspension steering-knuckle tie rods. (*Plymouth Division of Chrysler Corporation*)

1. Tie-rod-end assembly: short outer —left-hand thread
2. Tie-rod-end clamp bolts
3. Tie-rod-end assembly: short inner —right-hand thread
4. Steering gear
5. Tie rod: long
6. Tie-rod-end assembly: long outer —left-hand thread
7. Steering-knuckle arm: left
8. Tie rod: short
9. Tie-rod-end assembly: long inner —right-hand thread
10. Tie-rod-end clamp bolts
11. Steering-knuckle arm: right

[218]

camber of the wheel. One revolution of the bushing represents the full range of camber adjustments. After adjustment, tighten the lock screw.

4. *Checking toe-in.* With wheels in a straight-ahead position, roll the car ahead one wheel revolution and then measure the distance between the center of the tire treads at the rear of the tires. Take the measurement at hub height from the floor. Use a toe-in gauge such as that shown in Fig. 8-28. Mark the points on the tires

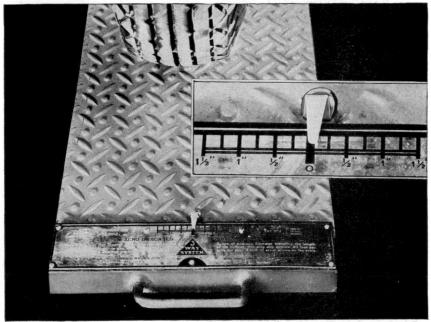

FIG. 8-30. Wee-gee board for checking toe-in. (*Dodge Division of Chrysler Corporation*)

at which the measurement is taken. Then roll the car ahead until marks are in front, hub-high. Take the measurement again between the same markings. The difference between the two measurements is the toe-in or toe-out. If the markings are closer together at the front than they were at the rear, the wheels are toed in. Actual toe-in should be slight—between zero and $\frac{1}{16}$ inch. Adjustment is made by loosening the clamp bolts and turning the tie rods (Fig. 8-29).

A device called the *wee-gee board* may be used to check toe-in directly (Fig. 8-30). This device contains a ball-bearing-supported

[219]

Fig. 8-31. Turntables being used to check toe-out on turns. (*Plymouth Division of Chrysler Corporation*)

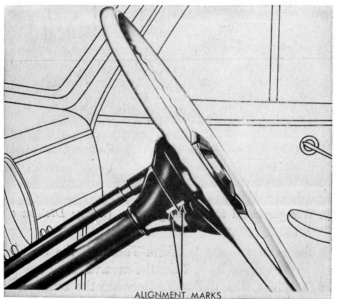

Fig. 8-32. Steering-wheel alignment marks. (*Ford Motor Company*)

plate onto which the front wheel is rolled. The indicator and gauge at the front end of the board indicate the amount of toe-in or toe-out.

5. *Checking toe-out on turns.* Toe-out on turns is checked in a manner similar to that used in the Chevrolet service procedure (§122). Turntables (such as shown in Fig. 8-31) can be used for

[220]

this check. Improper toe-out on turns indicates a bent steering-knuckle arm or other steering-system part which must be replaced.

§**124. Front-wheel alignment—Ford** Items 1 to 8, below, discuss alignment procedures on the type of front suspension shown in Figs. 3-18 and 7-13. Items 9 to 12 discuss alignment adjustments on the ball-joint type of front suspension shown in Figs. 3-23 and 7-14. Note that on the ball-joint suspension, caster and camber are adjusted by installing or removing shims between the upper-suspension-arm shaft and the frame (see Fig. 3-23, upper right).

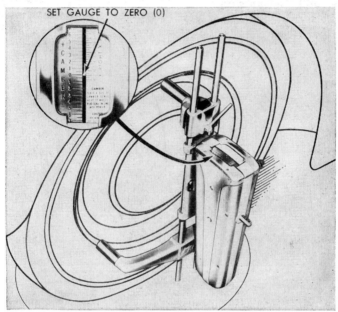

Fig. 8-33. Checking parallel plane of wheel. (*Ford Motor Company*)

Ford suggests that, when portable equipment is used, a level place be found on the floor. Then white circles can be painted to indicate where the wheels should be placed. Another special point is that while driving the car in the straight-ahead position, the steering-wheel hub and the steering column should be marked with pencil or chalk (Fig. 8-32) to indicate the straight-ahead position. After making the other preliminary checks as already outlined (§§ 117 to 121), proceed as follows:

1. Camber check. Place front wheels in center of the white spots which indicate a level floor. Adjust gauge-holder set screws to fit

[221]

wheel rim, and adjust gauge-holder rod to center of wheel. Tighten rod set screws. Put gauge holder on wheel with the three set screws against the outer edge of the rim, and turn the clamping handle one-fourth turn clockwise to lock holder in place (see Fig. 8-33). Make sure all three contact points are tight against rim.

Raise front wheels off floor and install the gauge on the holder spindle with the plus side of the camber scale toward the wheel. Turn the wheel slowly and note the range of pointer movement. This indicates the amount of wheel run-out. If it is more than ⅛ inch, the wheel is bent and should be replaced. If the run-out is

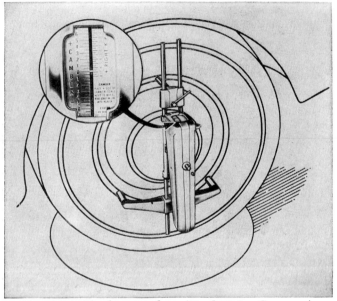

Fig. 8-34. Checking camber. (*Ford Motor Company*)

not excessive, stop the wheel at the point exactly at which the pointer is in the center of its movement. Then place a pedal jack on the brake pedal, or turn one brake cam adjustment to hold the wheel stationary in this position.

Turn the wheels straight ahead (check markings on steering-wheel hub and steering column), and lower wheels to floor. *Make sure gauge-holder rods clear the floor before lowering the wheels.* Otherwise, the gauge may be damaged. With car weight on wheels, read the camber on the camber scale (Fig. 8-34). Repeat the procedure at the other wheel. If the camber is incorrect, check the kingpin inclination. If the camber is within specified limits, omit the kingpin-inclination check.

2. *Kingpin-inclination check.* The wheels must be turned out 20 degrees and then in 20 degrees to check kingpin inclination. Portable turntables simplify the check. If they are not available, use the turn indicator as explained below.

Raise wheels and turn to straight-ahead. Lower wheels and install brake-pedal jack to keep wheels from rotating. Put gauge on

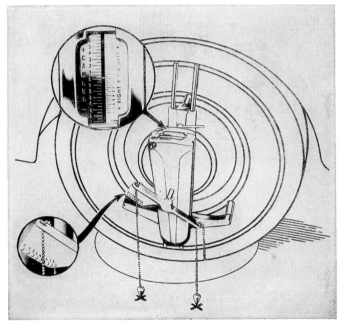

FIG. 8-35. Checking kingpin inclination. (*Ford Motor Company*)

holder in position 90 degrees from camber-checking position (Fig. 8-35). Install turn indicator in spindle and set the indicator so that the chain will be in line with the numeral 6 as shown in Fig. 8-35. Tighten thumbscrew. With wheels in straight-ahead position, adjust chains so the plumb bobs just clear floor. Draw two short lines on floor just under the points of the plumb bobs, as shown.

Move gauge until the pointer is at zero on the camber scale and tighten thumbscrew to hold it in this position. Raise front wheels to just clear the floor. Adjust plumb bobs until they almost touch the floor. Turn wheels until the front plumb bob aligns with the

[223]

rear mark on the floor (Fig. 8-36). This is the 20-degree outward turn. Lower the wheels to the floor and adjust the zero point on the kingpin-inclination scale to align with the pointer. Raise the wheels to clear the floor and turn them until the rear plumb bob aligns with the front mark on the floor (Fig. 8-37). This is the 20-degree inward turn. Lower wheels and note the reading on the kingpin-inclination scale.

3. *Caster check.* Install gauge on holder using same hole as for checking camber (Fig. 8-34). Install turn indicator, set it so the

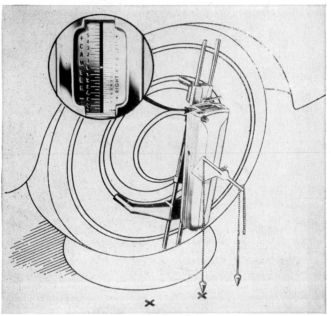

Fig. 8-36. Measuring 20-degree outward turn. (*Ford Motor Company*)

chain is in line with numeral 6 (Fig. 8-38), and tighten thumb-screw. Put front wheels in straight-ahead position. Make marks on floor under plumb bobs as when checking kingpin inclination. Raise wheels from floor and turn them until the front plumb bob is in line with the rear mark (Fig. 8-39). Lower the wheels and turn them to correct any misalignment of the plumb bob with the floor mark. Turn the knob on the gauge until the zero on the caster scale lines up with the pointer. Raise the wheels clear of the floor, and turn them until the rear plumb bob lines up with the front mark on the floor (Fig. 8-40). Lower the wheels, correct any misalignment

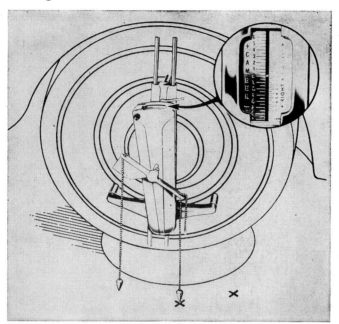

Fig. 8-37. Measuring 20-degree inward turn. (*Ford Motor Company*)

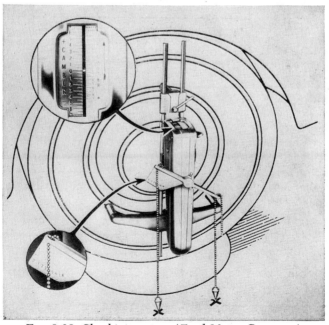

Fig. 8-38. Checking caster. (*Ford Motor Company*)

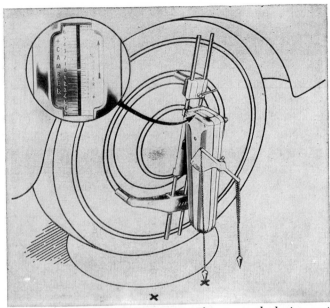

Fig. 8-39. Front plumb bob in alignment with rear mark during caster check. (*Ford Motor Company*)

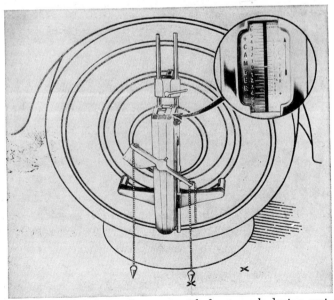

Fig. 8-40. Rear plumb bob in alignment with front mark during caster check. (*Ford Motor Company*)

with the mark on the floor by turning them, and then read the caster angle.

4. Toe-in check. To check toe-in, push the car backward about six feet and then pull it forward about three feet. This takes up all the freeness in the steering linkage in the forward direction. Put telescope gauge between the front wheels with the ends of the chains just touching the floor (Fig. 8-41). Set scale to zero. Pull the car forward until gauge is on rear side with both chains just touching the floor. Read the toe-in on the scale.

5. Adjusting camber. To adjust camber, loosen the clamp bolt at the upper end of the spindle support. Install special tool on the

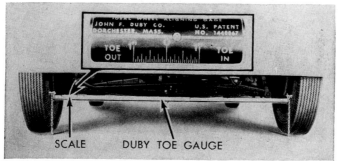

Fig. 8-41. Checking toe-in with telescoping type of toe-in gauge. (*Ford Motor Company*)

support bushing as shown in Fig. 8-42 and turn upper spindle-support bushing. After correcting camber, tighten clamp bolt to 25 to 30 lb-ft torque. Make sure the bolt does not bind in the bushing groove since binding would prevent proper tightening.

6. Adjusting caster. Caster is adjusted by turning the lower spindle-support bushing with a special tool as shown in Fig. 8-43. Additional caster adjustment can be made by turning the front-suspension lower-arm inner shaft, or the front-suspension upper-arm inner shaft. The lower-arm inner shaft—when disconnected from the frame cross member—can be turned clockwise one turn (viewed from front) to increase caster; it can be turned counter-clockwise one turn to decrease caster. Arm must be supported by a jack when it is disconnected. The upper-arm inner shaft—when disconnected from the frame cross member—can be turned ½, 1, or 1½ turns. Clockwise turning (from front) decreases caster.

[227]

Counterclockwise turning increases caster. When either of the arm inner shafts are turned, make sure they still have enough movement so the clamp bolts will not bind in the bushing grooves when tightened. This would prevent normal tightening.

7. *Toe-in adjustment.* Note the position of the steering-wheel spoke and make the adjustments as noted in Fig. 8-44.

8. *Kingpin inclination and toe-out on turns.* These are not adjustable. If incorrect, then steering or suspension parts are bent and must be replaced.

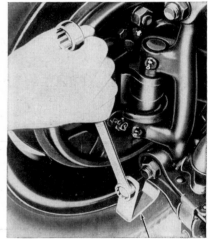

Fig. 8-42. Adjusting camber. Arrow points to adjusting tool. (*Ford Motor Company*)

Fig. 8-43. Adjusting caster. Arrow points to adjusting tool. (*Ford Motor Company*)

9. *Ball-joint suspension—caster adjustment.* Caster and camber adjustments are interrelated. If caster is adjusted, then camber must be checked and adjusted, if necessary. Likewise, camber adjustment requires a caster check and adjustment.

To adjust caster, loosen the two bolts that attach the upper suspension-arm shaft to the frame and insert or remove shims between the shaft and frame. One-sixteenth inch of shim added at the front bolt adds a negative caster of ½ degree. One-sixteenth inch of shim removed at the front bolt will add a positive caster of ½ degree. Shims are available in ⅟₃₂- and ⅛-inch thicknesses. When the caster is correct (0 to + 1½ degrees), tighten bolts to 70 to 80 lb-ft torque.

Caution: Caster on the two wheels of a car should be within ½ degree of each other.

10. *Ball-joint suspension—camber adjustment.* Camber is adjusted by inserting or removing shims between the shaft and frame, just as with caster. However, to adjust *caster,* shims are added or removed *at the front bolt only.* When adjusting *camber,* shims must be removed or added *at both the front and the rear bolts.* Each 1/16 inch added (at both bolts) gives ¼ degree of negative camber. Each 1/16 inch removed (at both bolts) gives ¼ degree of positive camber. When the camber is correct, it should be 0 to + ¾ degree.

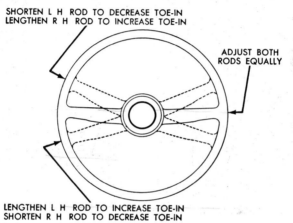

FIG. 8-44. Steering-wheel spoke adjustment. (*Ford Motor Company*)

Caution: Camber on the two wheels of a car should be within ¼ degree of each other.

11. *Ball-joint suspension—theoretical kingpin inclination.* Since this suspension has no kingpin, kingpin inclination can be theoretical only. No adjustment of the theoretical kingpin inclination on this suspension is provided. However, the angle should be 7 degrees when the camber angle is + ¾ degree.

12. *Ball-joint suspension—toe-in.* Toe-in is adjusted as in other suspensions (see Fig. 8-44).

§**125. Other caster and camber adjusting methods** In addition to the adjusting devices discussed above for adjusting caster and camber, other types of adjusting devices have been used. One type (shown in Fig. 8-45) makes use of $\frac{1}{16}$-inch-thick C-shaped washers, which are installed or removed from between a spacer plate and control-arm pivot. Removing washers at both *A* and *B* increases camber, while installing washers at both *A* and *B* decreases camber. Installing washers at *B* only increases caster; installing washers at *A* only decreases caster.

When the front wheels are not independently suspended but are attached through the spindles to an I-beam axle, camber and king-

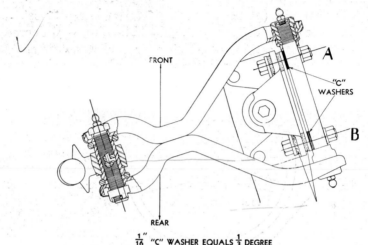

FRONT

"C" WASHERS

A

B

REAR

$\frac{1}{16}''$ "C" WASHER EQUALS $\frac{1}{3}$ DEGREE

REMOVAL OF "C" WASHER AT BOTH **A** AND **B** INCREASES CAMBER.

ADDITION OF "C" WASHER AT BOTH **A** AND **B** DECREASES CAMBER.

ADDITION OF "C" WASHER AT **B** ONLY INCREASES CASTER.

ADDITION OF "C" WASHER AT **A** ONLY DECREASES CASTER.

FIG. 8-45. Method of adjusting caster and camber by installing and removing C-shaped washers at *A* and *B*. (*American Motors Corporation*)

pin-inclination-angle adjustment must be made by bending the axle with special correcting tools. Slight caster adjustments can be made by inserting wedge-shaped shims between the spring seat on the axle and the spring; major caster adjustments are made by use of correcting tools that bend the axle. Figure 8-46 illustrates the use of a correcting tool to decrease the caster on the right side. This tool merely twists the axle slightly to correct the caster. Figure 8-47 illustrates the use of a correcting tool to correct the camber and kingpin-inclination angles. This tool slightly bends the axle to make the correction. Correction can be made by this method only

FIG. 8-46. Correcting tool being used to decrease caster on the right side. (*Chevrolet Motor Division of General Motors Corporation*)

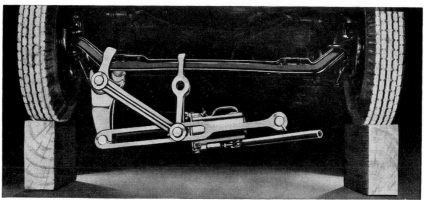

FIG. 8-47. Correcting tool being used to adjust camber and kingpin inclination. (*Chevrolet Motor Division of General Motors Corporation*)

when both camber and kingpin inclination are off the same amount. When one is off more than the other, the wheel spindle is bent and should be replaced; in addition, the axle may require bending to bring the two angles within specifications.

CHAPTER CHECKUP

Because automobiles are bigger, heavier, and faster than they used to be, proper front-end alignment is more important than ever. Proper front-end alignment assures maximum steering stability and maneuverability. Thus, you should have a good understanding of the factors

[231]

involved in front-end alignment, and how each of these factors are adjusted. The chapter you have just completed covers the use of three types of alignment-checking devices. The questions in the checkup that follows give you a chance to check yourself and find out if you remember the details of how these various devices are used and how alignment adjustments are made. Don't worry if you have trouble with some of the questions. That simply means that you should review the chapter again. Rereading and reviewing the material and then answering the questions will really fix the important facts in your mind so you won't forget them.

Completing the Sentences

The sentences below are incomplete. After each sentence there are several words or phrases, only one of which will correctly complete the sentence. Write down each sentence in your notebook, selecting the proper word or phrase to complete it correctly.

1. Before front-wheel alignment is checked, several items should be checked, including tire inflation, bearing condition, and   *wheel run-in*   *wheel run-out and balance*   *kingpin run-out*   *toe-in on turns*

2. Weights can be attached to the wheel rim to correct   *wheel run-out*   *wheel turn-out*   *wheel balance*   *wheel alignment*

3. Wheels must be checked for balance in two ways,   *statically and at rest*   *statically and dynamically*   *at high speed and at low speed*

4. On Chevrolet, caster is adjusted by turning the   *lower control-arm pin*   *kingpin*   *clamp bolt*   *upper control-arm pivot pin*

5. On Chevrolet, camber is adjusted by turning the   *lower control-arm pin*   *kingpin*   *clamp bolt*   *upper control-arm pivot pin*

6. On Chevrolet, one full turn of the upper control-arm pivot pin represents the full range of   *camber adjustment*   *caster adjustment*   *toe-in adjustment*

7. On Chevrolet, kingpin inclination   *is adjusted by turning eccentric*   *is adjusted by turning knuckle*   *cannot be adjusted*

8. On Chevrolet, toe-in is adjusted by loosening the clamp bolts on the left-hand tie rod and   *turning the tie rod*   *replacing the tie rod*   *adding shims under tie rod*   *turning the pivot pin*

[232]

9. On Plymouth, incorrect kingpin inclination indicates the need for   *camber adjustment*   *caster adjustment*   *replacement of bent parts*

10. On Plymouth, the caster angle   *is adjusted by turning pin*   *is adjusted by turning eccentric*   *is not adjustable*

11. On Plymouth, the camber angle   *is adjusted by turning eccentric bushing*   *is adjusted by turning the knuckle*   *is not adjustable*

12. On Plymouth, toe-in is adjusted by loosening the clamp bolts and   *turning the tie rod*   *adding shims under tie rod*   *turning the eccentric*

13. On Ford, camber is adjusted by turning   *upper spindle-support bushing*   *lower spindle-support bushing*   *kingpin bushing*

14. On Ford, caster can be adjusted by turning   *upper spindle-support bushing*   *lower spindle-support bushing*   *kingpin bushing*

15. On Ford, additional caster adjustment can be made by turning the   *lower arm or the upper arm*   *inner shaft*   *outer shaft*

Servicing Procedures

In taking the following test, write down in your notebook the procedures asked for. Do not copy from the book, but write in your own words, the way you would explain it to another person. Thinking out and then writing down the procedure is a fine way to fix the procedure in your mind.

1. Make a list of the preliminary checks and corrections to be made before front wheels are aligned.

2. How are wheels checked for balance, and how are corrections made?

3. Explain how to check and adjust caster and camber on Chevrolet.

4. Explain how to check kingpin inclination on Chevrolet. What should be done if kingpin inclination is incorrect?

5. Explain how to check and adjust toe-in on Chevrolet.

6. Explain how to check and adjust camber on Plymouth.

7. Explain how to check and adjust camber on Ford (both suspension systems).

8. Explain how to check and adjust caster on Ford (both suspension systems).

9. Explain how to check and adjust toe-in on Ford.

10. What should be done if toe-out on turns is incorrect?

[233]

SUGGESTIONS FOR FURTHER STUDY

Because of the increasing importance of proper front-end alignment—due to heavier cars and higher speeds—a variety of alignment-checking devices has become available in recent years. Only three types of devices were covered in the chapter; there are other types. It may be that you can find other alignment-checking devices in your local school shop or in an automotive service shop. If you can, see how they are used. If possible study the instruction manual issued by the equipment manufacturer. Notice how the various factors in front-end alignment are checked and adjusted on different automobiles. Be sure to write down in your notebook any important facts you come across.

9: Manual steering-gear service

THIS CHAPTER explains how to check, adjust, and repair various types of manually operated steering gears used on passenger cars. Chapter 6 describes trouble-shooting methods for determining the causes of different steering and suspension troubles. The following sections discuss the adjustments and repairs required to eliminate causes of trouble in manually operated steering gears. The next few chapters describe power-steering checks, adjustments, and repairs.

§126. Steering-gear adjustments As noted in Chap. 5, a variety of steering-gear designs have been used on automobiles. All have two basic adjustments: one for taking up the worm-gear and steering-shaft end play, and the other for removing backlash between the worm and the sector (or roller or lever studs). In addition, some designs have a means of adjusting the sector-shaft (pitman-arm-shaft) end play.

Before attempting to adjust a steering gear to take up excessive end play or to relieve binding, make sure the condition is not the result of faulty alignment or of wear in some other component of the linkage or front suspension. Adjusting and repair procedures on various manual steering gears follow.

§127. Chevrolet steering-gear adjustments Adjustments of manual steering gears are described for two models of Chevrolet: the earlier model used until 1948 (Fig. 9-1), and the model used since that time (Fig. 5-17). The earlier-model steering gear (Fig. 9-1) has various adjusting screws and nuts, as shown, by means of which three adjustments can be made. The first step in adjustment is to disconnect the steering connecting rod from the pitman arm. Then check the steering-gear mounting bolts for tightness. Next, check the worm-shaft end play first by setting the steering gear in the straight-ahead position and then pulling and pushing on the steering wheel.

[235]

To locate the straight-ahead position, turn the steering wheel in one direction as far as it will go, and then in the opposite direction as far as it will go, counting the number of wheel rotations. Next, turn the wheel back exactly halfway.

Caution: Be extremely careful to turn the wheel gently and avoid bumping it at the ends of turns since, with no load on the gear, such bumping may damage the sector roller.

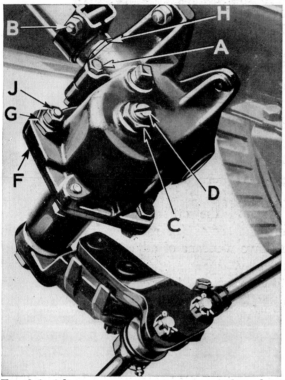

A. Housing clamp bolt
B. Mast-jacket clamp bolt
C. Sector-shaft adjusting-screw lock nut
D. Adjusting screw
F. Eccentric bolt
G. Eccentric sleeve
H. Worm-shaft adjuster
J. Eccentric-bolt lock nut

FIG. 9-1. Adjustments on steering gear. (*Chevrolet Motor Division of General Motors Corporation*)

If end play can be felt as the steering wheel is pushed and pulled, adjust by loosening the mast-jacket-clamp bolt *B* and the housing-clamp bolt *A* (Fig. 9-1). Check to make sure that there is backlash between the sector roller and the worm, and then turn the worm-shaft adjuster *H* clockwise to take up worm-shaft end play. Turn only a slight amount each time, and check the adjustment with a spring scale hooked on the steering wheel at a spoke next to the rim. The adjustment should be such that ½ pound is required to pull the wheel through the straight-ahead position (Fig. 9-2).

To remove sector-shaft end play, loosen the lock nut *C* (Fig. 9-1), and turn the adjusting screw *D* down tight, backing it off until it is free. Then turn it down again until it just touches the end of the sector shaft. Hold the adjusting screw in this position and tighten the lock nut *C*.

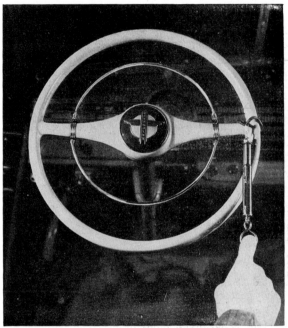

Fig. 9-2. Checking pull required to pull gear through straight-ahead position with a spring pull scale. (*Chevrolet Motor Division of General Motors Corporation*)

To remove backlash between the worm and the sector, first locate the straight-ahead position of the steering gear: turn the steering wheel in one direction as far as it will go and then in the opposite direction as far as it will go, count the number of wheel revolutions, and then turn back exactly halfway. Adjust by loosening the three cover bolts *E* and the eccentric-bolt lock nut *J* (Fig. 9-3). Next, using one wrench on the eccentric bolt *F* (Fig. 9-1) and a second wrench on the eccentric sleeve *G*, turn in opposite directions very small amounts (Fig. 9-3), noting the result after each slight adjustment by moving the sector shaft. This action causes the sector-shaft

[237]

assembly to move toward the worm, and excessive adjustment would damage the steering gear. Proceed slowly! Less than one-eighth turn will usually be found sufficient to eliminate backlash. To check adjustment, first tighten the cover bolts. Then hook a spring at right angles to a steering-wheel spoke at the rim. It should require not more than 1⅜ pounds to pull the gear through the center position (Fig. 9-2). Reassemble pitman arm and tighten nut securely.

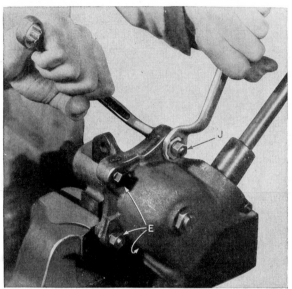

FIG. 9-3. Steering-gear cover bolts and eccentric-bolt-and-sleeve adjustment. Cover bolts (E) and eccentric-bolt lock nut (J) must be loosened to make the adjustment. (*Chevrolet Motor Division of General Motors Corporation*)

The steering gear shown in Fig. 5-17 is used on late-model Chevrolet automobiles. Adjustments required on this steering gear are somewhat different from those on the previous model. After the steering linkage is disconnected from the pitman arm, the lock nut should be loosened and the sector-shaft adjusting screw or lash adjuster—at end of pitman-arm shaft—turned back, to remove close meshing of sector teeth with worm. Then, the steering wheel should be turned all the way in one direction and then turned back one full turn. (Note the caution above about bumping the wheel at the end of a turn.) Then use a spring scale to measure pull at the steering-wheel rim (Fig. 9-2) required to keep the wheel in motion. It should be ⅜ to ⅝ pound. If not correct, adjust worm bearings.

[238]

Worm bearings are adjusted by loosening the large lock nut and turning the worm-bearing adjusting cup until there is no perceptible end play in the worm. Recheck pull on the steering wheel and make readjustment until the pull is within specifications. Then tighten the lock nut and make a final recheck.

Lash between sector teeth and worm is adjusted with the wheel turned to center position, as already explained (note caution). Mark center position on the steering wheel with tape. Then turn the lash adjusting screw in, to take out all lash, and tighten the lock nut to specified tension. Turn the wheel off center position and then, with a spring scale, pull the wheel through center. If the pull is not $\frac{7}{8}$ to $1\frac{7}{8}$ pounds, turn the wheel a half turn from center and loosen or tighten the adjusting screw as necessary. Always make a final check after retightening the lock nut.

§128. Chevrolet steering-gear service Servicing of the Chevrolet steering gear shown in Fig. 5-17 is discussed below. A disassembled view of this unit is shown in Fig. 9-4.

1. Removal. Remove horn button or cap and also blowing ring (where present). Pull steering wheel with special puller. Remove clamp bolt from shaft connector and toe-board grommet and seal. Take off the clamp holding mast jacket to instrument panel and detach gearshift-control-upper-support from mast jacket. Take off upper control shaft and support. Detach shifter housing from mast jacket and rotate housing out of way. Then, in engine compartment, remove metal splash guard protecting the steering gear and take off nuts and bolts that hold the steering gear. Remove air duct from left fender skirt. Rotate steering gear so it clears fender skirt and lift it up and out of engine compartment.

2. Disassembly. With steering gear in vise, remove nut and lock washer from pitman-arm shaft and pull pitman arm with special puller. Back off lash adjuster a few turns. Loosen worm adjuster lock nut and back off adjuster cup a few turns. Put a pan under steering gear to catch lubricant, take out the bolts attaching side cover, and remove side cover with sector and shaft. If sector will not come out, turn worm shaft by hand so sector will pass through the opening in the housing. Then remove the adjuster cup, the lower worm bearing, and the worm and shaft assembly. Unscrew lash adjuster from cover.

3. *Inspection.* Handle all parts with care and keep them clean. Remember that very small scratches or dirt on the worm, sector, or bearings may cause trouble later after the unit is back in operation. Use a magnifying glass to check the worm, sector, and bearing after cleaning them in solvent. Check the fit of the sector

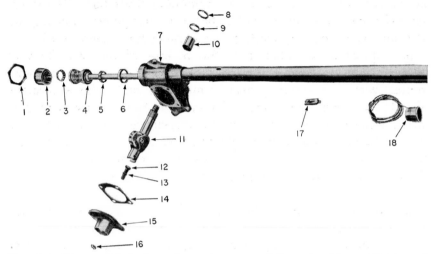

Fig. 9-4. Disassembled view of steering gear. (*Chevrolet Motor Division of General Motors Corporation*)

1. Worm-bearing adjuster lock nut
2. Worm-bearing adjuster cup
3. Lower worm-shaft roller bearing
4. Worm-shaft assembly
5. Upper worm-shaft roller bearing
6. Upper worm-shaft roller-bearing race
7. Housing and mast jacket assembly
8. Sector-shaft packing retainer
9. Sector-shaft packing
10. Sector-shaft bushing
11. Sector-shaft and roller assembly
12. Lash adjuster
13. Lash-adjuster shim
14. Housing side-cover gasket
15. Housing side cover
16. Lock nut
17. Horn wire retainer
18. Mast jacket bearing assembly

(pitman-arm) shaft in the bushings. Replace the bushings, if necessary. Replace shaft packing if it is worn or shows signs of leakage. Bearings and bearing cups should be replaced if worn. Bearing cups require special remover and replacer.

4. *Assembly.* Put upper worm bearing on worm shaft and install shaft in housing. Make sure the horn wire is in place. Put lower worm bearing in place and turn adjuster cup into housing loosely. Put lash adjuster, with shim, into the slot in the end of the sector

shaft. End clearance between the button on lash adjuster and bottom of slot should be 0.002 inch or less. If more, install a thicker shim. Start cover on sector shaft and insert screw through hole in cover to turn lash adjuster into cover as far as it will go. Use new gasket and install cover on housing. Make sure there is some lash between worm and sector before tightening cover bolts. The steering gear may be adjusted on the bench by temporarily putting the steering wheel on the shaft. Use the procedure given above.

5. *Installation.* Installation is the reverse of removal. Be sure to put the steering wheel on the shaft so that the spokes are horizontal with the steering gear centered (front wheels straight ahead). Steering connecting rod may have to be adjusted to give straight-ahead wheel position when steering gear is centered. This is done by loosening the connecting-rod adjuster clamps and turning the adjusting sleeve one way or the other to lengthen or shorten the connecting rod. Then tighten clamps.

§129. Ford steering-gear adjustment The Ford steering gear (see Fig. 5-16) requires four adjustments, as explained below.

1. *Sector-shaft end play.* This is adjusted by a screw located at the end of the pitman-arm, or sector, shaft. With lock nut loose, the screw should be turned in just enough to remove all shaft end play without causing a bind between the screw and shaft. Hold screw in this position and tighten nut.

2. *Worm bearing preload.* This is controlled by the shim pack (gaskets) between the housing and the housing upper cap (see Fig. 5-16). To check, disconnect steering linkage from pitman arm and turn steering wheel two full turns away from the straight-ahead position. Use a spring scale as shown in Fig. 9-2 and note pull required to keep wheel moving (make a full turn of the wheel during the check). Proper bearing preload will give a pull of ½ to 1¼ pounds. If the reading is too high, a shim or shims must be added. If too low, a shim or shims must be removed. To add or remove shims, remove the screws that hold the housing upper cap to the housing and push the cap and column jacket up (steering wheel may have to be removed). To add a shim, split the shim at one point and then install shim, split upward. Be sure split ends do not overlap as this would double the thickness. To remove a shim, separate the first shim on the pack from the rest with a knife

[241]

blade. Work blade all the way around carefully so as to not damage the other shims. Remove or add shims, one at a time, checking the worm-bearing preload each time. The steering column and housing upper cap must be attached to the housing each time the preload is checked.

3. *Worm and roller-mesh preload.* This is adjusted by rotating the sector-shaft housing. The sector-shaft housing has an eccentric boss that seats in the steering-gear housing. When the four cap screws attaching the two housings are loosened, the sector-shaft housing may be turned one way or the other to move the sector toward or away from the worm. This results in a tighter or a looser mesh between the worm and roller. Adjustment is checked by measuring the pull, with a spring scale, required to pull the wheel past the center point. It should be at least ½ pound more than the worm-bearing preload previously checked but not more than 2 pounds. To increase the mesh preload, loosen the four cap screws and use a mallet to tap the cover in a clockwise direction so all backlash is removed. Check backlash by moving the pitman arm. Tighten cap screws and recheck with spring scale, as above. If reading is now too high, loosen cap screws and back off adjustment slightly. Tighten cap screws and recheck.

4. *Steering-wheel spoke position (Fig. 8-44).* The steering-wheel spokes should be horizontal when the front wheels are straight ahead and the pitman arm should be pointing straight back. The steering wheel can be centered by turning the connecting rod sleeves after loosening the clamp bolts.

§130. **Ford steering-gear service** Servicing of the Ford steering gear shown in Fig. 5-16 is discussed below.

1. *Removal.* Remove the horn button or ring, nut, and steering wheel. Detach steering column from instrument panel. Disconnect lower gearshift levers from gearshift rods by removing attaching nuts. Detach and remove gearshift tube, tube pin, and levers. Loosen steering-column clamp and pull column off steering-gear shaft. Then, from engine compartment, remove pitman arm from shaft with special puller after taking off nut. Take off three bolts attaching steering gear and remove steering gear from underside of car; raise the car, if necessary, to remove it.

2. *Disassembly.* Drain lubricant. Scratch a mark with sharp

punch on the sector housing and steering-gear housing so they can be replaced in same alignment. Separate two housings by removing attaching bolts. Remove the two spacers from the sector shaft; then take out gasket. Take housing cap off steering-gear housing after removing attaching screws. Pull steering-gear shaft out of housing and then slide shim pack, bearing cup, and upper bearing off shaft. Tie shim pack together so you don't loose shims. Lift lower worm bearing and cup from housing. Press needle bearings out of sector-shaft housing.

3. Inspection. Clean all parts in solvent and check the worm, roller, and bearings for signs of cracks, scratches, or other damage. Replace all worn or damaged parts.

4. Assembly. Put the bearings, with spacer between them, into sector-shaft housing. Press oil seal into place. Put upper worm bearing and cup and shim pack on worm shaft. Put housing cap on shaft. Install lower bearing and cup in housing. Then put worm shaft into housing and attach cup to housing with screws. Put the two thrust washers on the sector shaft, install shaft in housing, and attach two housings. Be sure alignment marks previously scratched on the housings line up.

5. Installation. Working beneath the car, position steering gear on frame but do not tighten attaching bolts and nuts. Put column tube assembly on shaft. Attach column to instrument panel and then attach and connect gearshift lever and other parts. Install pitman arm and tighten lock nut to 110 to 130 lb-ft torque. Add lubricant and adjust steering gear, as above.

§131. Plymouth steering-gear adjustments The Plymouth steering gear (Fig. 5-18) requires two adjustments, as follows:

1. Sector shaft adjustment. To check for free play, jack up the front of the car and turn the wheels until they are straight ahead. Rotate steering wheel first clockwise until resistance is felt, then counterclockwise until resistance is felt. Remove the lock nut and lock plate (Fig. 9-5) and tighten the adjusting screw until no free play can be felt at the steering wheel. No free play should be noticeable when the steering wheel is turned through the straight-ahead position. The pull needed to turn the steering wheel through straight-ahead can be checked with a spring scale. It should be 1 to 2½ pounds if the worm-bearing adjustment is correct.

2. *Worm-bearing adjustment.* This can be checked by shaking the front wheels from side to side (while car is jacked up). There should be no up-and-down movement of the steering wheel. If there is, end play is excessive and it must be decreased by removing one or more shims (see Fig. 5-18). With the sector-shaft assembly

Fig. 9-5. Adjustments of steering gear. 1, adjusting screw; 2, adjusting screw lock nut; 3, adjusting-screw lock plate; 4, lubricant filler plug; 5, bearing-adjusting shims. (*Plymouth Division of Chrysler Corporation*)

removed, the worm bearings—when properly adjusted—will produce a ⅜- to ¾-pound pull on the wheel rim (Fig. 9-2). With the sector-shaft assembly installed and adjusted, the pull should be 1 to 2½ pounds.

Caution: At least one shim is required to provide a grease seal at the housing cover. If all shims must be removed to get proper worm-bearing adjustment, then parts are worn and should be replaced.

[244]

§**132. Plymouth steering-gear service** *1. Steering-gear sector shaft.* The sector, or pitman-arm, shaft can be removed and replaced without removing the steering gear from the car. The pitman arm and cover cap screws should be removed first. Then the shaft can be driven upward with a soft hammer. As the roller tooth clears the worm, check the shaft and bushings for wear by moving the shaft from side to side. If the shaft is loose, new bushings should be installed. Remove the upper bushing from the top and the lower bushing from the bottom. Then press in new bushings and burnish them.

Inspect the roller for signs of wear and also for looseness on the shaft. If loose or worn, the shaft assembly should be replaced. To reinstall the shaft, first put oil seal in housing. Then wrap masking tape over serrations on shaft to protect the oil seal. Install shaft assembly, with adjusting-screw washer in place, in housing. Secure with gasket and cover and attach pitman arm.

2. Tube and worm assembly. If the tube and worm assembly must be replaced, the assembly can be removed without removing the column jacket or gearshift controls. First take out sector shaft. Then remove the lower cover and shims and take out worm and tube assembly. Conditions requiring replacement include worn, cracked, or scratched bearing cups or worm. On reinstallation, the adjustments previously noted must be made.

§**133. Recirculating ball-and-nut steering-gear adjustments** The steering gear illustrated in Figs. 5-19 and 5-20 requires two adjustments, worm-shaft end play and backlash. To make the adjustments, disconnect the steering tie rod from the pitman arm, turn the wheel all the way in one direction and then back one turn (observe caution about bumping at the end of travel). Then check for lash by working the pitman arm. If no lash can be felt, loosen the lock nut and turn the pitman-shaft adjusting screw (Fig. 9-6) in a counterclockwise direction until lash can be felt in the pitman arm. Then loosen the large lock nut and turn the worm-bearing adjuster (Fig. 9-7) until a slight load is felt when the steering wheel is turned near extreme positions. The adjustment is correct when the pull on the steering-wheel rim needed to turn the wheel near the extreme positions in $\frac{7}{8}$ to $1\frac{1}{8}$ pounds. Tighten the lock nut and recheck the adjustment.

After the worm bearing has been adjusted, recheck backlash with

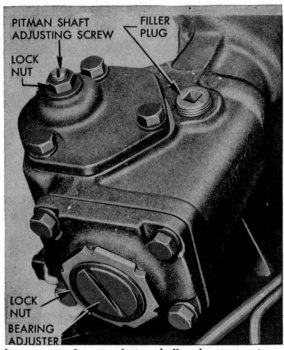

Fig. 9-6. Adjustments of recirculating ball-and-nut steering gear. (*Buick Motor Division of General Motors Corporation*)

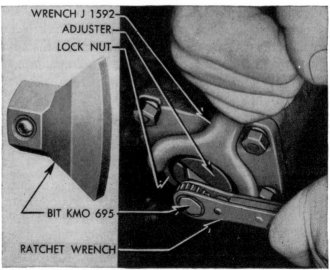

Fig. 9-7. Adjusting worm bearing with special tools. (*Buick Motor Division of General Motors Corporation*)

the wheel in the center, or straight-ahead, position. Adjust back-lash, as necessary, by turning the pitman-shaft adjusting screw. Turn clockwise to reduce backlash. When adjustment is correct, no pitman-arm movement can be felt in the straight-ahead position. After adjustment is completed, turn the steering wheel to see if there are any tight spots. If there are, back off the pitman-shaft adjusting screw slightly (counterclockwise) to increase lash. Then recheck the adjustment. With adjustment correct, it should require a pull of 2 to 2¼ pounds to pull the wheel through center position.

§134. Recirculating ball-and-nut steering-gear service *1. Removal.* On some models, air cleaner must be removed and fuel and vacuum lines disconnected from carburetor in order to have enough room to remove the steering gear. Detach steering tie rod from pitman arm. Disconnect wires from steering column at connectors and detach transmission selector rod and springs. In driver's compartment, disconnect braces holding steering column to cowl or instrument panel. Remove steering column pad and other parts on toe board to permit column to pass through toe board. Move front seat all the way back and cover it with cloth. Remove steering wheel, shift control lever, and direction-switch control lever (where present). Then, in engine compartment, remove bolts holding steering gear to frame. With assistant in driver's compartment to keep steering column from being damaged or from damaging finish, move steering gear to rear as far as possible, turn it so pitman arm is up, lift it up, and pull it forward and out of car.

2. *Disassembly (Fig. 9-8).* Pull pitman arm with puller, after removing nut and lock washer. From upper end of steering column, remove dial housing (automatic transmission) and direction signal (leave hanging loose on wire). Other parts on the column—shift-control lever housing, back-up light switch, neutral safety switch—can be removed and the wires pulled through slot in column. Then the steering gear itself can be disassembled. Loosen lock nut on pitman-shaft adjusting screw and take off side cover with pitman shaft attached. Separate the two by unscrewing the adjusting screw. Loosen worm bearing adjuster several turns after loosening lock nut. Take off end cover and gasket. Steering shaft with ball nut and bearings can then be removed from housing. Ball nut can be taken off worm by removing guide clamps and guides and dumping balls out of nut.

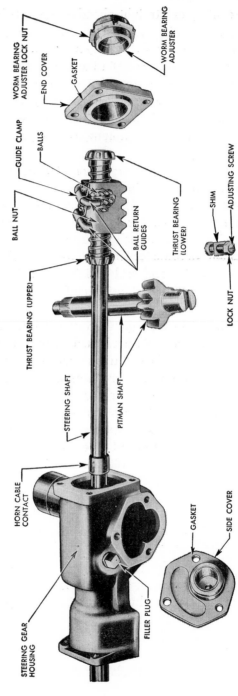

FIG. 9-8. Disassembled view of a recirculating ball-and-nut steering gear. (*Buick Motor Division of General Motors Corporation*)

WORM BEARING ADJUSTER LOCK NUT

WORM BEARING ADJUSTER

END COVER

GASKET

GUIDE CLAMP

BALLS

BALL NUT

BALL RETURN GUIDES

THRUST BEARING (LOWER)

SHIM

ADJUSTING SCREW

LOCK NUT

THRUST BEARING (UPPER)

STEERING SHAFT

PITMAN SHAFT

HORN CABLE CONTACT

STEERING GEAR HOUSING

FILLER PLUG

GASKET

SIDE COVER

3. *Inspection.* After cleaning steering-gear parts in solvent, inspect balls, races, worm, and bearings for wear, scores, or other damage. Damaged parts must be replaced. Replace pitman-shaft bushings in housing and side cover if they are worn. Pitman-shaft oil seal in housing should be replaced. Feather edge of new seal should be toward inside of housing. Check fit of adjusting screw in slot in end of pitman shaft with shim in place. If clearance between button on screw and bottom of slot is more than 0.002 inch, install a thicker shim.

4. *Reassembly.* Reassembly is reverse of disassembly. Use new gaskets to avoid leaks. When installing balls in nut, be sure to put 30 balls in each of the two circuits in the ball nut. Use care when inserting pitman shaft in housing so that the serrations do not cut the oil seal. Pitman arm should go on shaft so it is parallel with steering column when steering gear is in straight-ahead position. Steering gear should be adjusted (§133) before installation. A steering wheel can be put on the steering shaft temporarily for the adjustments.

5. *Installation.* During installation, leave the steering-gear attaching bolts loose until steering-column bracket and spacers (if originally installed) are in place. Attach parts previously removed from steering column (dial housing, direction signal, wiring, and so on). When attaching tie rod to pitman arm, make sure the bearings seat around the ball stud and that the dust cover closes off the opening around the ball stud. Turn tie-rod plug up until it is solid, back off two turns, and install cotter pin. Put specified lubricant in steering-gear housing.

CHAPTER CHECKUP

As a rule, steering gears give little trouble and, aside from lubrication, require attention only when wear of parts has progressed to such an extent that readjustment or replacement of parts is required. Nevertheless, for a well-rounded education in automobiles, you should know how various steering gears are adjusted and repaired. The information in the chapter covers this subject; the questions that follow will help you to review the information and find out how well it has stayed with you.

Completing the Sentences

The sentences below are incomplete. After each sentence there are several words or phrases, only one of which will correctly complete the sentence. Write down each sentence in your notebook, selecting the proper word or phrase to complete it correctly.

1. There are two basic adjustments on steering gears, one for taking up worm-gear and steering-shaft end play, the other for removing steering-gear   *frontlash*   *side play*   *backlash*
2. A third adjustment on many steering gears has the purpose of adjusting sector-shaft   *bushing fit*   *bearing fit*   *end play*   *side play*
3. One of the most important precautions to observe in turning the steering wheel with the linkage disconnected from the pitman arm is to avoid   *bumping at the ends of turns*   *bumping at center of turns*   *spinning wheel slowly*
4. On some models, worm-bearing adjustment, or preloading, is made by turning a bearing adjusting cup; on other models it is made by means of   *adjusting nuts*   *roller bearings*   *shims*   *bushings*
5. Generally speaking, the steering-gear backlash is adjusted by moving the sector in relation to the   *pitman shaft*   *worm*   *steering wheel*   *pitman arm*

Servicing Procedures

Write down the procedures asked for in the following questions in your notebook. Do not copy from the book, but write the procedures down in your own words, just as though you were explaining to a friend how to do the jobs.

1. How is a late-type Chevrolet steering gear adjusted?
2. Explain how to remove, repair, and replace a Chevrolet steering gear.
3. How is the Ford steering gear adjusted?
4. Describe the procedure for removing, disassembling, assembling, and reinstalling a Ford steering gear.
5. Explain how to adjust a Plymouth steering gear.
6. Describe how to remove the sector shaft from a Plymouth steering gear.
7. Explain how to adjust a recirculating ball-and-nut steering gear.
8. Explain how to remove, disassemble, assemble, and reinstall a recirculating ball-and-nut steering gear.

[250]

SUGGESTIONS FOR FURTHER STUDY

When you are in your local school or automotive service shop, examine various steering gears that are available. Note how the automotive mechanic makes adjustments to steering gears and, if possible, how he removes and tears one down for complete service. If you have a chance to study automotive shop manuals, be sure to note the details of servicing of their steering gear. Write down in your notebook any important facts you learn.

10: Saginaw power-steering service

THIS CHAPTER describes the trouble-shooting, adjusting, removal, repair, and reinstallation of the Saginaw power-steering units. Section 67 describes the operation of these units. Chapter 6 discussed trouble-shooting procedures on steering and suspension generally. The material that follows carries this a step further into power steering and includes complete repair procedures on the Saginaw units.

§135. Trouble-shooting chart (Saginaw power steering) These units were described in detail in §67. The list, below, of trouble symptoms, causes, and checks or corrections is provided to give you a means of logically analyzing trouble and quickly locating the cause. Once the cause is known, the trouble is usually easy to cure. Following the trouble chart are several sections that describe the repair procedures on the Saginaw power-steering units.

NOTE: The troubles and possible causes are not listed in the chart in the order of frequency of occurrence. That is, item 1 does not necessarily occur more often than item 2, nor does item *a* under Possible Cause necessarily occur more often than item *b*.

SAGINAW POWER-STEERING TROUBLE-SHOOTING CHART

(See §§136 to 150 for details of checks and corrections listed.)

Complaint	*Possible Cause*	*Check or Correction*
1. Hard steering	*a.* Tight steering-gear adjustment	Readjust
	b. Pump drive belt loose	Tighten
	c. Low oil pressure	Check—see item 3, Low oil pressure, below
	d. Air in hydraulic system	Bleed system

Complaint	Possible Cause	Check or Correction
	e. Low oil level	Add oil
	f. Low engine idle	Adjust idle
2. Poor centering (or recovery from turns)	a. Valve sticky or off center	Free up, relocate
	b. Tight power-rack	Readjust
	c. Steering shaft binding	Align, replace bushings
	d. Incorrect steering-gear adjustments	Readjust
3. Low oil pressure	a. Loose pump belt	Tighten
	b. Low oil level	Add oil
	c. Mechanical trouble in pump	Check relief valve, rotor parts
	d. Oil leaks, external	Check hose connections, 0 sealing rings at cover, etc.
	e. Oil leaks, internal	Replace cylinder adapter, valve cover, or upper housing seal
	f. Engine idling too slowly	Set idle speed to specifications
4. Pump noise	a. Oil cold	Oil will warm up in a few minutes
	b. Air in system	Bleed
	c. Oil level low	Add oil
	d. Air vent plugged	Open
	e. Dirt in pump	Clean
	f. Mechanical damage	Disassemble pump, replace defective parts
5. Gear noise	a. Loose power-rack adjustment	Adjust
	b. Loose over-center adjustment	Adjust
	c. Loose thrust-bearing adjustment	Adjust
	d. Loose power-rack pin	Replace
	e. Air in system	Bleed
	f. Oil level low	Add oil
	g. Hose rubbing body or chassis part	Relocate hose

§136. Trouble diagnosis (Saginaw power steering) The chart above lists possible troubles, causes, and corrections. When trouble is reported on the steering system, the following checks should be made in an attempt to pinpoint the trouble. Often, it may be some simple thing like a loose belt that can be corrected without difficulty.

1. Check belt tension. As noted in the chart, low belt tension can cause low oil pressure and hard steering. A quick check of belt tension can be made—while the engine and pump are warm—by turning the steering wheel with the front wheels on a dry floor. As the wheel is turned, maximum pressure is built up and this imposes full load on the belt. If the belt now slips, the tension is too low. To check tension accurately, turn engine off and push in

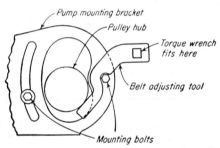

Fig. 10-1. Belt-tension adjusting tool in position. (*Chevrolet Motor Division of General Motors Corporation*)

on belt midway between pulleys. Belt should deflect about one-fourth inch with a push of about 6 pounds. Loosen mounting bolts and move pump out to increase tension. Then tighten bolts.

Some adjusting procedures call for the use of a special belt-adjusting tool (Fig. 10-1). The tool fits under the pulley hub and over the outer mounting bolt. With both bolts loose, the tool is positioned as shown, a torque wrench is inserted into the square opening in the tool, and an outward pull is exerted. (Chevrolet calls for 17 lb-ft, Cadillac 13 to 15 lb-ft.) Then the inner bolt is tightened, the tool removed, and the outer bolt tightened.

2. Check oil level. If oil level is low, add oil to bring level up to marking on side of reservoir. Use only the special oil recommended —automatic transmission oil. If the oil level is low, the possibility exists that there is an oil leak; check all hose and power-steering connections for signs of a leak. Leakage may occur at various points in the power-steering unit if seals are defective. Check around

[254]

the piston and valve housings for leakage signs. Replace seals or tighten connections to eliminate leaks.

3. *Checking steering action.* A check of the power-steering action can be made with a pull scale hooked to the wheel rim (Fig. 9-2). Oil in the system must be warm before this test is made, and the front wheels must be resting on a level, dry floor. If the oil is cold, set the hand brake, start the engine, and allow it to idle for several minutes. While idling, turn the steering wheel back and forth so as to build up pressure in the system; this hastens the warming of the oil. With the oil warm, hook the pull scale on the steering-wheel rim, and see how much pull it requires to turn the front wheels first in one direction and then in the other. The amount of pull specified varies with different models (due to tire and wheel size, linkage design, and so on), but in general, if pull exceeds about 10 pounds, the unit is not working properly and oil pressure should be checked.

NOTE: Be sure engine is idling at specified speed. If it is idling too slowly, it may not be driving the pump fast enough to build up normal pressure.

4. *Checking oil pressure.* A special hydraulic-pressure gauge is required to check oil pressure from the pump. To use the gauge, disconnect the pressure hose from the pump and connect the gauge between the pressure fitting on the pump and the pressure hose (Fig. 10-2). Then, with oil and pump warm, with engine idling at specified speed, and with front wheels resting on a level, dry floor, turn steering wheel to right and left. Pressure should build up to between 700 and 900 psi (pounds per square inch). Do not hold wheel at either end of travel since this will maintain high pressure and cause excessive oil temperatures and possible wear of internal parts.

If pressure does not build up satisfactorily, close the manual valve on the gauge while the engine is idling and quickly note the pressure. Then open valve.

Caution: Do not leave valve closed more than a few seconds since this causes pump to work against maximum pressure and without oil circulation.

If pressure goes up satisfactorily when the manual valve is closed, it means that the pump is operating satisfactorily and loss of pres-

[255]

sure is therefore due to leakage in the steering gear (or externally). See item 2, check oil level, above, for possible points at which leakage might occur.

If pressure remains below specifications when the manual valve is closed, then loss of pressure is due to some condition in the pump itself. If the pump belt is properly tightened and the oil level at proper height, then possibly the pressure-relief valve is stuck or rotor parts are sticking or are worn.

Fig. 10-2. Special hydraulic-pressure gauge connected into pressure line from pump to check oil pressure that pump can develop. (*Buick Motor Division of General Motors Corporation*)

§137. Bleeding hydraulic system   Air will enter the hydraulic system while oil lines are being disconnected and reconnected, after the pump or steering gear has been removed and replaced, or possibly because of a low oil level in the reservoir. The air must be removed; otherwise the unit will operate noisily and unsatisfactorily. To bleed the system, fill the oil reservoir to the proper level and allow car to sit for several minutes. If a Vickers pump (right, Fig. 5-27) with manifold is used, remove pipe plug from top of manifold and when oil starts to flow out of opening, reinstall plug finger tight.

[256]

After waiting for several minutes, start engine and run it at fast idle for several minutes. Then turn steering wheel from one extreme to the other several times. This will work air out of system; pump will quiet down as air is bled out. If necessary, add more oil, and repeat waiting and bleeding procedure. Finally, tighten plug (on Vickers pump).

§138. Adjusting Saginaw steering gear on car Three steering-gear adjustments are required, thrust-bearing, over-center, and power-

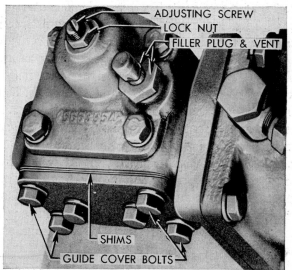

Fig. 10-3. Steering-gear adjustments. Over-center adjustment is made by turning the adjusting screw. Power-rack adjustment is made by removing or adding shims, thus changing mesh of rack with sector. (*Buick Motor Division of General Motors Corporation*)

rack. Over-center and power-rack adjustments can be made on the car, but the thrust bearing must be adjusted with the unit removed from the car.

1. Over-center adjustment. This adjustment determines the amount of pull required to turn the steering wheel through the center position. The adjustment is made by turning the adjusting screw in or out (Fig. 10-3). This moves the pitman shaft endwise. First, on the type of steering gear shown in Fig. 10-3, the four corner guide-cover bolts must be loosened (do not touch the two center bolts) so as to remove any load between the power rack and sector teeth. On the type of steering gear with a single power-rack adjusting screw, loosen the lock nut and back out adjusting screw one-fourth turn. Then, loosen the lock nut and back off the pitman-shaft adjusting screw. Disconnect the steering connecting rod from the pitman arm.

Turn steering wheel through complete range (avoid bumping at ends of turns) to check for free action. Then turn wheel to mid-position and turn adjusting screw back in just enough to take out all lash in gear teeth (check for lash by moving pitman arm back and forth). Tighten lock nut. Turn wheel off center position and then check, with scale, the number of pounds required to pull wheel through the center position (Fig. 9-2). Pull should be ½ to 1 pound. Readjust adjusting screw and recheck as necessary to attain proper over-center pull. Tighten four corner guide-cover bolts, or adjust power-rack screw as described below and tighten lock nut.

2. *Power-rack adjustment (guide-cover type).* After completing the over-center adjustment and tightening the guide-cover bolts, recheck the pull required to pull the wheel through the center position. Pull should now be somewhat higher—by only a fraction of a pound—due to loading of rack and sector teeth. If pull has increased too much, remove guide cover and add one 0.003-inch shim, and recheck. Add shims as necessary until the pull required is only ⅛ pound more than pull required in previous paragraph.

But if pull required does not increase, then remove one 0.003-inch shim and recheck. Remove additional shims as necessary to get the pull to increase ⅛ pound.

Caution: Total over-center load (due to adjusting-screw adjustment and also to installation of shims) should not exceed 1¼ pounds.

Reattach the steering connecting rod to pitman arm.

3. *Power-rack adjustment (adjusting-screw type).* On this type, tighten the adjusting screw (with special tool) so that the over-center pull is ⅛ to ¼ pound greater than with power-rack screw loose. Then tighten lock nut and recheck adjustment. Reattach steering connecting rod to pitman arm.

§139. Saginaw power-steering gear removal The procedure for removing the steering gear varies to some extent from one make of car to another because of individual variations in the installation.

As a first step, it is recommended that the battery cables be disconnected. Disconnect the grounded terminal cable first. Disconnecting the battery guards against an accidental short or ground when other electrical devices are being disconnected and removed.

The removal procedure for the power-steering gear is very much like the removal procedure for the manual gear described in Chap. 9. Refer to the car shop manual for other details of removal.

SAGINAW OFFSET POWER-STEERING SERVICE

§140. Saginaw power-steering-gear disassembly   Figure 10-4 is an exploded view of the steering gear for which disassembly procedure is given below. Before disassembly, clean exterior of the steering gear thoroughly with solvent. Bolt the steering gear to a suitable bracket clamped in a vise.

Caution: Make sure that the workbench, your hands, and the tools are clean. Remember, it takes only a very little dirt in the mechanism to cause faulty action or damage.

1. If steering gear was removed with mast jacket in place, remove jacket by taking out attaching screws.
2. Remove two hoses, two large valve-to-cylinder tubes, and small bypass line between power cylinder and gear housing. Allow oil to drain from valve and power cylinder. Drain lubricant from gear housing by removing filler plug.
3. It is not necessary to remove the elbow fittings (see Fig. 10-5) unless the sealing O rings require replacement.
4. Turn steering shaft clockwise as far as possible and remove the power-rack guide cover (see Fig. 10-3) and shims by taking out the four corner bolts.
5. Take off power-cylinder-and-rack assembly, with cylinder gasket, after removing attaching bolts.
6. Remove piston-and-rack assembly, with adapter (Fig. 10-5), from cylinder by pushing rack all the way in and then pulling it out smartly to break seal between O rings and cylinder. Piston can then be removed from rod by taking off nut. Thrust washers, adapter, and stop plate will then slide off rod.
7. Turn steering shaft counterclockwise to center the ball nut. Then remove the gear-housing side cover and gasket with pitman shaft attached (by removing four screws). Take off lock

[259]

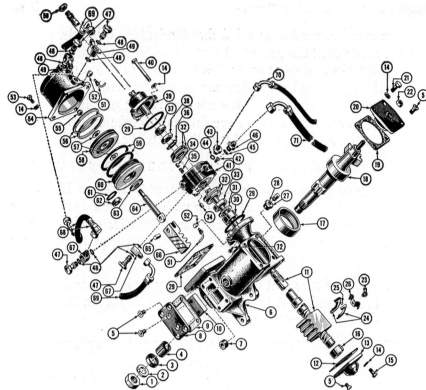

Fig. 10-4. Disassembled view of Saginaw power-steering gear. (*Lincoln-Mercury Division of Ford Motor Company*)

1. Nut
2. Lock washer
3. Seal
4. Bushing
5. Screw
6. Housing
7. Plug
8. Cover
9. Shim
10. Guide
11. Shaft and ball nut
12. Gasket
13. Cover
14. Lock washer
15. Cap screw
16. Bearing
17. Bearing
18. Pitman shaft

19. Gasket
20. Cover
21. Cap screw
22. Nut
23. Screw and washer
24. Guide
25. Ball
26. Bracket
27. Plug
28. Breather
29. O ring
30. Bearing
31. Washer
32. Thrust bearing
33. Seal
34. Plunger
35. Spring
36. Tab lock

37. Seal
38. Nut
39. Cover
40. Bolt
41. Valve cover
42. Check valve
43. Fitting
44. Seal
45. Seal
46. Fitting
47. Fitting
48. Seal
49. Union
50. Nut
51. Bleeder tube
52. Fitting
53. Cap screw
54. Housing

55. Nut
56. Rings
57. Washer
58. Piston
59. O ring
60. Adapter
61. Washer
62. Seal
63. Plate
64. Rod
65. Pin
66. Rack
67. Union
68. Hose assembly
69. Hose
70. Hose assembly
71. Hose assembly
72. Screw

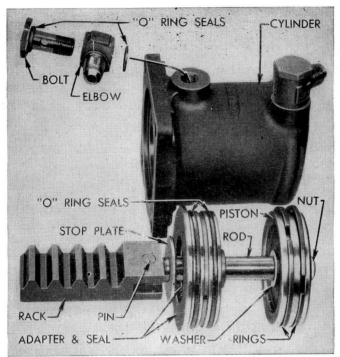

FIG. 10-5. Power cylinder and rack parts. (*Buick Motor Division of General Motors Corporation*)

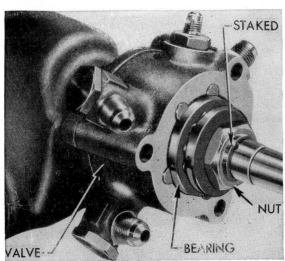

FIG. 10-6. Location of thrust bearing and lock nut, showing the staking method of locking the nut into place. (*Buick Motor Division of General Motors Corporation*)

nut from adjusting screw, and run adjusting screw in through cover to separate cover and pitman shaft. Take adjusting screw and shim from shaft.

8. Mark hydraulic-valve cover, valve, and housing so they can be reassembled in exactly the same relationship. Then remove bolts and take off valve cover. The thrust-bearing lock nut

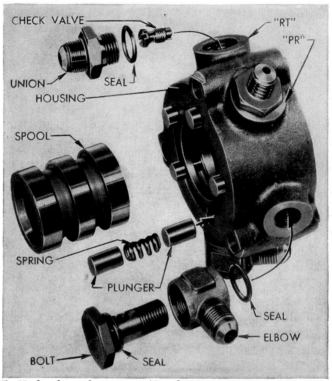

Fig. 10-7. Hydraulic valve parts. (*Buick Motor Division of General Motors Corporation*)

must now be backed off. On some models, this nut is locked in place with a tang lock washer. On others, it is staked into the shaft keyway (Fig. 10-6). Remove nut and thrust bearing.

9. With shaft horizontal, remove the hydraulic-valve assembly. Be careful to hold valve assembly horizontal so spool and plungers do not fall out (Fig. 10-7).

10. Check valve and plungers for possible sticking in housing. Then remove these parts and the centering springs. Remove

unions, elbows, and check valve as necessary (if sealing O rings require replacement).

Caution: Handle spool and plungers with care. Put them aside in a safe place where they will not be bumped, scratched, or otherwise damaged.

11. Remove gear-housing end cover and then take out steering shaft and ball nut from housing.
12. Take clamps and ball-return guides from nut, turn nut over to allow balls to run out, and then remove nut from shaft.

§141. Saginaw power-steering-gear inspection Wash all parts in clean kerosene or solvent and wipe dry with clean, lintless cloths. Then check, repair, or replace parts as follows:

1. Make sure that steering shaft is straight and ball-bearing and needle-bearing races are in good condition and not worn or brinelled (that is, have developed worn pockets due to shock loads on race through balls or needles).
2. Check teeth of ball nut and sector. If teeth are worn, replace part.
3. Check fit of adjusting screw in end of pitman shaft. With shim in place, clearance between button on end of adjusting screw and slot in shaft should be 0.002 inch or less. If it is excessive, fit a new shim.
4. Replace bushings in housing or replace cover assembly if pitman-shaft bushings are worn excessively.
5. If the needle bearing in the gear housing requires replacement, remove it with a punch and use special tool to install the new bearing (Fig. 10-8). Remove seal from gear housing with a punch and install a new seal, *spring side out*, with special tool (Fig. 10-8).
6. If bearing in end cover requires replacement, use special removing tool as shown in Fig. 10-9. Turning the screw will expand plates under the bearing and will force the tool and bearing out. Use special tool to locate and drive new bearing into position.
7. Install new pitman-shaft seal with feather edge toward inside of gear housing.
8. Replace shaft bearing in gear housing, if necessary.
9. Check piston rod, teeth, and guide-bearing surface of power

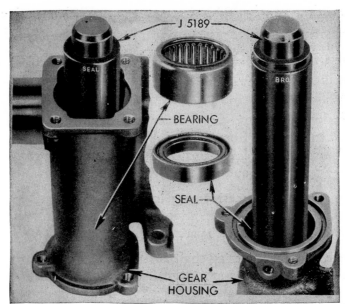

Fig. 10-8. Installing new bearing and seal in gear housing. (*Buick Motor Division of General Motors Corporation*)

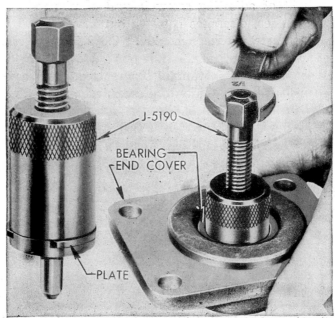

Fig. 10-9. Removing bearing from end cover. (*Buick Motor Car Division of General Motors Corporation*)

rack for wear or scoring. Replace worn parts. Piston rod and rack can be separated by driving out old pin. Use new pin to reconnect the two and stake pin at three places on each side. File down burrs raised in staking.

10. Inspect power-cylinder bore and rings for scores or wear, either of which requires replacement of the part. If adapter seal is worn or damaged, install a new seal.

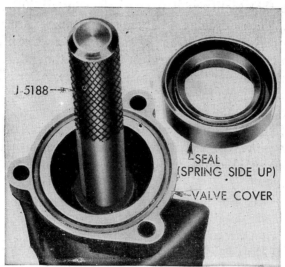

Fig. 10-10. Installing valve cover seal. (*Buick Motor Division of General Motors Corporation*)

11. If valve housing, spool, and centering plungers are scored, nicked, or otherwise damaged, replace them. Make sure spool and plungers slide freely in the housing.

    NOTE: Spool and housing are serviced as a unit because they are selectively fitted at the factory.

12. Test the check valve by blowing through both ends. Ball should seat when you blow through small end. It should allow air to go through when you blow into slotted end.

13. Remove seal from valve cover with a punch and use special installer to install a new seal (Fig. 10-10). Install with the spring side of seal out.

14. Discard all old O sealing rings and use new O rings on reassembly.

§142. Saginaw power-steering-gear assembly Refer to Fig. 10-4 for the relationship of the parts in the unit. Be sure that all parts are really clean and that you are working on a clean bench and using clean tools. Lubricate parts with clean engine oil during assembly. Proceed as follows:

1. Put steering shaft on bench with upper end of shaft to your right. Install ball nut on worm so that the *deeper* side of the teeth is nearest you when the teeth are on top. Turn ball nut over so that teeth are down and then install 30 balls in each circuit. A circuit includes not only the passage through the ball nut, but also the split ball-return guide. Part of the 30 balls will go in the ball-nut circuit, the rest in the guide. Then, the ball guide can be pushed down into place. After all balls and both guides have been installed, secure with clamp, using lock washers under the screws.

2. Run ball nut to upper end of worm and then install shaft in gear housing. Work shaft through worm seal in housing carefully to avoid damaging seal. Install end cover with new gasket.

3. Install lower thrust bearing on shaft with large race out. Put a new O ring in groove in face of gear housing.

4. Install check valve in RT (return) port of valve housing (Fig. 10-7) and tighten securely.

5. Install hose unions with new O rings. Union with smaller outer threads goes in PR (pressure) port. Install elbows and bolts at other ports with new seals on both sides of elbows. Do not tighten these parts.

6. Put valve housing on bench with RT port to right of PR port (both pointing away from you). Install valve spool with the counterbored end upward. Be very careful to start the spool squarely, and work it into alignment before pushing it down. Do not force it. If it is held square, it will go in easily.

7. Install five centering springs and ten plungers in housing. Drill-spotted ends of plungers should go inward, against the springs.

8. With steering shaft horizontal, install valve assembly with the counterbored end of the valve spool toward free end of shaft (Fig. 10-11). Be careful so spool or plungers do not slide out of housing.

9. Turn steering gear so shaft is upward to make sure thrust balls are seated in their races. Align markings on valve and gear

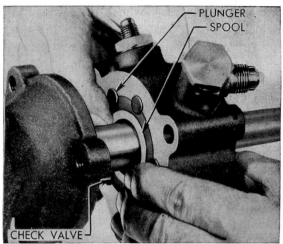

FIG. 10-11. Installing valve body. Counterbored end of valve spool is toward the free end of shaft. On later models, location of check valve is not as shown but is under the RT union. (*Buick Motor Division of General Motors Corporation*)

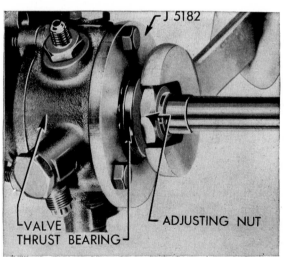

FIG. 10-12. Adjusting thrust-bearing nut with adapter (J5182) in place. (*Buick Motor Division of General Motors Corporation*)

housings, install adapter plate (designated as J5182 in Fig. 10-12), and tighten attaching bolts securely.

10. Install upper thrust bearing with large race toward valve. Make sure balls are seated in the races. Turn on a *new* bearing nut. Adjust nut as follows.

[267]

11. Temporarily put steering wheel on shaft and turn shaft counterclockwise until centering springs are fully compressed by the pressure of ball nut against the end cover. Hold wheel in this position and tighten nut just enough to seat the thrust bearing against the valve spool (Fig. 10-12).

12. Use pull scale on rim of steering wheel and check the pull required to turn wheel steadily. Pull should be ¼ to ½ pound. Adjust nut as required to obtain this reading, then stake outer

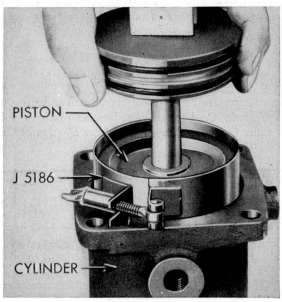

PISTON

J 5186

CYLINDER

Fig. 10-13. Installing piston in cylinder, using special ring compressor (J5186) to compress rings. (*Buick Motor Division of General Motors Corporation*)

edge of nut down into keyway of shaft. Make sure nut does not turn during the staking operation. (Some models also use tang lock washers. On these, tangs should be bent up against flats of nut.)

13. Remove steering wheel and adapter. Put bushing protector over end of steering shaft and install hydraulic-valve cover with a new O ring seated in the cover groove. Align markings (or dowel pin on some models) and attach cover with bolts and lock washers.

14. Put adjusting screw, with shim, in slot in pitman shaft (make sure clearance is 0.002 inch or less), and attach side cover to

shaft by running screw part way into cover. Turn lock nut on finger tight.

15. Prepare to install power cylinder by assembling it. Put new O rings in both grooves of power-cylinder adapter. Put stop plate on piston rod, and then use rod inserter to protect the seal as the rod is pushed through the seal and adapter. Install thrust washer, piston with rings, thrust washer, and nut on the rod, and tighten nut securely. Use ring compressor to compress rings and install piston in power cylinder (Fig. 10-13). Push

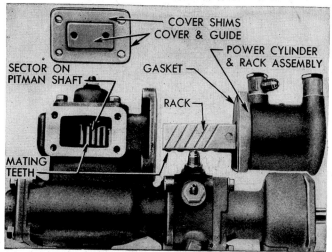

Fig. 10-14. Position of rack and sector for installation of power cylinder. (*Buick Motor Division of General Motors Corporation*)

down so adapter is flush with cylinder flange. Then install elbows and bolts on power cylinder using new O rings, but do not tighten the bolts as yet.

16. From this point on, the assembly procedure follows one of two different paths, depending on whether the two sectors on the pitman shaft are opposite each other (as in Fig. 10-15), or are separated and near the two ends of the shaft (as in Figs. 10-4 and 10-14). On some models, the power cylinder is offset to one side so the sector on the pitman shaft that meshes with the power rack is also offset. On other models, the power cylinder is directly above the steering shaft; on these, the rack sector is directly above the ball-nut sector (Fig. 10-15).

[269]

17. To complete the assembly of the offset type (Figs. 10-4 and 10-14), turn the steering shaft until the ball-nut teeth are centered and then install pitman shaft so center tooth of sector is between two inner teeth of ball nut. Be careful, as you slide the pitman shaft through the seal, to avoid damaging seal. Install side-cover bolts and tighten securely. At this point, check the over-center adjustment (§138) and adjust as necessary. Now turn steering shaft clockwise to limit of its travel and push power rack in against stop plate (see Fig. 10-14). Use new gasket and install power-cylinder-and-rack assembly

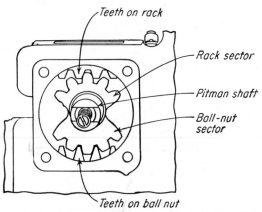

Teeth on rack

Rack sector

Pitman shaft

Ball-nut sector

Teeth on ball nut

Fig. 10-15. Relationship of sector teeth on pitman shaft and teeth on rack and ball nut. In this unit, the two sectors are opposite each other on the pitman shaft and are not offset as in the unit shown in Fig. 10-14. (*Chevrolet Motor Division of General Motors Corporation*)

on gear housing. Make sure that the end tooth of the rack enters the sector between the two end teeth, as shown (Fig. 10-14). Then install power-rack guide with original shims and tighten cover bolts. Adjust power rack by adding or removing shims, if necessary (see §138).

18. To complete the assembly of the opposed-sector type (Fig. 10-15), install the power-cylinder-and-rack assembly on gear housing with a new gasket. Then center the rack and turn wheel as necessary to center the ball nut. Now, when the pitman shaft is installed, the sector teeth and the rack and ball-nut teeth will mesh properly as shown in Fig. 10-15. The pitman shaft can now be installed, along with the end cover. The

over-center adjustment, followed by the power-rack adjustment, should then be made (§138).

19. Finally, on both types, install the small bypass line and the two large valve-to-cylinder tubes, tightening the elbow bolts. Fill lines with automatic transmission oil (specified for use in the unit), and remove unions on valve and fill it with oil. Unit should be as full of oil as possible when reinstalled to minimize necessity for bleeding the system.

20. Put gear lubricant in gear housing through the filler opening.

SAGINAW IN-LINE POWER-STEERING SERVICE

§143. **Saginaw in-line power-steering service**   The servicing of the in-line power-steering unit is described in the following sections. This unit is shown in Figs. 5-28*a* to 5-28*d* and is described in §67.

§144. **Control-valve assembly**   Figure 10-16 shows the control-valve body mounted on the power-steering unit. It is removed by taking out the mounting bolts. Valve assembly then can be slid out of the valve body after the retaining snap ring is removed. To disassemble the valve into its component parts (Fig. 10-17), the valve link must be backed out of the valve spool.

If either the valve spool or body is defective, both parts must be replaced as a unit since they are supplied in matched sets.

To reassemble, oil with Dynaflow oil and replace all parts in the order shown (Fig. 10-17), tightening link to 8 to 10 lb-ft torque. Place valve assembly in body, using care to avoid scratching parts, and secure with snap ring.

§145. **Pitman-shaft assembly**   To disassemble the pitman shaft, first remove valve body. Then remove side-cover bolts (Fig. 10-16), turn cover one-half turn, align pitman gear with opening (by turning worm shaft), and tap end of pitman shaft to take it from housing. If the adjusting screw is removed from the side cover, the nylon pin in the screw will be damaged and a new screw is required. The pitman-shaft-seal assembly can be replaced by removing the retaining snap ring.

To replace the pitman shaft, turn worm shaft to align center of rack piston with center of pitman-shaft bushing. Install pitman shaft so the center tooth in the sector meshes with the center groove in

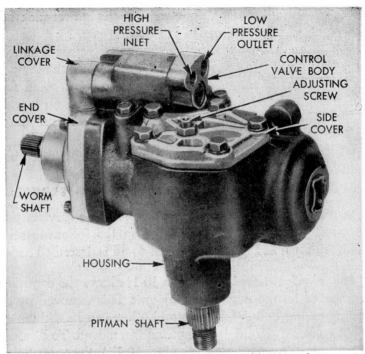

FIG. 10-16. Right side of power-steering-gear assembly. (*Buick Motor Division of General Motors Corporation*)

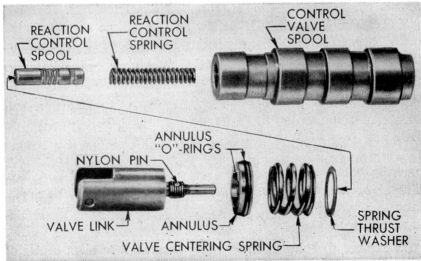

FIG. 10-17. Disassembled view of control-valve-spool assembly. (*Buick Motor Division of General Motors Corporation*)

the rack piston. Splines on end of shaft should be covered with a single layer of tape so they do not cut the oil seal. Install and tighten cover bolts.

§146. Rack-piston and worm assembly   Disassemble by first removing valve assembly and pitman shaft. Then pull actuator lever out of end cover and remove flexible coupling. Mark coupling flange and worm shaft, drive pin out, and remove coupling flange. Remove end cover by taking out retaining bolts. Remove oil seal if it requires re-

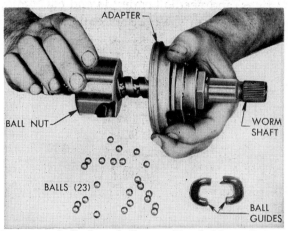

Fig. 10-18. Removing balls from ball nut. (*Buick Motor Division of General Motors Corporation*)

placement. Rack-piston and worm assembly can be disassembled by unstaking and removing ball-nut retaining screw (with Allen wrench). Slide ball nut and worm assembly out with screw hole down to prevent loss of balls. Remove guides and turn nut with the guide holes down (Fig. 10-18). Turn worm back and forth to work balls out. Remove ball nut and adapter from worm.

Use new seals and gaskets on reassembly. Lubricate parts with Dynaflow oil. On adapter, install O ring, oil seal, washer, and ring. Put adapter on worm. Put ball nut on worm, chamfered edge away from adapter. Align guide holes with worm groove and load 17 balls into nut. Drop balls into hole farthest from adapter and rotate worm slowly so balls feed through the circuit. Put remaining 6 balls in one half of guide, put other half of guide on top, plug ends with grease so balls will not fall out, and install guide in ball nut.

[273]

On end of worm, put steel washer, Teflon seal (rubber toward worm), bronze washer, retaining ring washer, and ring. With ball nut back against adapter and retaining screw hole down and aligned with screw hole in rack piston, install worm in rack piston. Install, tighten, and stake nut retaining screw.

Use piston-ring compressor to install rack-piston assembly in housing. Align actuator-lever relief slot in adapter with valve mounting face on housing. Push rack piston into housing. Install the four valve centering springs between the adapter and thrust bearing. Install seals, O rings, and needle bearing in end cover and, using seal protector on end of worm shaft, install end cover and secure with

Fig. 10-19. Checking pitman-shaft adjustment. (*Buick Motor Division of General Motors Corporation*)

retaining bolts. Then install other parts, including actuating lever, coupling on worm shaft, flexible coupling, pitman shaft, and control valve. Pitman shaft must be adjusted before unit is reinstalled on car. This is done by turning the adjusting screw to get the proper pull (Fig. 10-19) to carry the gear through the high point of maximum pull required (1¼ to 1¾ pounds on model shown).

§147. **Reinstallation**   In general, the reinstallation procedure is the same as the removal procedure, but performed in reverse. Use a bearing protector on the end of the steering shaft to protect the upper bearing in the jacket when inserting the shaft in the jacket. Check the pull required to pull the steering wheel through center (after installation is complete). If pull has increased from what it was on the bench, then the upper bearing in the jacket has been damaged or else there is misalignment somewhere. After reconnecting the oil lines between the oil pump and steering gear, fill the reservoir and bleed the system as already explained (§137).

§**148. Oil pump service**   Two types of pumps have been used, the Eaton and the Vickers (Fig. 5-27). Several models of these have been used, and thus the disassembly-assembly procedures that follow may be only typical and may vary somewhat with different models. Basic differences lie in the location and type of valving used. To remove the pump from the engine, disconnect hoses from pump and fasten them in an elevated position so they do not drain. Put caps on all pump connections. Take off pulley nut and pump-mounting bolts. Then remove pump. Drain oil from reservoir after removing cover.

§**149. Vickers pump (see Fig. 10-20)**   The Vickers pump uses a series of vanes assembled in slots in the rotor.

1. Disassembly. The pump is disassembled by removing the reservoir—and the manifold on earlier models. On the pump without the manifold, there are spacers in the attaching-bolt holes. Remove these, and the cork gaskets, from the pump.

Figure 10-21 shows the location of the valve parts in one pump model. Other models have a combination relief and flow-control valve inside the cover; it is removed after the cover is taken off. Note the location and relationship of the valve parts as you remove them.

Take off the pressure plate which fits over two dowel pins extending through the rotor ring. The rotor ring is the flat piece located between the cover and the body of the pump. As the rotor ring comes off, the rotor, with vanes, will come out. Remove and discard the O rings.

Use snap-ring pliers to compress the bearing-retaining snap ring and remove it. The shaft with outer bearing can then be pressed from pump body (see Fig. 10-22). Seal can be driven from pump body with a long punch, and the inner bearing can be removed.

2. Inspection. The outer bearing is of the sealed type and must not be washed in cleaning solvent. This would remove the lubricant and cause short bearing life. The inner bearing and other parts should be cleaned with solvent. If a new outer bearing is required, press it on the shaft with a tool that applies pressure to the inner

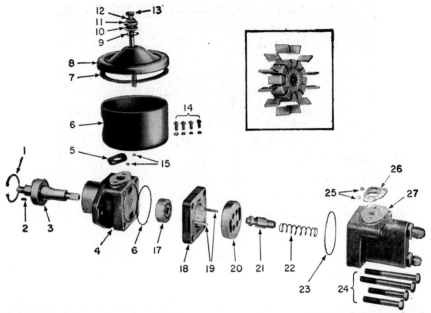

FIG. 10-20. Exploded view of vane type of pump. (*Studebaker-Packard Corporation*)

1. Snap ring	10. Guide	20. Pressure plate
2. Key	11. Spacer	21. Flow and pressure
3. Shaft and bearing	12. Lock washer	control-valve
assembly	13. Bolt	assembly
4. Pump-body assembly	14. Reservoir screws	22. Spring
5. Gasket	15. Gasket spacers	23. O ring
6. Reservoir	16. O ring	24. Pump-cover screws
7. Cover gasket	17. Impeller assembly	25. Gasket spacers
8. Cover	18. Cam, or rotor, ring	26. Gasket
9. Gasket	19. Dowels	27. Pump cover

race only. Stamped face of bearing should be toward threaded end of shaft.

Check the fit of the vanes in the rotor slots; they should fit snugly but should be free to move. Tightness may be relieved by thorough cleaning or removal of irregularities. Check ground surfaces of the ring for roughness or irregular wear. Slight irregularities may be removed with an Arkansas hard stone. The flat faces of the ring and body should be checked for wear or scoring. The faces may be repaired by lapping them until they are smooth and flat; wash away all lapping compound after the job is done. Check the fit of the valve in the cover. Excessively worn parts must be replaced.

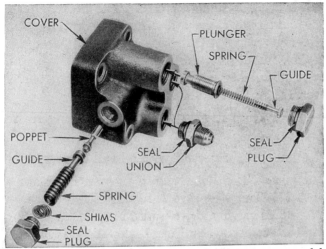

FIG. 10-21. Location of relief and flow-control valves in one model of pump. (*Buick Motor Division of General Motors Corporation*)

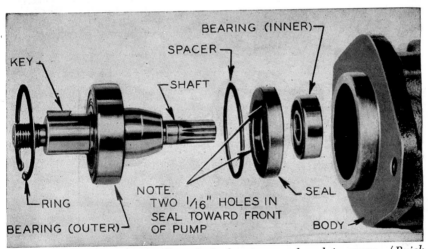

FIG. 10-22. Relationship of drive shaft, bearings, and seal in pump. (*Buick Motor Division of General Motors Corporation*)

3. *Reassembly.* Make sure all parts are really clean. Bench and tools must be clean also. Put inner bearing in pump body, stamped face down. Tap it into place to make sure it is seated. Install shaft seal, two small $\frac{1}{16}$-inch oil holes toward front of pump (Fig. 10-22). Use a tube with an outside diameter of $1\frac{5}{8}$ inches to push the seal home. Put drive shaft, with outer bearing, into pump body and then

[277]

secure with bearing-retaining snap ring. Put dowel pins in holes in pump body and then place rotor ring on body, aligning it with dowel pins. The arrows in the ring should point *in the direction of pump rotation.* Install rotor and vanes. Rounded edges of the vanes should point outward toward the rotor ring. Put valve in cover and install cover. Install reservoir or manifold.

Caution: Always use new O sealing rings during reassembly to assure good seals.

On reinstallation, fill reservoir with oil and bleed system (§137).

§150. Eaton pump The Eaton pump uses an inner and an outer rotor (Fig. 5-27). There are several models of this pump in use, differing in details of valving, drive-pulley attachment, and so on. Disassembly of the type shown in Figs. 10-23 to 10-25 follows.

1. Disassembly. Remove large hex cap and seal from the flow director adapter. Leave hose connector in place. Remove hose unions and seals from pump cover. Then remove adapter bolts and install special studs, one at a time, at the two locations shown in Fig. 10-23. Loosen stud nuts and two remaining adapter bolts evenly

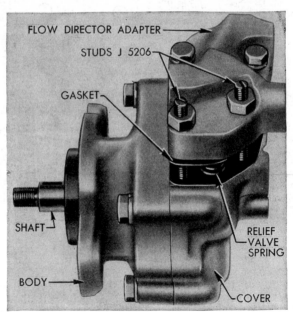

Fig. 10-23. Removing the flow director adapter with special studs. (*Buick Motor Division of General Motors Corporation*)

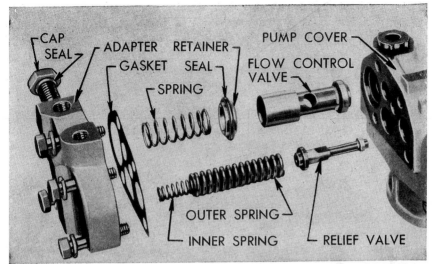

Fig. 10-24. Relief and flow-control valves and springs in one model of Eaton pump. (*Buick Motor Division of General Motors Corporation*)

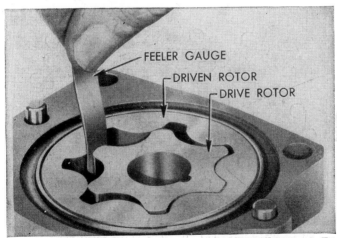

Fig. 10-25. Checking clearance between rotors. (*Buick Motor Division of General Motors Corporation*)

to relieve the spring pressure. Then remove the springs, seal ring, and tubular retainer from the large hole. Turn pump over so that valves slide out (Fig. 10-24). Handle valves carefully so that they will not be damaged or become dirty.

Remove cover bolts and tap cover loose with a soft mallet.

[279]

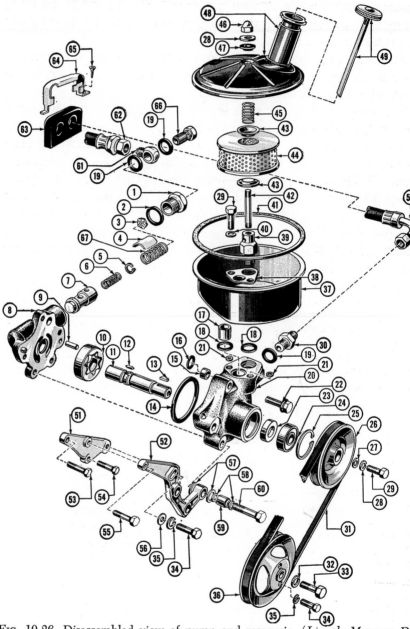

FIG. 10-26. Disassembled view of pump and reservoir. (*Lincoln-Mercury Division of Ford Motor Company*)

Remove seal, rotors, and drive pin from body. Then use snap-ring compressor to remove retainer ring so that shaft and bearing can be pressed from pump body.

Another pump model, similar in general construction and operation, is shown in disassembled view in Fig. 10-26. Follow this illustration to disassemble the pump.

2. *Inspection.* Do not wash the bearing in solvent as this could dissolve the lubricant sealed in the bearing. Clean other pump parts in solvent and check pump, body, and rotors for wear. Worn parts should be replaced. Rotors are supplied in matched sets for replacement. Check clearances between the rotors at all points with feeler gauge (Fig. 10-25) and replace rotors if clearance is over 0.006 inch. Then lay a straightedge on pump body and check between it and the sides of the rotors. Replace pump body if clearance is over 0.0025 inch. Finally, check clearance between the outer rotor and pump body. Replace body if clearance is over 0.006 inch.

3. *Reassembly.* Make sure all parts are clean. Reverse above disassembly procedure to reassemble the pump. Install shaft and bear-

1. Valve cap adapter	23. Oil seal	46. Nut
2. O ring	24. Ball bearing	47. Seal
3. Orifice plate	25. Retainer	48. Cover and filler tube
4. Spring damper	26. Pulley	49. Dip stick and cap
5. Retainer	27. Washer	50. Elbow
6. Spring	28. Lock washer	51. Bracket
7. Valve	29. Bolt	52. Bracket
8. Cover	30. Union	53. Cap screw
9. Dowel	31. Belt	54. Cap screw
10. Rotor assembly	32. Lock washer	55. Cap screw
11. Shaft	33. Cap screw	56. Washer
12. Drive pin	34. Cap screw	57. Seal
13. Key	35. Lock washer	58. Washer
14. Gasket	36. Pulley	59. Bushing
15. Retainer gasket	37. Reservoir	60. Bolt
16. O ring	38. Plate	61. Union
17. Retainer gasket	39. Orifice body	62. Fitting
18. Seal	40. Lock washer	63. Insulator
19. Seal	41. Gasket	64. Bracket
20. Body	42. Stud	65. Screw
21. Washer	43. Seat	66. Union
22. Cap screw and lock washer	44. Filter	67. Spring
	45. Spring	

ing as an assembly, and press against the outer race to seat the bearing in the body. Use new rubber seals and a new adapter gasket on reassembly. When assembly is complete, rotate the pump shaft to make sure it is free.

On reinstallation, fill reservoir with oil and bleed the system (§137).

CHAPTER CHECKUP

With the widespread adoption of power steering, it becomes increasingly important for everyone in the automotive field to know how these units operate, what can go wrong with them, and how they are repaired. Thus, the chapter just finished, on one make of power steering, is of special importance to you. Now that you have completed the chapter, let's find out how well you remember the important points covered in the chapter. The checkup test that follows covers the essential facts discussed in the chapter. If you have any trouble answering any of the questions, reread the chapter. The review is very important and helps you to remember the basic facts discussed.

Correcting Trouble Lists

The purpose of this exercise is to help you spot related and unrelated troubles in a list. For example, in the list *Hard steering: tight steering-gear adjustment, pump drive belt loose, low oil pressure, full oil reservoir, air in hydraulic system,* you can see that the term *full oil reservoir* is the only item that does not belong because it will not cause hard steering. Any of the other conditions in the list could.

In each list, you will find one item that does not belong. Write down each list in your notebook, but *do not write down* the item that does not belong.

1. Poor centering: spool valve sticky, tight power-rack adjustment, steering shaft binding, pump pressure above 700 pounds, incorrect steering-gear adjustments.
2. Low oil pressure: loose pump belt, low oil level, mechanical trouble in pump, excessive caster, oil leaks, engine idling too slowly.
3. Hard steering: tight steering-gear adjustment, pump drive belt loose, low oil pressure, air in hydraulic system, low oil level, engine idles too fast.
4. Pump noise: oil cold, air in system, oil level low, air vent plugged, tires overinflated, dirt in pump, mechanical damage.
5. Gear noise: loose power-rack adjustment, loose over-center adjustment, loose thrust-bearing adjustment, loose power-rack pin, air in system, oil level low, steering gear tight on car frame, hose rubbing.

Completing the Sentences

The sentences below are incomplete. After each sentence there are several words or phrases, only one of which will correctly complete the sentence. Write down each sentence in your notebook, selecting the proper word or phrase to complete it correctly.

1. The Saginaw steering gear requires three adjustments, power-rack, over-center, and   *oil pressure*   *thrust bearing*   *push bearing*

2. Of the three adjustments, the one that has to be made with the unit removed from the car is adjustment of the   *thrust bearing*   *power rack*   *oil pressure*

3. Turning the adjusting screw to make the over-center adjustment causes   *endwise movement of ball nut*   *endwise movement of pitman shaft*   *endwise movement of worm shaft*   *endwise movement of steering shaft*

4. Power-rack adjustment is made, on some models, by   *adding or removing shims*   *turning adjusting cam*   *adding or removing balls*

5. In the disassembly process, when the hydraulic-valve assembly is removed, it must be held horizontal so the   *spool and plungers do not fall out*   *steering shaft does not come off*   *oil does not run out*

6. On reassembly, all the old O sealing rings should be   *discarded*   *tested and reused if good*   *used if not split*

7. The reassembly procedure follows one of two directions, depending on whether the two sectors on the pitman shaft are separated and near the two ends of the shaft, or are   *on the same side*   *opposite each other*   *removed from shaft*

8. The Vickers pump has   *two rotors*   *vanes in the rotor*   *two gears*   *three rotors*

9. The Eaton pump has   *two rotors*   *vanes in the rotor*   *two gears*   *three rotors*

10. On reassembly, the arrows on the rotor ring of the Vickers pump should point in the direction of   *pump rotation*   *vane installation*   *dowel pin installation*   *rotor alignment*

Servicing Procedures

Write down the procedures asked for in your notebook. Do not copy from the book, but write the procedures in your own words. This will help you to remember them.

[283]

1. Pick a car equipped with a Saginaw power-steering unit and describe in detail the procedure in removing the steering gear.
2. Explain how to test the steering gear (belt tension, oil level, steering action, oil pressure).
3. Describe the procedure in bleeding the hydraulic system.
4. Explain how to make the over-center and power-rack adjustments.
5. List the main steps in disassembling the Saginaw power-steering unit.
6. List the main steps in inspecting steering-unit parts.
7. List the main steps in assembling the steering unit.
8. List the main steps in oil-pump service, including removal, disassembly, inspection, and reassembly.

SUGGESTIONS FOR FURTHER STUDY

When in your local school or automotive service shop, examine power-steering components that are available. If possible, be on hand when a power-steering gear is being disassembled. Note how the job is done. If you can, study the shop manual issued by the manufacturer, which gives detailed instructions on the repair procedure. Be sure to write down in your notebook any important facts you learn.

11: Gemmer Hydraguide power-steering service

THIS CHAPTER describes the trouble-shooting, adjusting, removal, repair, and reinstallation of the Gemmer Hydraguide power-steering unit. Section 68 describes the operation of this unit. Chapter 6 discussed trouble-shooting procedures on steering and suspension systems generally. The material that follows carries this a step further into power steering and includes complete repair procedures on this equipment.

§151. Trouble-shooting chart—Gemmer power steering This unit was described in §68. The list, below, of trouble symptoms, causes, and checks or corrections will give you a means of logically analyzing trouble so the causes can be quickly located. Once you know the cause, you normally have little difficulty eliminating the trouble.

NOTE: The troubles and possible causes are not listed in the chart in the order of frequency of occurrence. That is, item 1 does not necessarily occur more often than item 2, nor does item a under Possible Cause necessarily occur more often than item b.

GEMMER POWER-STEERING TROUBLE-SHOOTING CHART

(See §§152 to 162 for details of checks and corrections listed.)

Complaint	Possible Cause	Check or Correction
1. Lack of steering assistance	a. Pump (generator) drive belt loose	Tighten
	b. Low oil level	Add oil
	c. Pump coupling broken	Replace
	d. Low oil pressure	See item 2, Low oil pressure, below
	e. Piston seals worn	Replace seals
	f. Engine idle low	Adjust idle

Complaint	Possible Cause	Check or Correction
2. Low oil pressure	a. Belt loose	Tighten
	b. Coupling broken	Replace
	c. Flow-control valve stuck	Free, clean if necessary
	d. Mechanical trouble in pump	Repair or replace pump
3. Steering aid in one direction but not in other	a. Gear-to-jacket alignment off	Realign
	b. Valves stuck in gear body	Clean, free up
4. Extremely sensitive steering	Flow-control valve stuck closed	Clean, free valve
5. Excessive free play in steering wheel	a. Steering gear loose on bracket	Tighten bolts — recheck gear-to-jacket alignment
	b. Bracket loose on frame	Tighten bracket-attaching bolts
	c. Steering connections loose	Check, tighten connections
	d. Excessive valve-gear backlash	Adjust
	e. Worm and roller backlash excessive	Adjust
6. Poor centering, or recovery from turns	a. Steering column misalignment	Realign
	b. Incorrect front-wheel alignment	Realign front end
	c. Binding in linkage	Check linkage, eliminate binding
7. Noises	a. Attaching bolts (gear or bracket) loose	Tighten
	b. Looseness in linkage	Tighten linkage connections
	c. Valve gears out of adjustment	Readjust
	d. Column-jacket bearing out of line with steering tube	Replace, realign
	e. Oil level low	Add oil to reservoir
	f. Oil cold	Idle engine for 3 minutes before using power steering

§152. Trouble diagnosis—Gemmer Hydraguide power steering The chart above lists possible troubles, causes, and corrections. When trouble is reported, the following checks will help to locate accurately the cause of trouble:

1. *Checking oil pressure.* Connect special gauge into the pressure line at the pump as shown in Fig. 11-1. Start engine and turn the steering wheel. Gauge should show at least 500 pounds pressure when wheel is in either extreme position. If pressure does not go

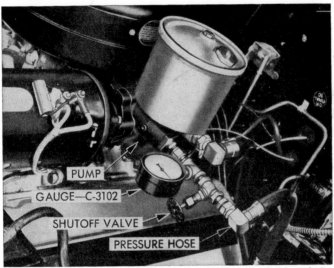

FIG. 11-1. Checking pressure the pump develops with a special gauge connected into the pressure line from the pump. (*De Soto Division of Chrysler Corporation*)

this high, check the pump by momentarily closing the shut-off valve on the gauge. If pressure does not go up, the trouble is in the pump (loose generator-pump drive belt, drive coupling broken, valve stuck, and so on). If pressure does go up, trouble is in the gear assembly (lack of steering power when pump can develop adequate pressure is probably due to leakage at the piston seals, which should be replaced). *Do not leave shutoff valve on gauge closed for more than a few seconds.*

If a gauge is not available, a fairly accurate check of pump pressure can be made by noting whether or not the high pressure hose flexes as wheel is turned to extreme positions. If hose does not flex, adequate pressure is not developing in hose.

2. *Checking pump.* If pump is not developing sufficient pressure,

first note whether or not the drive belts are tight and are driving the generator at normal speed. Then, remove the reservoir cover from the pump and close center hole at top of filter with finger or plug. Start engine and turn steering wheel. If oil flows through the filter, the flow control-valve plunger is probably stuck. Shut off engine, take off high-pressure hose at pump, and insert a ¼-inch clean probe—dull-ended so it does not scratch—into the fitting. If you can push the plunger inward ³⁄₁₆ inch, plunger was stuck and will probably function now that it is loosened. Recheck pressure, as above, after reconnecting hose. If pressure is still low, there is probably mechanical trouble in the pump and it should be replaced.

If oil does not flow through the filter in the above test (center hole plugged), then it is likely that the drive coupling is broken. Remove pump and take coupling off, after removing snap ring. Turn pump shaft at least 10 revolutions. If it turns freely, install a new coupling and reinstall pump on generator. If shaft binds, replace both pump and coupling. If generator shaft appears damaged, replace generator.

3. *Check oil level.* If oil level is low in reservoir, there is a possibility that leaks exist, either at hose connections or internally, at seals. When adding oil, bleed the system as noted in §153, below.

4. *Checking for internal leaks.* To check for leakage in the steering gear, a special manometer has been developed. This device is mounted on the steering gear at the filler-plug opening. Leakage of high pressure past any of the seals will be indicated by manometer action, as described below.

    a. Figure 11-2 shows the setup for testing the unit off the car. The steering gear is mounted in a vise with long hoses connecting it and the pump on the car. Notice that the pressure gauge is connected in the pressure line at the pump. Figure 11-3 shows the details of mounting the manometer on the steering gear. If pressure builds up in the steering gear, it will push the water up in the free end of the tube.

    b. With test setup arranged as pictured in Figs. 11-2 and 11-3, fill manometer tube with clean water, as shown. Put enough additional oil in pump reservoir to fill long hoses and steering gear (it may be necessary to add more oil during test).

    c. With engine running and warmed up, check pump pressure as noted in item 1, above.

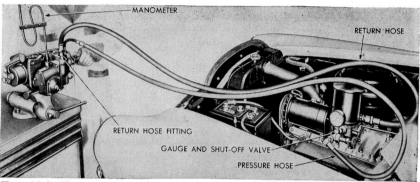

FIG. 11-2. Testing steering-gear assembly for leakage with unit off the car. (*De Soto Division of Chrysler Corporation*)

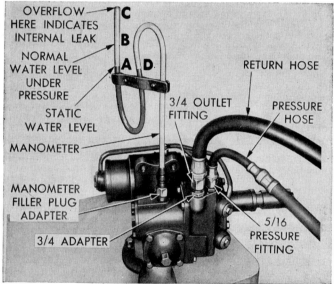

FIG. 11-3. Steering-gear assembly mounted in vise with manometer and test hoses installed. (*De Soto Division of Chrysler Corporation*)

d. Bleed system (§153).

e. Wipe all oil from outside of steering gear.

f. With engine idling, watch water level in manometer. It should slowly rise at the free end about one inch from the static level (or to *B* in Fig. 11-3).

g. Turn gear shaft through at least 20 cycles—10 to left and 10 to right. Apply enough effort at the end of each turn to cause the relief valve to "buzz" slightly. Do not hold the shaft in this extreme position for any length of time. Turn shaft to left and hold in this position until valve buzzes. Pump pressure should be 500 to 700 pounds (shutoff valve open). If pressure varies considerably, piston rings are not sealing and should be replaced.

h. If water in the manometer continues to go up and spills out of the open end (*C* in Fig. 11-3), there is a defective seal in the gear assembly which must be replaced (§154).

5. Check for centering. If the steering wheel does not come back to center readily after a turn is completed, there could be binding in the steering linkage, misaligned front wheels, or steering column misaligned with the steering gear. As a first step in locating the cause of trouble, raise the front end of the car so the front wheels are free. Check tire pressure. Check kingpins, intermediate and steering arms, drag links, and tie-rod ends for frictional drag, or binding. Make whatever corrections are necessary to restore the linkage and wheel suspension to normal condition. Then proceed as follows:

a. With engine running and front wheels suspended, put your two hands on the sides of the tire of the left-front wheel and turn the wheel first to the right and then to the left. Note carefully the amount of resistance to wheel turn in either direction. Repeat the check several times. If more effort is required to turn the wheel in one direction than in the other, center the steering wheel, lower the car to the floor, and continue as indicated below.

b. Check and tighten, if necessary, the screws attaching steering-column shroud to the instrument panel.

c. If rubber insulator at the lower end of the column jacket has not completely entered the jacket, remove the steering wheel, pull the column up so insulator can be positioned and the jacket telescoped over it. Put liquid soap on the insulator so it will slip into place.

d. Apply chalk on the gear and bracket at the bolt bosses so lines can be scribed across the two. This shows exact alignment between the steering gear and the bracket. Now, loosen the steering-gear attaching bolts just enough to permit the gear to move on the bracket.

[290]

e. With engine running, turn the steering wheel exactly one-fourth turn off center position *in the direction that the wheels turned without resistance.* Hold the steering wheel in this position and retighten the attaching bolts. This procedure allows the steering gear to align itself with the steering tube.

f. If the scribe lines remain in the same position—that is, if the steering gear does not shift on the mounting bracket—it is likely that the adjustment holes in the mounting bracket are not large enough to permit proper alignment. This means that shims must be added between the frame and the bracket to bring the gear into alignment. See chart below.

g. Road-test the car. If wheels now do not return from the opposite direction, perhaps the steering gear has moved too far. Check the scribe lines. If the gear has shifted more than ⅛ inch, move the gear back ¹⁄₁₆ inch, retighten the bolts, and recheck.

ADJUSTING AND SHIMMING CHART FOR ADJUSTMENT OF CENTERING

If steering will not recover from	Front wheels are	Scribe marks on gear should be	Scribe marks did not move enough to equalize turning efforts
Left turn	Harder to turn right	Moved back toward dash	Add shims under two front bolts between bracket and frame
Right turn	Harder to turn left	Moved forward	Add shim under single rear bolt between bracket and frame

6. *Checking for noises.* The type of noise and the steering action that produces it are often good indications of the cause of the noise. For example, if a thump is heard when the steering wheel is reversed, it is probable that there is looseness in the steering gear or linkage. When the steering forces are reversed by reversal of the steering wheel, the loose parts shift suddenly and with a thump.

[291]

Parts that could be loose include the pitman shaft, piston arm on shaft, piston plugs, pitman arm, steering gear on bracket or frame, steering column, tie rods, intermediate arm, drag link.

A snap in the steering system when the steering wheel is turned at the start or end of travel (in either direction) could be due to a loose intermediate arm or loose arm-bearing adjustment, a loose column-shaft-coupling retaining-cap screw, or a loose pitman-arm bolt drag link.

A clatter at slow speeds may be due to loose valve spur-gear adjustment or to inoperative dash pots in valves.

If the relief valve sings, or buzzes, it means that there is extremely high pressure in the system. This will occur when the steering wheel is held in either extreme position or when the wheels are against a curb. In effect, this is a warning to the driver to release the steering wheel: continued operation under this condition will cause an excessive amount of heat to develop in the pump. In extremely cold weather, when the oil is cold, buzzing may occur briefly until the oil is warmed up.

§153. Bleeding steering-gear assembly   If oil has been lost or removed from the system, air will probably have gotten into the steering gear. The air must be bled out and the oil restored to the proper level in the reservoir. First, fill the reservoir slightly higher than normal and put cover on to avoid spilling of oil. Start engine and allow it to run for a short time so oil circulates. Stop engine and fill reservoir again to proper height. You may have to do this more than once if the steering gear was empty to begin with. Finally, with engine idling, turn the steering wheel back and forth several times from one extreme to the other to bleed any remaining air from system. Check and refill the oil reservoir, if necessary.

§154. Maintenance of seals   It is obvious that the seals in the power-steering assembly must be in good condition for normal power-steering action. Some of the seals are required to withstand pressures of several hundred pounds. Location of various seals and related parts in the assembly are shown in Fig. 11-4. The paragraphs below (*A* to *L*) refer to the lettered items in Fig. 11-4.

A. Pitman-shaft outer seal. This seal can be replaced with the steering gear in the car. Do not damage shaft when removing old seal. Clean cavity with solvent. Wrap the end of shaft with cellophane tape so the seal lip will not be cut by the shaft serrations. Lubricate seal thoroughly and slide it over the shaft, spring-loaded lip *inward.* Use special tool to seat it. *Do not drive seal*—tap it lightly into place.

B. *Snap ring.* Snap ring should be installed with tapered surface outward. If ring does not fit groove, lay ring flat on abrasive paper and move it back and forth. When installed, snap ring should exert a slight inward thrust on seal.

C. *Pitman-shaft outer bearing.* When steering gear is disassembled or when a new bearing is installed, bearing should be installed

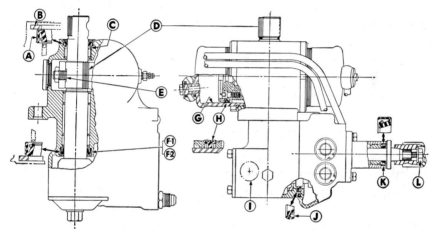

Fig. 11-4. Location of seals and related parts in the power-steering-gear assembly. Descriptions and names of parts are given in text. (*De Soto Division of Chrysler Corporation*)

—with special drift tool—0.005 inch below the flat surface or recess.

D. *Shaft serrations.* If the serrations are sharp, the sharp edges should be removed with a stone or fine abrasive paper. Lubricate shaft thoroughly before installing seals.

E. *Piston-arm set screw.* This Allen set screw must be very tight, and locked securely with the lock nut. The set screw can be reached through the access plug.

F. *Pitman-shaft inner seal.* Two different seals are used here, depending on depth of seal recess. It may be ⅜ or ½ inch deep. Install proper seal with sealing lip facing cylinder housing.

G. *Cylinders.* Cylinders and pistons should be carefully examined for scoring when new seals are installed, or when the steering

[293]

gear is disassembled. If scores are present, replace cylinder, piston, and rings.

H. Piston rings. New rings should be installed every time the cylinders are removed or whenever the steering gear is disassembled.

I. Identification. The model number of the unit is stamped at the point indicated on the housing.

J. Worm-shaft seal. Install this seal with the sealing lip facing the valve body.

K. Steering-tube-gear seal. This seal must be installed with the sealing lip facing the steering gear.

L. Steering-tube coupling bolt. This bolt must be tight. If it is not, noise will result.

§155. Gemmer power-steering-gear removal The procedure for removing the steering gear varies to some extent from one make of car to another because of individual variations in the installation. As a first step, disconnect the battery to guard against accidental grounds when the steering-column wiring is being disconnected. Then proceed as follows: (The following procedure is typical only, and may vary on different cars to some extent.)

1. Remove steering wheel by first centering wheel, removing horn ring ornament (press down and turn counterclockwise), and then disconnecting horn wire from terminal on plate. Remove bushing, travel plate, contact-ring spring, and triangular ground plate. Then curl and push horn wire into the steering tube to make room for steering wheel puller. Remove wheel nut and use puller to pull wheel.

2. Remove clutch, accelerator, and brake pads. Fold carpet back out of way and remove draft pad from around steering column. Disconnect accelerator rod from bell crank in engine compartment. Remove screws and take out floor board with accelerator pedal and rod still attached. Disengage rod from transmission lever and disconnect horn wire.

3. Remove connector-bracket assembly from steering column and then disconnect the six turn signal wires from the connectors.

4. Disconnect transmission-shaft rod from control arm.

5. Remove two top bolts (leaving bottom bolt) attaching steering gear to frame bracket. Remove starting motor.

6. Move brake pedal out of way by removing the bolt that attaches the push rod to the pedal. Then remove pedal bushing lock (horseshoe type) and slide pedal out on shaft far enough so it clears stop screw. It can then be pushed toward the rear of the car.
7. Disconnect pressure hoses from pump and support them in an elevated position so oil will not leak out.
8. Now remove the third screw (lower one) that attaches steering gear to bracket. Take out screws attaching jacket shroud to instrument panel and remove steering assembly.

§156. Gemmer power-steering-gear disassembly Figures 11-5 and 11-6 are disassembled views of the valve body and the power-steering cylinders and pistons. Study these illustrations to determine relative locations of various parts in the assembly. Before disassembly is begun, drain oil from the steering gear by removing the access plug, turning the assembly over, and turning the steering coupling to the extreme right to force out the oil. Then remove the filler plug and drain the worm gear housing. Plug all openings and carefully clean the outside of the assembly so all dirt is removed.

Caution: Extreme care must be used to prevent dirt from getting into the steering gear. Particles of dirt on the valves or other internal parts can scratch finished surfaces or clog passages and cause trouble after the unit is reassembled.

1. Remove pitman arm by taking out bolt.
2. Use socket wrench to unscrew the tube-fitting bolts. Remove tubes and sealing rings from tube fittings.
3. Remove four bolts holding valve body to cylinder housing.
4. Disassemble valve body further by using special snap-ring pliers to remove snap rings holding valves in body. Then take out valves (Fig. 11-7).

   Caution: Handle each valve assembly separately. Put the four valves into four separate containers. Parts must not be mixed between assemblies since they are selective fits in each valve (piston to sleeve, check valve to piston).

5. Handling each valve assembly separately, clean parts in a suitable solvent. Check bleeder hole and clean it if it is

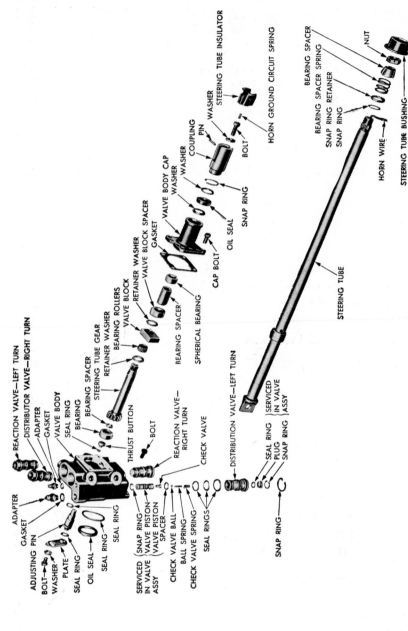

Fig. 11-5. Disassembled view of the valve body and related parts in the power-steering gear. (*De Soto Division of Chrysler Corporation*)

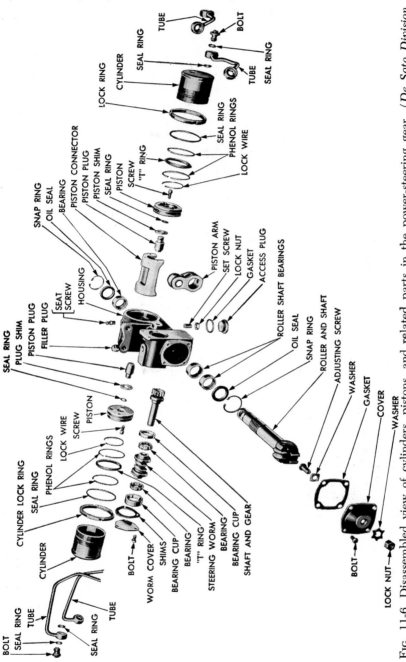

FIG. 11-6. Disassembled view of cylinders, pistons, and related parts in the power-steering gear. (*De Soto Division of Chrysler Corporation*)

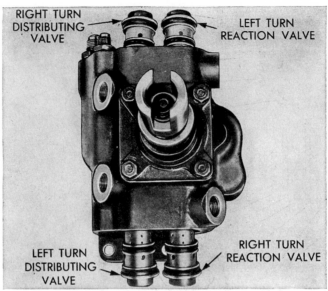

Fig. 11-7. Location of valves in valve body. (*De Soto Division of Chrysler Corporation*)

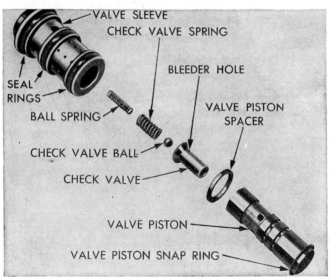

Fig. 11-8. Disassembled view of a valve—either distribution or reaction. (*De Soto Division of Chrysler Corporation*)

[298]

plugged. Figure 11-8 shows the essential parts in a valve. Note that there are three seal rings on the valve sleeve. Valve assemblies differ somewhat. One type uses a valve piston spacer as shown in Fig. 11-8. Another type does not. *Two different types of valves must not oppose each other.* That is, both distribution valves must be of the same type, and both reaction valves must be of the same type. It should seldom be necessary to replace valves, but if it is, be sure to replace valves in sets (both reaction valves, or both distribution

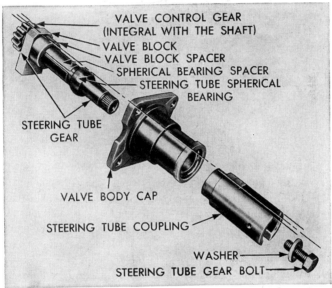

VALVE CONTROL GEAR
(INTEGRAL WITH THE SHAFT)
VALVE BLOCK
VALVE BLOCK SPACER
SPHERICAL BEARING SPACER
STEERING TUBE SPHERICAL
BEARING

STEERING TUBE
GEAR

VALVE BODY CAP

STEERING TUBE COUPLING

WASHER
STEERING TUBE GEAR BOLT

Fig. 11-9. Disassembled view of valve body cap and related parts. (*De Soto Division of Chrysler Corporation*)

valves). Also, remember that the valve sleeve and piston must be purchased as a fitted assembly.

6. Remove valve body cap by taking out four bolts holding it to the valve body.
7. Disassemble valve body cap (Fig. 11-9) by removing bolt that holds coupling to steering-tube gear. Then use special puller to remove steering-tube coupling from steering-tube gear. Gear can then be slid from body cap. Steering-tube-gear oil seal (this is *K* in Fig. 11-4) can be removed after lock ring is removed with special snap-ring pliers. On some models,

there is a valve-block spacer and bearing spacer (as shown in Fig. 11-9). Later models do not have these two spacers. On the earlier model, drive out the inner washer and oil seal from valve body cap with a drift. On later models, drive out the thrust washers, spherical bearing, and oil seal through upper end of valve body cap with a special drift that is large enough to contact the lower thrust washer around its outer diameter.

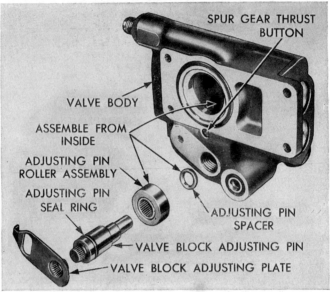

Fig. 11-10. Valve-block adjusting pin and related parts. (*De Soto Division of Chrysler Corporation*)

8. Valve-block adjusting pin (Fig. 11-10) may require removal so that a new seal ring can be installed if leakage occurs around pin. If new roller bearings are required, drive out old bearing and install new one using special tools. On assembly, assemble the adjusting plate to the splines of the pin in such a way that enough space is allowed for the plate to swing in a clockwise direction (as shown in Fig. 11-11). This will allow for adjustment after assembly. Secure plate with bolt and washer.

9. Steering-gear cylinders and pistons may be removed from the cylinder body by unscrewing them. First, mark the cylinders and body with scratch marks (do not use punch marks), as shown in Fig. 11-12. Put one scribe mark on one side and two

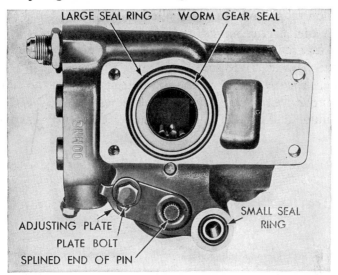

Fig. 11-11. Position of adjusting plate on reattachment. This allows plate to be moved clockwise for adjustment after reassembly of the steering gear. (*De Soto Division of Chrysler Corporation*)

Fig. 11-12. Scratch marks on the cylinders and body to aid in correct reassembly. (*De Soto Division of Chrysler Corporation*)

on the other to make sure cylinders will be restored to proper side and in proper relationship.

10. To unscrew cylinders, first loosen lock rings with a spanner wrench (Fig. 11-13). Back off lock rings several turns. Then install special studs into the tube fitting holes in the end of the cylinder and use a pry bar between the studs to turn the cylinder and loosen it from the cylinder body. Loosen both

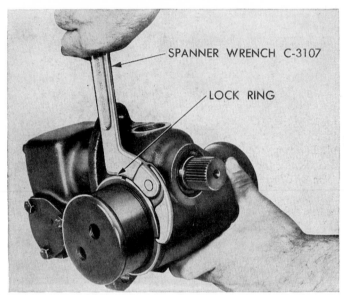

SPANNER WRENCH C-3107

LOCK RING

Fig. 11-13. Loosening lock ring with special spanner wrench. (*De Soto Division of Chrysler Corporation*)

cylinders in this manner. Then unscrew *both* cylinders and remove them both at the same time from the body.

Caution: If both cylinders are not removed at the same time, the piston rings may be damaged.

11. Use a screw driver to pry the lock wire from the end of one piston and take out Allen screws so piston can be slid away from the piston connector (Fig. 11-14). Then swing the piston arm against the plug of the remaining piston by turning the worm gear (as shown in Fig. 11-14). Piston and connector assembly can then be slid from cylinder body as shown.

12. Examine cylinder bore and pistons for scratches. Very light

scores or scratches can be removed by crocus cloth. But any part that is worn or damaged should be replaced. Discard old piston rings and install new ones.

13. Steering-gear shaft (also called pitman shaft) can be removed, along with the worm, by first removing the snap ring on the outside of the shaft outer oil seal (the seal is *A* in Fig. 11-4). Then a special tool can be used to remove the seal. Remove

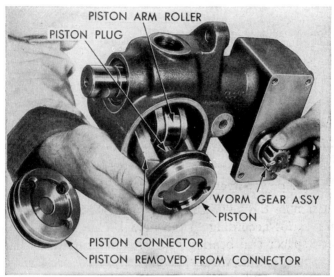

FIG. 11-14. Removing piston and connector from body. (*De Soto Division of Chrysler Corporation*)

the piston arm set screw and lock nut. Now, take off the pit-man-shaft-adjusting-screw lock nut and washer. Remove the four screws attaching the shaft cover. Turn adjusting screw in (or out of cover) and slide it out of slot in pitman shaft. Remove pitman shaft from piston arm and housing. Remove three cover bolts, lift off cover and shims (save shims), and remove worm assembly (Fig. 11-15). Check roller tooth on steering-gear shaft for free movement. Side play or sticking bearings require a new shaft and roller assembly.

14. If pitman-shaft bearings require replacement, remove snap rings, oil seals, and bearings with special tools. New bearings should be installed, also with special tools. When installing seals, refer to Fig. 11-4 to show direction of installation.

[303]

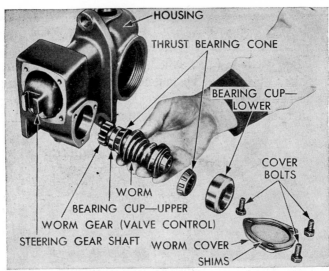

Fig. 11-15. Removing worm gear from housing. (*De Soto Division of Chrysler Corporation*)

§157. Gemmer power-steering-gear reassembly

1. Reassemble the valve body cap (Fig. 11-9). Assembly procedure varies according to the model. One model has a valve-block spacer and bearing spacer, another does not have these two spacers. This was explained in §156, 7. On the type with the spacers, first install the inner washer against the shoulder in the cap. Use a special driver tool and install a new oil seal (lip inward) far enough to allow installation of the outer washer and snap ring. Install outer washer and snap ring with snap-ring pliers. Then, position the steering-tube-gear assembly in the cap and install the coupling on the tube gear with bolt and washer. Tighten bolt to 20 lb-ft torque.

On the type without spacers, install the lower valve-block retainer washer, valve block with bearing rollers, and upper retainer washer. Then use new upper and lower spherical-bearing thrust washers. Put lower (smaller) washer in the cap from the upper end. Install spherical bearing and then large thrust washer. Then install snap ring (beveled side down). Slide steering-tube gear into valve body cap, install coupling, and secure with washer and bolt.

2. Install worm assembly in housing. Put shims in position under

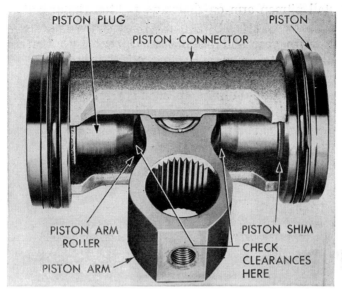

Fig. 11-16. Clearance check points between piston-arm roller and piston plugs. (*De Soto Division of Chrysler Corporation*)

the worm cover and tighten bolts securely. Turn the worm gear to see if it binds. If it does, add shims to eliminate binding (cover shims are available in various thicknesses). If worm turns freely, remove shims until there is a slight drag, but no binding. Then, remove bolts, one at a time, put sealing compound on them, replace them, and tighten to 17 lb-ft torque.

3. Install pistons and plugs on piston connector. Check clearances between the plugs and the piston-arm roller, as shown in Fig. 11-16. Clearance should be as close to zero as possible so as to eliminate all lash. Shims of various thicknesses are available. After clearance has been corrected, remove one piston and plug in readiness for further assembly.

4. Put steering (pitman) shaft and piston arm in housing so arm splines mesh with shaft splines. Put adjusting screw in slot in end of shaft, and install shaft cover—with gasket—by turning screw into cover. Put sealing compound on cover bolts and install bolts. Put washer and lock nut on adjusting screw but do not tighten nut.

5. Install pitman shaft outer seal (lip facing inward) with special tool. Install snap ring over seal. See §154, A and B.

[305]

6. Install pitman arm on shaft and tighten clamp bolt to 100 to 120 lb-ft.

7. Set worm gear and piston arm at center position and mark center position on gear as shown in Fig. 11-17. Then hold the pitman arm as shown and check backlash by turning the worm gear. Adjust by turning pitman-shaft adjusting screw in to eliminate backlash. There should be no backlash felt when the worm gear is turned 90 degrees on either side of center, as shown. With adjustment correct, tighten lock nut on screw.

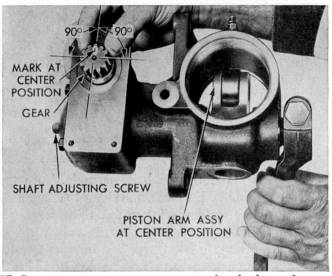

Fig. 11-17. Centering piston arm in preparation for checking adjustment of the pitman shaft. (*De Soto Division of Chrysler Corporation*)

8. Turn piston arm to one extreme position. Install piston (one) and connector assembly with plug against piston-arm roller. Then, turn worm gear to center piston arm. Assemble other piston, with plug, to connector. Tighten Allen screws and install lock rings.

9. Assemble cylinders to housing with pistons centered so both extend from housing an equal amount, as follows: (*a*) lubricate cylinder bores, piston rings, and pistons with engine oil; (*b*) install both cylinders, at same time, over pistons; (*c*) make sure rings are not damaged as they enter the cylinder bores; and (*d*) after both cylinders have been properly started on the pistons, thread both simultaneously into the housing until cylinders bottom in the gear housing.

10. Turn the worm gear counterclockwise and at the same time unscrew the upper cylinder as shown in Fig. 11-18. Continue to turn the worm gear and unscrew the cylinder. Piston head should very closely follow the top of the cylinder or should actually bear against it. Turn worm gear exactly 1⅝ turns (*no more*) with piston bottomed in cylinder. Note scribe marks previously made (see Fig. 11-12). If they do not line up, turn the cylinder in (*never out*) to align the hydraulic-tube fitting holes in the cylinder. In some cases, this means

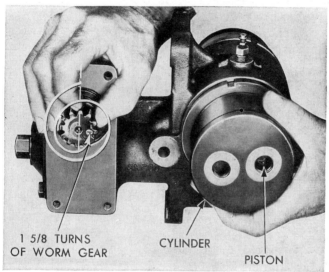

1 5/8 TURNS
OF WORM GEAR   CYLINDER

PISTON

Fig. 11-18. Adjusting cylinder to piston travel. (*De Soto Division of Chrysler Corporation*)

the cylinder will be turned in as much as ½ turn from scribe marks.

11. Repeat the above procedure for the other cylinder, turning the worm gear clockwise while backing out the cylinder. Do not exceed 1⅝ turn of worm gear. With both cylinders properly positioned, recheck worm gear rotation; *it must not exceed 1⅝ turn from center in either direction* to cause piston to contact cylinder end. Tighten lock rings by putting special studs in the tube fitting holes and using bar to hold cylinder stationary. Then use spanner to tighten lock rings (Fig. 11-13).

12. After the above operations, install and tighten the Allen set screw in the piston arm to 30 to 35 lb-ft. You need a special

[307]

fitting to measure torque on this screw. The fitting can be made by cutting a 2-inch length from a ¼-inch Allen wrench and welding it on a socket that will fit a torque wrench. It is very important to tighten this screw properly; otherwise, the steering system will feel "lumpy" or will seem to catch while operating.

13. To assemble valve body, refer to Fig. 11-5. Insert steering-tube gear—with cap—into valve body, using a new gasket.

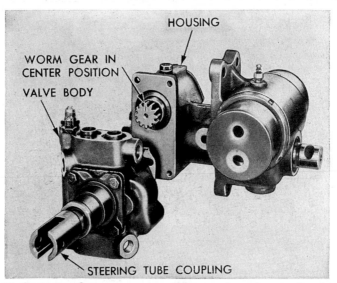

FIG. 11-19. Centering the worm gear and the steering-tube coupling in preparation for attaching valve body to housing. (*De Soto Division of Chrysler Corporation*)

Secure with four bolts. Then install the four valves in the valve body and secure with snap rings. Beveled edges of rings go out. Install worm-shaft seal (*J* in Fig. 11-4) with lip facing valve body. Then install large and small seal rings in valve body.

14. Remove bolt and turn adjusting plate (see Fig. 11-11) counter-clockwise (when facing plate). This permits assembly of the valve body to the gear housing. Now, with worm gear and steering-tube coupling in center position, as shown in Fig. 11-19, bring valve body to housing, engage gears, and attach with four bolts.

15. Eliminate backlash between the spur gears. Turn the adjusting plate clockwise (facing plate) until backlash is no longer
felt at the coupling. Install and tighten adjusting-plate bolt.
(Further adjustment may be necessary after steering gear is
installed in the car.)

16. Use new seal rings (coated with Lubriplate) and install
hydraulic-tube fittings. Tighten fitting bolts to 16 to 20 lb-ft.

§158. Gemmer power-steering-gear installation Before installing the
assembly on the car, be sure to remove shipping caps from fittings

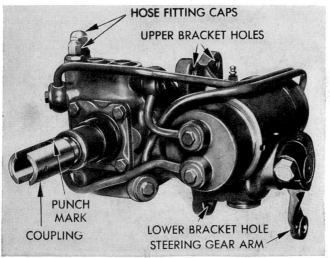

Fig. 11-20. Punch mark on coupling to identify centered position. (*De Soto Division of Chrysler Corporation*)

of any replacement part that has been installed. Otherwise, when
the coupling is turned, as below, seals will be damaged.

1. Remove caps from pressure-and-return-hose fittings and turn
   coupling to extreme left or right position. Then turn back
   approximately 1⅝ turns to center (Fig. 11-19). Put punch
   mark as shown in Fig. 11-20 to indicate center position.

2. Install gear through floor-board opening from driver's compartment. Attach with one upper bolt, leaving bolt just barely
   loose enough so assembly can be pivoted for alignment.

3. Prepare steering tube for installation by making sure upper
   parts are in place—snap ring, retainer, bearing-spacer spring,

spacer—and that the insulator and horn-contact spring are in position at the lower end. Then put rubber steering-gear-to-jacket insulator on upper part of steering gear.

4. Install steering tube by indexing insulated tongue into tube-coupling slot. The punch mark on coupling and the master serration for steering wheel should be in alignment as shown in Fig. 11-21. Attach tube by inserting tube insulator pin and peening over both ends of pin.

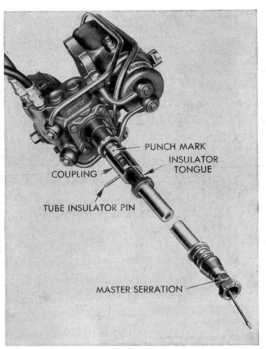

FIG. 11-21. Alignment of punch mark on coupling and master serration on upper end of steering tube. (*De Soto Division of Chrysler Corporation*)

NOTE: The following applies to S17 De Soto specifically. Alignment procedure on other models is somewhat different.

5. Slide jacket assembly down over steering tube. Install spacer tool (¼ inch thick) between end of jacket with gear housing. As jacket is pushed down against the spacer, the collar at the end of the steering gear will engage the collar inside the jacket to form a rigid connection between the jacket and steering gear.

6. Pivot jacket upward so studs on jacket shroud enter holes in instrument panel. Put rubber insulator between jacket shroud and panel.
7. Then, from engine side, install other two bolts that attach gear to frame bracket. Tighten all three bolts to 75 lb-ft.
8. Check jacket and shroud alignment with instrument panel opening. If alignment is off, loosen upper two bolts attaching bracket to the frame and shift entire assembly to right or left, as necessary. Then retighten bolts to 50 to 65 lb-ft.

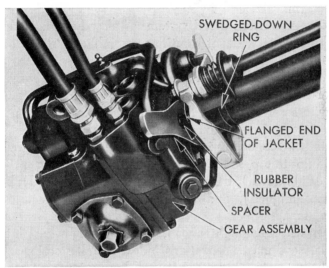

SWEDGED-DOWN RING

FLANGED END OF JACKET

RUBBER INSULATOR

SPACER

GEAR ASSEMBLY

Fig. 11-22. Installing column jacket to steering-gear assembly, using space- tool to secure alignment. (*De Soto Division of Chrysler Corporation*)

9. Remove alignment spacer tool (see Fig. 11-22) and push jacket down against steering-gear insulator.
10. Adjust insulated wedge between jacket shroud and lower instrument panel so jacket shroud fits tightly against both the lower instrument panel and instrument cluster panel when stud nuts are installed. Install and tighten nuts.
11. Install horn contact to jacket with two screws. Connect horn wire and six turn-signal wires. Attach transmission cross-over rod and install hairpin clip.
12. Working under car, slide the brake pedal back into position and secure with new bushing lock, or horseshoe. Connect master-cylinder push rod to brake pedal with bolt. Connect

[311]

brake-pedal extension with spring clip installed on bolt between push-rod end and pedal extension. Secure with nut, washer, and cotter pin.

13. Working under hood, remove plugs from pressure-and-return fittings (if present) and connect the hoses from pump. Hose with the small fitting at the gear-assembly end should be connected to the pump. Hose with the large fitting at the gear-assembly end should be connected to the pump reservoir. *Do not reverse these connections!* Then connect drag link to pitman arm.

14. Fill reservoir and bleed system, as already explained (§153).

15. In front compartment, continue assembly by reinstalling floor board—with accelerator rod. Rod goes beneath offset crook in gearshift control rods. Fasten end of rod to bell crank. Attach floor board with screws, slide draft pad into place and attach it with screws, fold the floor mat back into place, and reinstall the clutch, brake, and accelerator-petal pads.

16. Install the following in steering wheel: triangular ground ring (red dot to top, screw holes aligned), contact ring spring (concave side down), travel plate (screw holes aligned), horn ring (holes aligned), and three screws with fiber and rubber insulators.

17. With wheels straight ahead, slide steering wheel into place. Make sure master serrations index. Install steering-wheel nut and tighten to 35 to 40 lb-ft. Pull horn wire from folded position, install bushing and connect wire to terminal on travel plate. Put steering-wheel-medallion retaining spring in place (concave side down) and install medallion, turning it clockwise.

§159. Gemmer power-steering adjustments   1. Spur gear adjustment must be checked in 12 positions, or for each 30 degrees turn of steering wheel, because the gears have 12 teeth. With engine running, pull steering wheel up and release it. Then turn wheel 30 degrees and repeat until all 12 positions are checked. If wheel fails to drop in any position, loosen the adjusting-plate lock bolt (see Fig. 11-11) and turn adjusting-plate until wheel will drop. Tighten lock bolt and recheck all 12 positions. If adjusting plate has been turned as far as it will go, remove the bolt, withdraw adjusting plate, and move it to the next serration. Then make adjustment as above.

2. Roller tooth and worm gear meshing is adjusted by turning the adjusting screw at the end of the pitman arm. To check, disconnect drag link from pitman arm, start engine, and turn steering wheel to mid-position. Attempt to move pitman arm to check backlash. If backlash is felt, loosen the lock nut and turn the adjusting screw. Adjust backlash with wheel at 90 degrees on each side of center. Backlash must be eliminated but there must be no binding. If you cannot eliminate backlash without causing binding, proceed as follows: (*a*) Remove access plug under piston arm, drain oil, and remove piston-arm set screw. Now adjustment can be made without causing binding between piston arm and pistons. (*b*) After adjustment, retighten piston-arm set screw (30 to 35 lb-ft), install access plug and gasket, bleed system, and give the adjustment a final check. (*c*) Connect drag link to pitman arm.

§160. Hydraulic-pump service   Two types of pumps have been used, the double-rotor type (shown dissassembled in Fig. 11-23) and the single-rotor type (shown dissassembled in Fig. 11-25). The latter is very much like the unit shown in Fig. 10-23. Service of the two types is covered in later sections.

Caution: Be extremely careful about dirt when working on the pumps. Even small particles of dirt can scratch or damage the rotor parts or can lodge in the pump and later circulate in the oil to the steering gear, where they will cause serious trouble. Be absolutely sure that the parts, the tools you use, your hands, and the work bench are really clean.

§161. Double-rotor pump service (Fig. 11-23)

1. Drain oil from reservoir after removing cover. Remove reservoir from pump—by taking out four screws. Do not lose one large and five small rubber seal rings between reservoir and pump body.
2. Remove drain tube from coupling chamber. On models using a rubber coupling, remove special lock screw and washer. This is a torque type of screw and should not be replaced by another type.

[313]

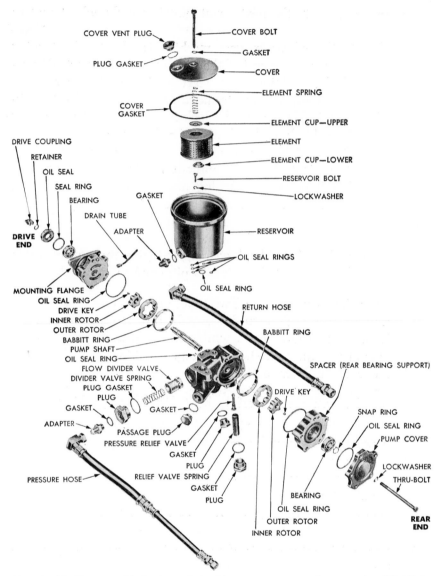

Fig. 11-23. Disassembled view of double-rotor pump and reservoir. (*De Soto Division of Chrysler Corporation*)

3. Remove five through bolts and take off rear cover. Remove and discard oil seal. Use snap-ring pliers to remove snap ring. Then tap side of rear spacer—the bearing support—with soft hammer to loosen it from dowels. Slide spacer, with bearing, off pump shaft. Remove and discard oil seal from pump body.

4. Turn pump over and shake it so rotors fall out. If inner rotor stays on shaft, pull it off with fingers and remove key. If outer rotor stays in pump, make two wire hooks and lift it out. *Never try to pry rotor out—this will ruin rotor and babbitt ring.*

5. Lift pump body off mounting flange. Remove rotors, as above, if they stick on shaft or in body.

Caution: Do not mix rotors. Keep front and rear sets separate, since they are not interchangeable.

6. Remove bearings and seals from mounting flange and spacer. Special bearing removal and replacement tool is required. The valve plugs (see Fig. 11-23) should also be removed.

7. Clean all parts in solvent and inspect bearings, rotors, babbitt rings, and pump shaft for scores, wear, cracks, and so on. Replace defective parts. (Worn rotors mean that a complete new pump assembly must be installed.) Then check end clearances of each set of rotors in its end of body by placing a straightedge across body face and measuring clearance with feeler gauge. Limits are 0.0010 to 0.0017 inch for the outer rotors and 0.0013 to 0.0020 inch for inner rotors. Excessive wear requires replacement of the complete pump assembly.

8. Start assembly of the pump by lubricating front bearing with engine oil and then using special driver to install it in the front flange. Coat oil seal ring with Lubriplate and install it over bearing. Coat lip of oil seal with Lubriplate and drive it into position over bearing and seal ring, using special tool.

9. Install rear bearing in rear spacer after lubricating it with engine oil.

10. Install plugs and valves in pump body. Note (Fig. 11-23) direction in which valve plungers are put into valve body. Use new gaskets under plugs. Tighten valve plugs with 45 to 50 lb-ft torque.

11. Insert seal-protector thimble into front-bearing oil seal until it bottoms, turn pump over, and place front outer rotor in

body. Then install pump shaft (drive tongue up) through outer rotor and into pump body (Fig. 11-24).

12. Put drive key in position and slide front inner rotor over shaft and key. Rotate shaft until two rotors mesh; then slide shaft in so drive key is centered in inner rotor.

13. Install bleed-hole seal ring and large seal ring on pump body after coating them with Lubriplate. Bring mounting flange—with thimble-seal protector still in it—into position and slide it

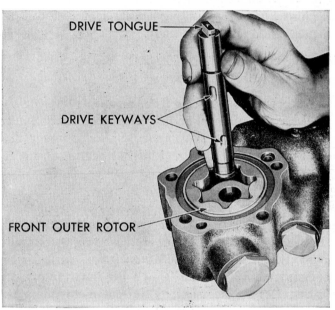

FIG. 11-24. Installing pump shaft in body of double-rotor pump. (*De Soto Division of Chrysler Corporation*)

onto pump body. Remove thimble from shaft, align locating dowels, and tap flange with a soft hammer to seat dowels.

14. Turn pump on end, with mounting flange down, and install rear outer rotor. Slide inner rotor over end of shaft and put drive key into position. Slide rotor down into place, meshing it with the outer rotor and aligning it with the drive key at the same time.

15. Put new seal ring, coated with Lubriplate, in pump body and slide rear spacer with bearing down over shaft. Align dowel holes and tap spacer down with soft hammer to seat them.

Put new seal ring, coated with Lubriplate, into spacer, install snap ring on end of shaft, and then install cover with through bolts and lock washers. Tighten bolts to 15 to 20 lb-ft.

16. Install coupling chamber drain tube, tightening the nut one-half to three-fourths turn beyond finger tight. If pump uses rubber coupling, install it by driving against flange (not lugs) with ⅝-inch steel rod. Tighten special lock screw and washer with 10 to 15 lb-ft.

17. Then install reservoir.

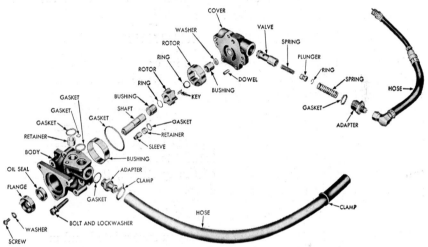

Fig. 11-25. Disassembled view of single-rotor pump. (*De Soto Division of Chrysler Corporation*)

§162. Single-rotor pump service (Fig. 11-25)

1. After draining oil from reservoir, remove reservoir from pump. Then remove coupling locking screw and coupling from pump. The locking screw is a special type and should not be replaced by an ordinary screw.

2. Put pump body in soft jaws of vise and take out the five cover-attaching bolts. Cover can now be separated from the body and the rotors and shaft can be removed.

3. Clean all parts in solvent and inspect shaft bushings, rotors, body, and cover for wear. End clearance, with rotors in body, should be not more than 0.0010 to 0.0017 inch. Check valves for scoring. Replace worn parts.

[317]

4. If any of the three bushings (outer-rotor babbitt bushing or two shaft bushings) requires replacement, use special tools to remove the old and install the new bushings. New seals should always be installed when bushings are replaced.
5. Refer to Fig. 11-25 and reverse disassembly procedure to reassemble the pump. Use seal-protector thimble in pump body before installing shaft. Use new seal rings and coat them with Lubriplate before installing them.
6. Tighten attaching bolts to 15 to 20 lb-ft torque. When installing coupling flange on pump, hold it with special tool and tighten it to 10 to 12 lb-ft.

CHAPTER CHECKUP

You may or may not plan to specialize in, or work on, power-steering equipment. But in any event, you will want to know how these units work, and the general servicing program they require. Thus, you will want to remember the high points of the chapter you have just finished. The checkup that follows will tell you how well you do remember what you have just studied. Don't be discouraged if you cannot answer, offhand, all of the questions. Most good students reread their lessons several times. When you can't answer all of the questions, it just means that you should reread the chapter once more.

Correcting Trouble Lists

The purpose of this exercise is to help you spot related and unrelated troubles on a list. Refer to the test instructions at the end of Chap. 10 for an explanation of how to take this test.

Write down the lists in your notebook, but do not write down the item that does not belong.

1. Lack of steering assistance: drive belt loose, low oil level, pump coupling broken, piston seals worn, engine idling too fast.
2. Low oil pressure: belt loose, coupling broken, flow-control valve stuck, mechanical trouble in pump, bracket loose on frame.
3. Steering aid in one direction but not in other: gear-to-jacket alignment off, valves stuck in gear body, drive belt loose.
4. Excessive free play in steering wheel: steering gear loose on bracket, bracket loose on frame, steering connections loose, excessive valve-gear backlash, valves stuck in body, worm and roller backlash excessive.
5. Poor centering, or recovery from turns: steering columns misaligned, front wheels misaligned, binding in linkage, pump coupling broken.

Gemmer Hydraguide Power-steering Service

Completing the Sentences

The sentences below are incomplete. After each sentence there are several words or phrases, only one of which will correctly complete the sentence. Write down each sentence in your notebook, selecting the proper word or phrase to complete it correctly.

1. When checking the oil pressure with the special gauge connected into the pressure line, failure of the gauge to show 500 pounds or more when the shutoff valve is closed means that there is trouble in the   *pump*   *gear assembly*   *distribution valve* *lines*

2. The special manometer is used to check the steering gear for *external leaks*   *valve action*   *internal leaks*   *centering*

3. If the relief valve sings, or buzzes, it means that there is   *high pressure in system*   *low pressure in system*   *lack of centering*   *lack of steering control*

4. During disassembly of the steering gear, when removing the cylinders, they must be removed   *one at a time*   *together with piston inside*

5. Worm assembly is adjusted by means of   *an adjusting screw* *an adjusting cam*   *an adjusting arm*   *shims under worm cover*

6. Clearance between the piston plugs and piston-arm roller should be   *as close to zero as possible*   *about 0.015 inch* *about 0.025 inch*

7. Meshing between the worm and roller tooth is adjusted by means of   *an adjusting screw*   *an adjusting cam*   *an adjusting plate*   *shims*

8. Backlash between the spur gears is eliminated by means of *an adjusting screw*   *an adjusting cam*   *an adjusting plate* *shims*

9. Two types of pumps have been used with the steering gear discussed in this chapter, double rotor and   *single rotor*   *triple rotor* *double gear*

10. Generally speaking, all seals or seal rings removed from the steering gear or pump during disassembly should be   *replaced with new seals or rings*   *cleaned in solvent and reused*   *reinstalled with Lubriplate*

Servicing Procedures

Write down in your notebook the procedures that are asked for. Do not copy from the book, but write the procedures in your own words. This will help you to remember them.

[319]

1. Pick a car equipped with a Gemmer power-steering unit and describe in detail the procedure for removing a steering gear.
2. Explain how to diagnose steering-gear trouble.
3. List the main steps in disassembling the steering gear.
4. List the main steps in assembling the steering gear.
5. List and describe the adjusting procedures required on the steering gear.
6. List the main steps in installing the steering gear on a car.
7. List the main steps in disassembling and reassembling a double rotor pump. A single rotor pump.

SUGGESTIONS FOR FURTHER STUDY

When you are in your local school or automotive service shop, examine power-steering equipment that is available. If possible, watch an expert mechanic remove, disassemble, and service a power-steering gear. If you can, study the shop manual describing the steering gear discussed in this chapter. Write down in your notebook any important facts you come across.

12: Linkage-type power-steering service

THIS CHAPTER describes the trouble-shooting, adjusting, removal, repair, and reinstallation of the linkage-type power-steering units. You will recall that there are two general types of linkage power-steering units, the integral type in which the valve and power cylinders are integral, and the type in which the two are separate. Both work in the same general manner (§§69 to 70). Chapter 6 describes trouble-shooting procedures on steering and suspension generally. The material that follows carries this a step further into linkage-type power steering and includes complete repair procedures on this equipment.

§163. Trouble-shooting chart (linkage-type steering) Refer to §§69 and 70 for descriptions of this unit. The list, below, of trouble symptoms, causes, and checks or corrections will give you a means of logically analyzing troubles so that their causes can be quickly located and eliminated. Not all of the troubles, causes, and corrections listed apply to all models of linkage power-steering units since there are some variations in design and operation from model to model.

NOTE: The troubles and possible causes are not listed in the chart in the order of frequency of occurrence. That is, item 1 does not necessarily occur more often than item 2, nor does item *a* under Possible Cause necessarily occur more often than item *b*.

LINKAGE-TYPE POWER-STEERING TROUBLE-SHOOTING CHART

(See §§164 to 167 for details of checks and corrections listed.)

Complaint	*Possible Cause*	*Check or Correction*
1. Hard steering	*a.* Low oil or leaks	Check for leaks, add oil

Complaint	Possible Cause	Check or Correction
	b. Low oil pressure	See item 2. Low oil pressure, below
	c. Binding in steering linkage	Check, adjust linkage as needed
	d. Power - cylinder piston rod bent	Replace rod or cylinder
	e. Low tire pressure	Inflate to proper pressure
	f. Incorrect front alignment	Align front end
	g. Binding in steering column	Align steering column
	h. Valve stuck or out of adjustment	Adjust. Remove valve and check for cause. Replace valve if it is damaged.
2. Low oil pressure	a. Pump belt slipping	Tighten to proper tension
	b. Relief and flow-control valve stuck	Remove and clean
	c. Valve spring weak or broken	Replace
	d. Drive coupling broken	Replace
	e. Pump rotors, body, or cover worn or broken	Replace rotors or pump
	f. Leaks past piston in power cylinder	Replace piston rings or cylinder
	g. Leaks past valve	Replace seal rings
3. Hard steering — one direction only	This could be caused by d, e, f, or g, listed under item 1, Hard steering, above, or by a misadjusted or sticky valve in the power cylinder or valve body.	
4. Poor centering or recovery from turns	a. Pitman arm and stud binding on power cylinder	Adjust to proper tension
	b. Bind in steering column or gear	Align column, adjust gear
	c. Bind in steering linkage	Check, adjust linkage as needed

Complaint	Possible Cause	Check or Correction
	d. Bent power-cylinder piston rod	Replace piston rod or cylinder
	e. Incorrect front alignment	Align front end
	f. Valve misadjusted or stuck	Free up, adjust
	g. Antiroll pin and bracket binding (on some models)	Align pin with bracket
5. Car wander	a. Uneven tire pressure	Inflate correctly
	b. Pitman arm and stud binding on power cylinder	Adjust to proper torque
	c. Valve stuck or misadjusted	Clean, replace
	d. Incorrect front alignment	Align front end
6. Noises	a. Low oil level	Replace oil, check for leaks
	b. Pump bushing worn	Replace bushing
	c. Dirty pump	Clean after disassembly, drain system, and refill with clean oil
	d. Looseness in steering linkage	Check, adjust, and tighten
	e. Tie rods improperly attached	Loosen clamps and retighten with bolts in proper position

§**164. Trouble diagnosis** The chart above lists possible troubles, causes, and corrections. When trouble is reported on the steering system, make the following checks to accurately pinpoint the cause:

1. Check belt tension. A quick check of belt tension can be made by turning the steering wheel to the extreme position while watching the belt (with engine operating). If the belt slips, the tension is too low. On the type of pump which is mounted on the generator, the belt is adjusted by loosening the adjusting-bracket bolt and pivoting the generator out as necessary to correct the tension. Then

tighten the bolt. On the type of pump that is driven by a separate belt, the pump-mounting bracket has slotted holes that permit the pump to be shifted outward to increase the tension as necessary (see §136, 1).

2. Check oil level in pump reservoir. If it is low, add oil to bring it up to the proper level. Also, check the pump, power-cylinder, and valve connections for signs of leakage.

3. Two additional tests, for steering effort required and for oil pressure developed, should be made. First, however, make sure that the wheel alignment, tire pressure, suspension, and shock absorbers are in normal condition. Then, to make the steering-effort check, use a pull scale hooked to the wheel rim (Fig. 9-2) and see what pull is required to pull the wheel through center, first in one direction, then in the other. Specifications vary, but Plymouth and Dodge state that any pull above 10 pounds is excessive (Mercury specifies 7 to 12 pounds) when the front wheels are on dry concrete.

Caution: Do not turn and hold wheel at extreme left or right position.

4. To check oil pressure, install special gauge in pressure line from pump. With engine idling and oil in steering system warmed up, turn steering wheel a full turn—either to left or right. Gauge should read high pressure (specifications vary on different units: 700 to 900 pounds on Mercury, 500 pounds on Plymouth and Dodge 6, 300 pounds on Dodge V-8, and so on). If pressure is too low, close shutoff valve, quickly read pump pressure, and open valve again. (Do not leave valve closed more than a few seconds, since this might damage pump.) If pump pressure goes up to specified value as valve is closed, it indicates that the pump is all right and that the loss of pressure is due to leakage at the power cylinder or valves. If pump pressure stays low as valve is closed, then the loss of pressure is due to a defect in the pump—relief or flow-control valve stuck or damaged, rotors worn or broken, and so on.

5. Bleed the system, if necessary, by adding oil to the reservoir, and turning the steering wheel to the left and right several times (do not bump wheel at extreme positions). Add more oil if level in reservoir falls too low.

§165. Servicing power cylinder and valve (separately-mounted type— see Figs. 5-34 to 5-38) *1. Power cylinder service.* The power cylinder is so constructed that repair of the unit in the field is not feasible if internal damage has occurred. Removal and installation of the power cylinder and replacement of piston-rod seal and fitting seals are covered in the following paragraphs.

a. To remove the power cylinder, first raise car on hoist, wipe the hose fittings at the power cylinder so they are really clean, detach the hoses, and let the system drain. For complete drainage, move wheels back and forth several times (Plymouth recommends that the engine be running). Remove nuts holding rod to frame-mounting bracket and to stud on linkage. Take power cylinder off. A new piston-rod seal can be installed by removing the snap ring—with snap-ring pliers—and then removing scraper and seal—with prick punch. Then lubricate new seal and install it and scraper with a ⅞-inch deep-well socket. Install lock ring.

b. To install power cylinder, first inspect the bushings and washers used to attach it and replace any that are worn. Then place a cup washer and rubber bushing on the piston rod, insert end of rod through hole in frame bracket, and place end of cylinder on linkage stud. Cylinder must be so aligned that the hoses are permitted to reach fittings, as on the original assembly. Secure cylinder with bushings, washers, and nuts as on the original assembly. Then attach hoses, fill reservoir with oil, and bleed system.

2. *Valve removal*

a. For valve removal, raise car on hoist, wipe hose fittings at the valve so they are really clean, detach hoses, and let the system drain. For complete drainage, move wheels back and forth several times.

b. Drive locking, or indexing, pin up into steering-arm rod just far enough to clear threads, as shown in Fig. 12-1. *Do not drive pin all the way in,* since the pin would then damage the threads on the opposite side of the valve.

c. Loosen sleeve clamping bolt.

d. Loosen pitman arm on stud by removing cotter pin and nut and then using special puller tool. *Do not use wedge-type tool or pry bar* to loosen pitman arm.

e. Raise valve and move ball stud forward to clear pitman arm

[325]

as shown in Fig. 12-2. Turn wheels to full left, and then turn valve counterclockwise to remove valve from rod. Drive indexing pin out of steering-arm rod.

3. *Valve disassembly.* Be very clean when working on the valve. Make sure your hands, the workbench, and the tools you use are clean. Even small traces of dirt are apt to cause damage to, and malfunctioning of, the valve assembly.

FIG. 12-1. Driving indexing pin into steering-arm rod. (*Lincoln-Mercury Division of Ford Motor Company*)

   a. Put valve assembly (Fig. 12-3) in soft jaws of vise, but do not tighten vise more than necessary since this could distort the valve. Cut and remove safety wire, remove two cap screws, and take off centering spring cover. Then take out spool adjusting nut, small and large washers, centering spring, spacer, and washer. Remove adapter plate and seal retainer.

   b. Remove two cap screws attaching sleeve to valve and separate sleeve and valve (Fig. 12-4). Remove valve spool by pushing it out of the spool-adjustment end of the housing with a finger

[326]

Fɪɢ. 12-2. Moving ball stud forward to clear pitman arm in preparation for valve removal. (*Lincoln-Mercury Division of Ford Motor Company*)

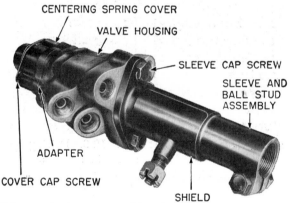

Fɪɢ. 12.3. Valve and sleeve assembly. (*Lincoln-Mercury Division of Ford Motor Company*)

(Fig. 12-5). Then remove retainer spacer, bushing, and seal from the sleeve end of the housing.

c. Disassemble sleeve assembly by clamping stop screw in vise (Fig. 12-6), removing lubricating fitting, pulling valve bolt out of sleeve to take up slack, and then driving pin from stop screw as shown in Fig. 12-6. Unscrew sleeve from stop screw. Then remove valve bolt from stop screw.

[327]

Fig. 12-4. Separating sleeve from valve housing. (*Lincoln-Mercury Division of Ford Motor Company*)

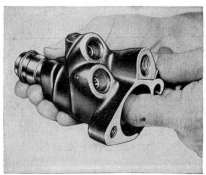

Fig. 12-5. Pushing valve spool from housing with finger. (*Lincoln-Mercury Division of Ford Motor Company*)

Fig. 12-6. Driving pin from stop screw in sleeve assembly. (*Lincoln-Mercury Division of Ford Motor Company*)

    d. Ball stud can be removed from sleeve by moving it toward enlarged part of slot in sleeve. Socket tube, plug, spring, and ball seats may then be removed.

    4. Valve-part inspection. Clean all parts in solvent and inspect them for wear, cracks, scores, or other damage that would require replacement of parts. If the valve spool has small burrs, they can be removed with very fine crocus cloth, provided the sharp edges of the spool *are not rounded off.*

    If the check valve must be replaced, then the return-line-fitting

[328]

seat must be removed. This is done by tapping the hole in the seat with a ⅜-inch starting tap and then using a ⅜-inch bolt, a washer large enough to fit over the port, and a nut as a puller tool to pull the seat. Then the check valve retainer, spring, and ball can be removed. Install new parts and put fitting seat in place in port. Screw a ⅝-18 bolt into port to force seat into position.

5. *Valve assembly*

a. Assemble sleeve by first putting ball stud seats, spring, plug, and socket tube into sleeve housing. Then insert ball stud through enlarged part of slot, making sure the seats properly align. Install stop screw with valve bolt in place and tighten screw until it is solid. Back it off to nearest hole. Check ball stud for freeness of motion. If still snug, back off screw one more hole. Then install pin in stop screw. Install lubrication fitting and dust shield.

FIG. 12-7. Installing seal in housing. (*Lincoln-Mercury Division of Ford Motor Company*)

FIG. 12-8. Installing adjusting nut on valve bolt (*Lincoln-Mercury Division of Ford Motor Com pany*)

b. Coat spool lightly with oil and install it in valve housing, rotating it while you enter it so it does not bind. Large-diameter end goes toward small end of housing. *Do not force spool!* Lubricate and install small seal over small end of spool, and work seal into housing with a screw driver (Fig. 12-7). *Be very careful not to damage seal!* Install bushing and retainer spacer in sleeve end of valve housing. Seat retainer spacer in housing. Lubricate and install large seal over large

[329]

end of spool. Work seal into housing, being careful not to damage it.

c. Put adapter plate on small end of housing and check the valve spool to make sure it is free to move back and forth. Then push bolt of the sleeve assembly through spool. Turn sleeve so ball stud is in line with the three ports in the valve housing (see Fig. 12-3), and attach sleeve to housing with two cap screws, tightened to 15 to 20 lb-ft.

d. Put large washer, spring spacer, spring, and large and small washers on valve bolt, compress the spring, and install adjusting nut (Fig. 12-8). Tighten nut until it is solid, then back it

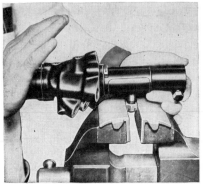 

FIG. 12-9. Checking valve spool for freeness of movement after assembly. (*Lincoln-Mercury Division of Ford Motor Company*)

FIG. 12-10. Checking distance between ball stud on pitman arm and inner ball stud on left connecting rod. (*Lincoln-Mercury Division of Ford Motor Company*)

off one-fourth turn. Check valve spool for freeness of action by moving ball stud back and forth along sleeve. Stud should be able to move about 0.060 inch. Install centering-spring cover, tightening the two cap screws four to six lb-ft. Put lock wire between two centering-spring-cover screws. Then put lock wire between two sleeve screws—on side opposite from dust shield.

e. Test valve freeness by putting castle nut on ball stud and locking nut in vise. Then push on centering-spring cover (Fig. 12-9). Rotate valve 180 degrees and push on sleeve end. This checks valve movement in both directions.

6. *Valve installation*

a. As a first step in installing the valve on the car, screw it onto the steering-arm rod until about four threads are showing on rod. Then put ball stud in pitman arm, and check the distance between ball stud in pitman arm and the inner ball stud on the left-steering-spindle-arm connecting rod (Fig. 12-10). This distance should be 5⅛ inches. To adjust, turn valve in or out on rod. Then line slot in sleeve with hole in rod and lock valve in this position with indexing pin. Tighten sleeve clamp bolt to 25 to 30 lb-ft.

b. Install ball-stud nut and tighten it to 60 to 65 lb-ft. Lock with cotter pin. Install pressure and return lines. Install short hose to cylinder—on forward hole of cylinder and lower hole of valve. Then install longer hose to cylinder—rearward hole of cylinder and upper hole of valve.

c. Lower car on hoist and make any adjustments necessary at tie-rod ends to secure straight-ahead position of steering and front wheels. Check and correct toe-in, if necessary.

d. Fill pump reservoir and start engine. Bleed system by idling for two minutes, adding more oil if necessary, and then increasing engine speed to 1,000 rpm (revolutions per minute) and turning wheels back and forth several times. Do not hit stops at extreme positions! Check connections for leaks and add more oil if necessary. Finally, check the steering effort with a pull scale as already explained (§164, 3).

§166. **Servicing Monroe power cylinder and valve (integral type— see Figs. 5-39 to 5-41)** In this unit—called a *power link*—the piston, cylinder, and valve are a single assembly. The unit incorporates a power-link valve adjustment. In addition, there are pitman-arm stop adjustments, and adjustment of the pitman-arm or drag-link attachments to the power link. The pump drive belt is checked and adjusted as previously described. Aside from adjustments, several parts and seals can be replaced in the power link, as detailed below. Valve parts cannot be replaced separately, since the valve spool is an extremely close fit to the valve body; it would not be possible to fit new parts and make internal adjustments without a great deal of special equipment available only at the factory. Thus, if steering difficulty is definitely caused by the valve parts, then the entire power link must be replaced. Other service operations are covered below.

Caution: When adding oil to the pump reservoir or when doing any work on the power link, be extremely careful about getting dirt into the unit. Remember that the valve parts are very close fits and that even tiny dirt particles can cause valve and steering trouble.

1. Adjustment of pitman-arm stop. Most vehicles using the power link have pitman-arm stops to limit the travel of the pitman arm and thereby prevent undue strain on the steering linkage and hydraulic system. To adjust the stops, loosen lock nuts and turn

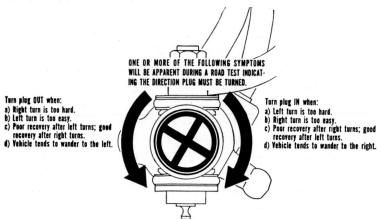

ONE OR MORE OF THE FOLLOWING SYMPTOMS WILL BE APPARENT DURING A ROAD TEST INDICAT- ING THE DIRECTION PLUG MUST BE TURNED.

Turn plug OUT when:
a) Right turn is too hard.
b) Left turn is too easy.
c) Poor recovery after left turns; good recovery after right turns.
d) Vehicle tends to wander to the left.

Turn plug IN when:
a) Left turn is too hard.
b) Right turn is too easy.
c) Poor recovery after right turns; good recovery after left turns.
d) Vehicle tends to wander to the right.

FIG. 12-11. Valve adjustment. (*Monroe Auto Equipment Company*)

pitman-arm stops in a few turns. Then turn steering wheel (engine *off*) to full right until right steering arm touches the lower-suspension-arm outer pivot or wheel stop. Turn the adjusting screw in the frame bracket or pitman arm out until the right steering arm is moved approximately ⅛ inch away from contact. Tighten lock nut. Repeat for a full left turn, adjusting the other stop screw.

2. Adjustment of power-link valve. Figure 12-11 shows various steering symptoms that would indicate the need for power-link valve adjustment together with the direction the plug must be turned to make the adjustment. Do not adjust the valve until you are sure that the steering trouble is caused by the valve (and not by misalignment of wheels, uneven tire inflation, binding steering linkage, and so on—see the trouble-shooting chart in §75).

a. Relay type of power-link-valve adjustment. Scribe a mark on the plug and valve body to indicate original position. Then remove the cotter pin and turn the plug one-sixth turn in proper direction (see Fig. 12-11). Road-test. Repeat adjustment if necessary. When adjustment is correct, install cotter pin. If you have to turn plug more than one-half turn altogether, and if the adjustment is still not correct, then the unit must be disassembled and examined for dirt, weak or broken springs, or other trouble that would prevent normal valve action.

b. Center-point power-link-valve adjustment. Remove spring-seat plug, spring, and ball seat from valve-end of power link and lift unit off bell-crank arm. Then, with an Allen wrench, back off valve-adjusting-plug set screw. Insert a wide-bit screw driver into end of unit and turn plug one-sixth turn in proper direction (see Fig. 12-11). Road-test, after reattaching link. Repeat adjustment if necessary, as explained in previous paragraph. If more than one-half turn is needed, altogether, unit must be disassembled as above.

3. Pitman-arm or drag-link attachment. The pitman arm or drag link is attached by the stud to the power link through the valve. When the stud is drawn properly (55 to 65 lb-ft torque) into the tapered hole in the pitman arm or drag link, the fit should be snug but not binding. If the fit is too snug, causing the rubber cushions to compress and the thrust washers to bind, the bind can usually be relieved by disengaging the pitman arm or drag link from the stud and removing one of the two metal thrust washers between the upper rubber cushion and the arm or link. If this does not correct the bind, it may be necessary to replace the pitman stud or arm or link.

4. Removal of frame-mounting-bracket parts (see Fig. 12-12). Remove cotter pin, nut and outer retainer, cushion, and locater from piston rod. Pull rod clear of frame bracket and remove inner locater (if present), cushion, and retainer.

5. Replacement of cylinder-end parts and seals. With piston rod disconnected from frame as noted in the previous paragraph, unscrew cylinder end plug or cap and pull out piston rod (Fig. 12-13). Pull rod out slowly and have a container ready to catch oil (throw oil away—do not reuse it).

Pull end plug, or cap, and rod guide from piston rod. Use care so threads on rod do not cut seals, if seals are to be reused. If parts

[333]

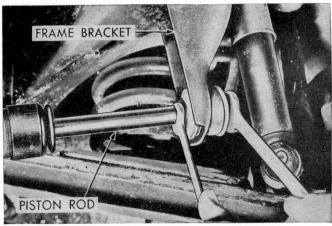

Fig. 12-12. Disconnecting piston rod from frame bracket. (*Monroe Auto Equipment Company*)

Fig. 12-13. Removal of piston rod assembly. (*Monroe Auto Equipment Company*)

require replacement, use parts kits supplied by manufacturer. Kits contain seals and other parts that should be replaced at time of overhaul.

Two types of T-ring retainers are used in the piston rod guide (Figs. 12-14 and 12-15). Also, one type contains the wiping ring (used when cylinder end is closed with a cap). To remove T ring

[334]

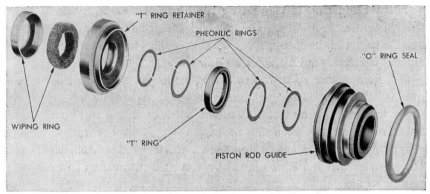

Fig. 12-14. Piston-rod-guide assembly showing relationship between parts. (*Monroe Auto Equipment Company*)

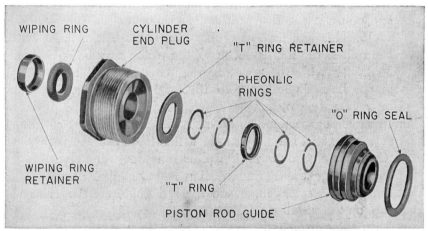

Fig. 12-15. Piston-rod-guide assembly, with cylinder-end plug. (*Monroe Auto Equipment Company*)

from rod guide, pry ring retainer from guide with screw driver. Take out T ring and two inner washers. When installing new T ring, be careful not to interlock the two fiber washers in seal recess. Put T ring over washers and press into guide recess with fingers. Rotate guide on fingers so washers and T ring will align and seat. Then put two more rings in recess in T ring. Install ring retainer on rod guide by tapping around outside of retainer.

The outer seal on the rod guide is removed by stretching the O ring over the retainer. If O-ring retainer is bent, nicked, or damaged, replace it.

[335]

The wiping ring in the T-ring retainer is removed by prying out the wiping-ring retainer. Use special tool to tap new wiping ring and retainer into position. Stake retainer in place with three equally-spaced punch marks at outer edge of retainer.

6. *Replacement of piston rod, rings, and piston.* On all but a few models, the piston and rod can be serviced separately. However, on some models, the end of the rod is spun over the nut so that the parts must be replaced as an assembly. With the rod assembly removed from the car, as noted above, inspect rod, piston, and rings. If rod or piston is badly nicked or scored, replace it. (Light scores can be removed with crocus cloth). If rings require replacement, use special ring service kit and install as explained below.

    a. Clamp piston rod in vise across wrench flats. Remove piston rings, cotter pin, nut, and piston. When installing piston, nut, and cotter pin, use special concentricity tool as shown in Fig. 12-16. This tool assures proper alignment of the piston with the rod. If the tool is not used, the piston may be out of concentricity with the rod and the assembly will bind in the power link. Tighten nut to 18 to 23 lb-ft torque. Then put piston rings on piston.

    b. Remove sharp edges on wrench flats and shoulder of frame-end of rod with emery cloth, a fine-tooth file, or a grinding wheel. *This is important!* Unless it is done, the sharp edges will damage the T ring causing leakage to occur. With the sharp edges removed, install the rod guide and end plug, or cap, on the piston rod.

    c. Lubricate piston and rings with type A automatic transmission fluid (the type of fluid used in the hydraulic system). Insert piston into cylinder, using piston-rod inserting tool, and rotate the piston to make sure rings enter without damage. Lubricate seal in rod guide with type A fluid, slide guide across threads on rod, and work it carefully over shoulder, across wrench flats, and onto rod. Put end plug or cap on in the same manner. Then slide rod guide in against shoulder in cylinder, screw end plug or cap onto cylinder, and tighten it. Stake it securely.

    d. Reattach piston rod to frame bracket. Tighten nut until rubber cushions are compressed even with outer edge of retainers. Replace cotter pin. Road-test car.

7. *Removal of power link from car.* The removal procedure varies according to the type of linkage—relay or center-point.

[336]

a. Relay type. Disconnect hoses from pump. Close pump fittings with caps to prevent entrance of dirt. Raise vehicle on hoist, pull hoses down from engine compartment, and disconnect tie rods from

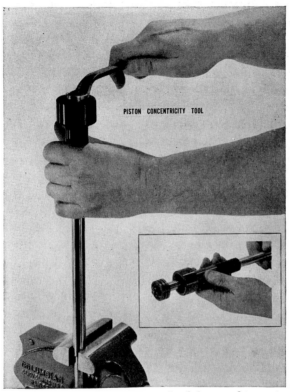

PISTON CONCENTRICITY TOOL

Fig. 12-16. Using piston concentricity tool while attaching piston to rod to assure concentricity between rod and piston. (*Monroe Auto Equipment Company*)

ball studs on the power link. Then disconnect piston rod from frame bracket (as explained above). Remove cotter pin and nut attaching pitman arm to stud in power link. Tap on side of pitman arm to loosen stud in the tapered hole of the pitman arm and take off the power link.

Caution: Do not push piston rod all the way into the cylinder; this will cause the wrench flat to damage the seals so that they would require replacement.

b. Center-point type. Raise vehicle on hoist. Disconnect piston rod from frame by removing cotter pin, nut, outer retainer, cushion,

[337]

and locater. Leave rod in frame bracket to support end of the power link. Then disconnect drag link from power link by removing cotter pin and nut from stud. Tap on side of drag link to loosen stud, and pull drag link from stud. Unscrew spring-seat plug from valve end of power link and lift unit off bell-crank ball. Lower vehicle on hoist. Disconnect hoses from pump and install caps on pump fittings. Lift unit from engine compartment.

8. *Installation of power link in car a. Relay type.* With vehicle raised on hoist, put inner retainer, cushion, and locater on piston rod. Insert rod loosely in frame bracket. Insert pitman stud into tapered hole in pitman arm. Install nut and cotter pin, tightening nut to 55 to 65 lb-ft torque. Install rest of parts on piston rod (see above) and tighten nut as already explained. Install tie-rod ends on ball-stud adapters on power link. Adjust tie-rod-end plugs by screwing them in tight and then backing them off one-fourth to one-half turn. Secure with cotter pin. Lubricate tie-rod end and pitman stud fittings with chassis lubricant. Push hoses up into engine compartment and lower car. Connect hoses to pump.

b. Center-point type. Put unit into position in engine compartment and connect hoses to pump. Put inner retainer, cushion, and locater on piston rod and insert rod loosely in frame-bracket hole. Raise car on hoist. Attach rod to frame by installing other parts and tightening nut as already noted above. Put ball housing (at valve end) on bell-crank ball. Push ball seat up against ball, place spring on spring-seat plug, and screw plug into end of unit. Adjust plug by turning in tight and then backing off one-fourth to one-half turn. Secure with cotter pin. Put drag link onto tapered valve stud and secure with nut. Tighten to 55 to 65 lb-ft torque and install cotter pin.

9. *Adding oil.* After installation is complete, fill pump reservoir with type A automatic transmission fluid, start engine, and turn wheels in each direction several times. Fill reservoir again, check steering operation, and inspect system for leaks.

Check front-wheel alignment, including toe-in, making whatever adjustments are necessary. Then road-test car and make whatever valve adjustments are necessary (see above). Since the hydraulic system is self-bleeding, all air will bleed out during initial operation. Make sure that, after all testing is completed, the reservoir is filled to the proper level before the car is delivered to the customer.

[338]

§167. **Pump service** The pumps used with the linkage-type power-steering units are similar to those used with the integral-type systems (Chaps. 10 and 11). Servicing procedures for these other systems that have already been discussed, will, in general, cover servicing of the pumps used with the linkage-type systems.

CHAPTER CHECKUP

Here is your chance to check up on yourself and find out how well you remember the important points in testing and servicing linkage-type power-steering units described in the chapter. Now that more and more cars are being supplied with power steering, it is important for you to know how all types are serviced. This chapter describes servicing procedures on one type of power-steering equipment. Preceding and following chapters describe other types. Thus, if you remember the procedures outlined in these chapters, you will have the basic knowledge that will assist you in working on power steering.

Correcting Trouble Lists

The purpose of this exercise is to help you spot related and unrelated troubles on a list. Refer to the test instructions at the end of Chap. 10 for an explanation of how to take this test.

Write down the lists in your notebook, but do not write down the item that does not belong.

1. Hard steering: low oil or leaks, low oil pressure, binding in steering linkage, piston rod bent, tight pump drive belt, valve stuck or out of adjustment.
2. Low oil pressure: pump belt slipping, valve stuck, drive coupling broken, pump defective, low tire pressure, leaks past piston or valve.
3. Poor centering or recovery from turns: pitman arm and stud binding on power cylinder, bind in steering column or gear, bind in steering linkage, bent piston rod, excessive oil in cylinder, incorrect fron' alignment, valve misadjusted or stuck.
4. Car wander: uneven tire pressure, pitman arm and stud binding on power cylinder, valve stuck or misadjusted, oil pressure low, front alignment incorrect.
5. Noises: low oil level, pump bushing worn, dirty pump, looseness in steering linkage, tie rods improperly attached, high oil level.

Completing the Sentences

The sentences below are incomplete. After each sentence there are several words or phrases, only one of which will correctly complete the sentence. Write down each sentence in your notebook, selecting the proper word or phrase to complete it correctly.

1. A quick check of belt tension can be made by turning the wheel to the extreme position; if the belt slips, it is   *too tight   too loose   undersized   worn and should be replaced*
2. If the oil pressure goes up to specifications when the shutoff valve on the gauge is turned off, it is likely that the oil pump   *is all right   is worn   needs a new belt   requires replacement*
3. If the separately mounted power cylinder is internally damaged, then it must   *be disassembled for adjustment   have internal parts replaced   be replaced as a unit*
4. One of the adjustments on the Monroe integral type of power-steering unit is to adjust the   *drag-link stop   pitman-arm stop   relay-closing voltage*
5. If right turn is too hard and left turn too easy on the integral type of power-steering unit, the valve plug should be   *removed   replaced   turned in   turned out*

Servicing Procedures

Write down in your notebook the procedures that are asked for. Do not copy from the book, but write the procedures in your own words just as you might tell a friend. This will help you remember them.

1. Pick a car equipped with separately mounted linkage-type equipment and describe in detail how to remove and replace the power cylinder and valve.
2. Describe how to disassemble and reassemble the valve.
3. Pick a car with the Monroe integral type of power-steering unit and describe how to remove and replace it.
4. Explain how to make the pitman-arm-stop, and the power-link-valve adjustments.
5. List and describe other servicing operations on the Monroe unit.

SUGGESTIONS FOR FURTHER STUDY

When you are in your local school or automotive service shop, examine various linkage types of power-steering equipment. If you have a chance, watch an expert disassemble or service this equipment. Study car manuals which explain how the units are serviced. Be sure to write down in your notebook any important facts you learn.

13: Coaxial and constant-control power-steering service

THIS CHAPTER describes the trouble-shooting, adjusting, removal, repair, and reinstallation of the coaxial and constant-control power-steering units used on Chrysler and De Soto cars. Section 71 described the operation of these units. Chapter 6 discussed trouble-shooting procedures on steering and suspension systems generally. The material that follows carries this a step further into the coaxial power-steering unit and includes complete repair procedures on this equipment.

§168. Trouble-shooting chart   The list, below, of trouble symptoms, causes, and checks or corrections will help you to analyze troubles and locate their causes in the power-steering unit. Later sections then describe procedures required to eliminate the troubles when servicing or repairing the unit.

NOTE: The chart covers the coaxial unit. Troubles on the constant-control unit are somewhat similar except for those special conditions resulting from the differences in construction.

NOTE: Troubles and possible causes are not listed in the chart in the order of frequency of occurrence. That is, item 1 does not necessarily occur more often than item 2, nor does item *a* under Possible Cause necessarily occur more often than item *b*.

TROUBLE-SHOOTING CHART

Complaint	Possible Cause	Check or Correction
1. Hard steering in both directions	a. Leak in hydraulic system	Correct leak, refill
	b. Fluid level low	Check for and correct leak, refill reservoir
	c. Pump belt slipping or broken	Tighten, install new belt
	d. Linkage not lubricated	Lubricate

Complaint	Possible Cause	Check or Correction
	e. Tire pressure low	Inflate tires properly
	f. Oil pressure low	See item 2, Low oil pressure, below
	g. Bind in steering column or gear	Align or adjust
	h. Front alignment off	Align front end
2. Low oil pressure	*a.* Belt loose	Tighten, replace if necessary
	b. Coupling broken	Replace
	c. Pump valve stuck	Free, clean if necessary
	d. Mechanical trouble in pump	Repair or replace pump *
	e. Pressure loss in steering gear	Repair, adjust steering gear
3. Oil leaks	*a.* Hose adapters	Tighten or replace adapters or gaskets
	b. At pump	Repair or replace pump *
	c. Between gear and worm housings	Tighten attaching screws, replace O ring
	d. Gear-shaft oil seal	Replace oil seal
4. Smaller turning radius in one direction	Wheel stops out of adjustment	Readjust wheel stops
5. Hard steering in one direction	*a.* Low tire pressure	Inflate tires properly
	b. Control valve out of adjustment	Readjust
	c. Bind in steering column or gear	Align or readjust
	d. Front alignment off	Realign front end
6. Car attempts to turn unless pressure is maintained on steering wheel	*a.* Tire pressure uneven	Inflate tires properly
	b. Control valve out of adjustment	Readjust

* For pump service, see §§160–162.

Complaint	Possible Cause	Check or Correction
7. Poor centering, or recovery from turns	a. Low tire pressure	Inflate tires properly
	b. Balls in worm connector are binding	Disassemble unit to clear or replace balls and connector
	c. Bind in steering column or gear	Align or readjust
	d. Bind in steering knuckles	Check kingpin and bushings, shim properly
	e. Worm bearing adjustment too tight	Readjust
	f. Front alignment off	Align front end
	g. Gear-shaft adjustment too tight	Adjust
8. Noises	a. Fan belt tension incorrect	Adjust
	b. Fluid level low	Check for leaks, fill oil reservoir
	c. Worn pump bearings	Repair or replace pump *
	d. Dirt or sludge in pump	Disassemble and clean pump,* drain system, refill, change filter element
	e. Noise in power unit	Check for air in system, hose clearance, gear-shaft adjustment

* For pump service, see §§160–162.

NOTE: The oil pressure developed by the oil pump can be checked with a special gauge as explained in §152. Gauge should read at least 600 pounds pressure with steering wheel in either extreme position. If it does not, close valve on gauge. Reading should now be at least 600 pounds. If it is low, the trouble is in the pump as noted in item 2, Low oil pressure, in the chart above. See also §152, 2 on checking the pump.

§169. Lubrication and oil changes The worm housing and the gear housing are separate and sealed off from each other. The worm housing is lubricated by oil added through a filler plug. The gear housing is lubricated by the oil flowing through it from the oil pump; it is actually a part of the hydraulic system. Lubricating the worm housing and draining and refilling the hydraulic system are discussed below.

1. *Checking fluid level in reservoir.* Clean cover or filler cap so dirt will not get into reservoir. Top of reservoir must be clean. Remove cover or cap and note oil level (should be ½ inch above highest point of filter element). Add SAE 10-W oil, as necessary. When temperatures are consistently below −10°F, drain hydraulic system and refill with SAE 5-W oil.

2. *Draining system.* Disconnect high-pressure (small) hose from gear housing and jack up front end of car so wheels are off floor. Put hose in a container; start engine, and allow it to idle. Turn steering wheel from one extreme position to the other until all fluid is forced from the unit. Do not run engine above idle. As soon as fluid starts to show great quantities of bubbles, stop engine. Then reconnect hose and refill reservoir.

3. *Refilling hydraulic system.* Fill reservoir slightly above normal full mark. Start engine and allow to run for a short time so oil is circulated through hoses. With engine idling, turn the steering wheel back and forth from one extreme to the other to bleed any air from system. Check oil level in reservoir and add oil if necessary. Total capacity of system is about 2 quarts.

4. *Worm housing lubrication.* It is not necessary to change oil in the worm housing. However, if the oil level drops, due to leakage, then it should be refilled (through filler-plug opening) with SAE 10-W oil. Fill level with opening. If the steering gear is removed for any reason, the oil can be drained and fresh oil put in after the gear is reinstalled on the car.

§170. Coaxial steering-gear removal

To remove the steering gear from the car, first turn steering wheel to extreme left position. Remove horn-control-ring ornament, cushion, and spring. Disconnect horn wire and remove steering-wheel nut and wheel. (If puller is used to pull wheel, control ring and contact plates will have to be removed.)

Remove steering-gear column-jacket-bearing spring and cone-shaped spacer. Remove three toe-board-cover screws and cover.

Remove accelerator and brake-pedal pads and floor mat. Remove six steering-column-jacket-toe-pad screws and slide toe pad up on jacket assembly. Remove floor-pan pedal-opening cover after taking out cover screws. Disconnect direction-signal indicator, horn, and selector-level indicator light wires.

Disconnect pressure and return hoses from steering-gear housing and cap fittings. Fasten ends of hoses above level of reservoir so oil does not leak out.

Remove cotter pin and disconnect gearshift control rod from rod lever. Remove steering-gear-arm (pitman-arm) nut and use special tool C-143 with short puller screw to remove steering-gear arm and drag link.

Remove access cover in left-front fender shield and remove front lower steering-gear-assembly-to-bracket screw, washer, and convex spacer. Note position of wedge between bracket and gear housing. Working through opening in toe board, remove front upper and rear screws, washers, and convex spacers attaching gear assembly to bracket. Do not lose spacers or wedge.

Hold jacket-and-shroud assembly in position and remove two steering-column-to-instrument-panel screws. Retaining plate and antisqueak pad may fall behind instrument panel when screws are removed.

Lower jacket-and-shroud assembly and remove insulator collar. Push steering-gear-column jacket-and-shroud assembly slightly toward passenger side of vehicle—so that gear shaft clears frame bracket—and remove assembly through toe board opening.

Place assembly on bench, loosen the gearshift-rod-lever nut, and slide lever and spacer off gearshift rod. Loosen two nuts on jacket-clamp assembly, and slide jacket and shroud from worm housing. The spring and the two spring seats may fall from gearshift rod when jacket and shroud are removed. Remove steering-gear-tube insulator pin, tube, and insulator from coupling.

§171. Servicing   Figure 13-1 is a completely disassembled view of the coaxial steering gear. This illustration shows the relative locations of the various parts in the assembly.

DISASSEMBLY

Caution: Extreme care must be used to keep all parts clean. During disassembly, parts should be washed in clean solvent, air-dried,

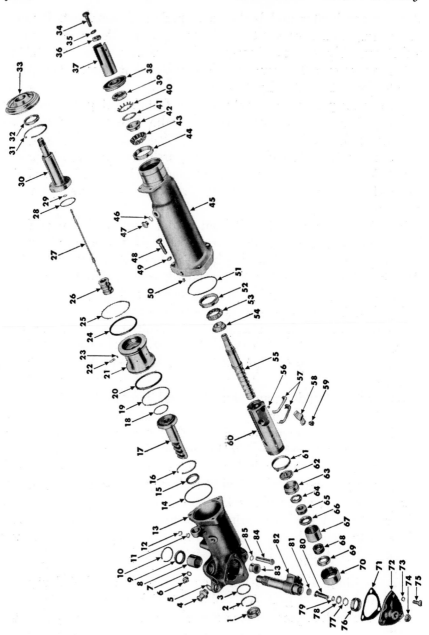

Fig. 13-1. Disassembled view of coaxial power-steering gear. (*De Soto Division of Chrysler Corporation*)

1. Housing cover
2. Housing-cover snap ring
3. Housing-cover O ring
4. Return hose adapter
5. Gasket
6. Pressure hose adapter
7. Gasket
8. Gear housing shaft bearing
9. Gear-shaft oil seal
10. Gear-shaft oil-seal lock ring
11. Roller support pin O ring
12. Piston rod support snap ring
13. Gear housing
14. Housing head O ring
15. Gear housing oil seal
16. Lower piston-rod snap ring
17. Lower piston rod
18. Lower piston-rod O ring
19. Piston ring—steel
20. Piston ring—neoprene
21. Piston
22. Piston pin
23. Piston-pin O ring
24. Piston ring—neoprene
25. Piston ring—steel
26. Valve piston
27. Valve rod
28. Upper piston-rod O ring
29. Valve-rod O ring
30. Upper piston rod
31. Upper piston-rod snap ring
32. Housing-head oil seal
33. Housing head
34. Screw
35. Lock washer
36. Tube coupling washer
37. Tube coupling
38. Worm-housing oil seal
39. Worm-bearing adjusting nut
40. Worm-bearing nut lock washer
41. Worm-bearing washer
42. Worm-bearing race
43. Worm-bearing cage and rollers
44. Worm-bearing cup—upper
45. Worm housing
46. Filler plug gasket
47. Worm-housing filler plug
48. Worm-housing screw
49. Lock washer
50. Worm-housing tube plug
51. Housing-head O ring
52. Worm-bearing cup—lower
53. Worm-bearing cage and rollers
54. Worm-bearing race
55. Worm
56. Worm ball
57. Worm-ball guides
58. Worm-ball-guide clamp
59. Screw and lock washer
60. Worm connector
61. Worm-connector nut lock
62. Valve-rod adjusting disk
63. Adjusting disk retainer
64. Upper piston-rod nut lock cup
65. Upper piston-rod nut
66. Valve-control-spacer-retainer
67. Valve control spacer
68. Valve-control-spacer seal
69. Valve-control-spacer retainer
70. Worm-connector nut
71. Gear-shaft cover gasket
72. Gear-shaft cover
73. Belleville washer
74. Adjusting screw lock nut
75. Gear-shaft cover screw
76. Gear-shaft cover bearing
77. Adjusting-screw snapring
78. Adjusting-screw seal
79. Adjusting-screw O ring
80. Adjusting screw
81. Adjusting-screw thrust washer
82. Gear shaft
83. Piston-rod support bearing
84. Piston-rod support pin
85. O ring

and put aside in a clean place. Do not wipe parts with cloths; lint might adhere and cause trouble later. Handle parts carefully to avoid nicking or burring them. Minor burrs or nicks can be removed with crocus cloth. Do not round off sharp edges of valve spool.

NOTE: Remove and discard all O rings and seals. Use new O rings and seals lubricated with Lubriplate when reassembling steering gear.

1. Drain gear housing through pressure-and-return connections by turning steering-tube coupling from one extreme to the other. Remove worm-housing filler plug and drain worm housing.
2. Attach holding fixture to steering gear and clamp fixture in vise (Fig. 13-2).

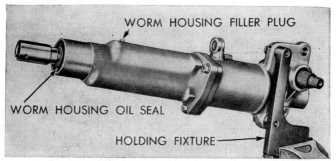

FIG. 13-2. Steering gear attached to special holding fixture clamped in vise. (*De Soto Division of Chrysler Corporation*)

3. Take coupling screw, lock washer, and washer from center of coupling and then use special tool to force coupling off worm shaft (Fig. 13-3). Remove oil seal with a screw driver, being careful to avoid damaging the housing or shaft.
4. Unlock bearing adjusting nut by bending down tang of lock washer. Remove worm-bearing adjusting nut, lock washer, and thrust washer by using two special tools and wrenches. One of the special tools fits on the adjusting nut; the other is a special nut with internal serrations that fit on the serrations of the worm shaft. With these, the worm shaft can be held stationary while the adjusting nut is backed out and removed (Fig. 13-4).
5. Remove three screws and lock washers and take worm housing

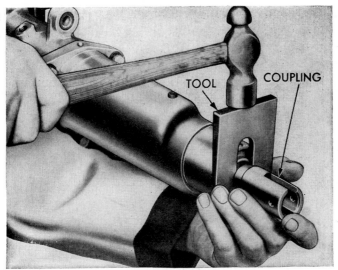

FIG. 13-3. Using special wedge-shaped tool to drive coupling from worm shaft. (*De Soto Division of Chrysler Corporation*)

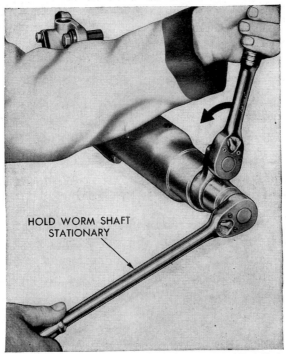

FIG. 13-4. Removing worm-bearing adjusting nut. (*De Soto Division of Chrysler Corporation*)

from assembly. It may be necessary to tap housing with a soft hammer to loosen it from the O ring in the housing head.

6. Remove inner bearing race from worm shaft and the lower bearing roller from housing. Inspect bearing roller and upper and lower bearing cups in housing. Do not remove cups from housing unless it is necessary to replace them. For removal and replacement, see Fig. 13-5.

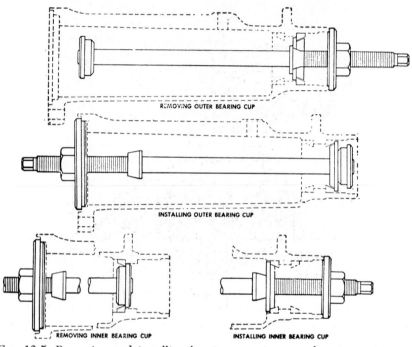

Fɪɢ. 13-5. Removing and installing bearing cups in worm housing, using special tools. (*De Soto Division of Chrysler Corporation*)

7. Remove worm connector by first taking off housing-head O ring and discarding it. Then unlock worm-connector-nut lock and slide lock back so the worm connector nut can be removed. Loosen nut with special tools as shown in Fig. 13-6. Slide worm-connector assembly from valve-control spacer.

8. Disassemble worm connector by removing the two guide-clamp screws, lock washers, clamp, and guide. Do not lose any of the 40 balls. Turn worm connector over and carefully thread the balls out by turning the worm in and out. *Do not*

bottom *worm shaft in either direction*—this could damage ball guides or worm. Remove worm from connector and slide connector-nut lock from connector.

9. Inspect guide rails on connector for nicks and burrs. Check balls for pits or cracks. If any ball is damaged, all 40 balls should be replaced as a set.

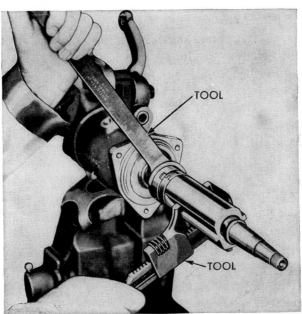

Fig. 13-6. Using special tools to remove the worm-connector nut. Worm connector is held stationary while nut is backed off. (*De Soto Division of Chrysler Corporation*)

10. Remove piston and rods from gear housing by first removing the pressure-and-return hose adapters and copper gaskets. Then remove steering-gear-shaft oil-seal lock ring and oil seal, using special tool. Remove the shaft-adjusting-screw lock nut and take out the three cover screws with lock washers and neoprene seals. Turn in the adjusting screw so the cover can be removed. Remove and discard old cover gasket. Steering-gear shaft can now be removed through the cover opening. Shaft may need to be aligned (use steering arm, if necessary) and tapped free with a fiber hammer. Adjusting screw, thrust washer, and washer may be removed from steering-gear shaft

[351]

by removing small snap ring from recess in shaft. Remove adjusting-screw O ring.

11. Inspect needle bearings in cover for broken needles or for wear and check bearing on shaft for pitting or for wear. If bearings require replacement, replace the cover-and-bearing assembly as a unit.

    Remove gear-housing cover by taking out snap ring. Remove O ring from housing. Put a suitable container under the assembly to catch trapped oil. Slide piston-and-rod assembly from housing. Handle carefully to avoid damaging sealing surfaces on housing head.

12. Start disassembly of piston-and-rod assembly by removing valve-rod adjusting disk from the valve rod. Then slide disk retainer from the upper piston rod. Remove upper piston-rod-nut lock cap. Then use special tool to remove upper piston-rod nut. Use extreme care to avoid damaging the housing head. Support upper piston rod on a block of wood, or wrap several layers of masking tape around the lower piston rod and clamp it in the soft jaws of a vise.

13. With the upper piston-rod nut removed, slide the valve-control spacer, seal assembly, and upper and lower valve-control-spacer seal retainers from the upper piston rod. Remove spacer seal retainers and slide seal assembly from spacer. Remove worm connector nut from upper piston rod.

14. Slide housing head off upper piston rod and remove O ring from head. Use a suitable drift and remove upper piston-rod seal from housing head.

15. Remove the two steel backup rings and D-type piston rings (neoprene) from piston (Fig. 13-7 shows the relationship of these rings).

16. Use special snap-ring pliers and remove lower piston-rod snap ring. Slide rod from piston. Now, slide the valve assembly out of the piston assembly. Do not bend the valve rod.

17. With a ¼-inch punch, drive the piston pin into the upper piston rod. Use snap-ring pliers, remove upper piston-rod snap ring and take rod from piston. Note carefully the type and position of the snap ring.

18. Use a wire hook to remove the piston pin and O ring from the piston rod. Make sure the oil passage is open in the rod. Re-

move the two small O rings in the two ends of the upper piston rod and the large O ring in the piston end of the rod.

19. Remove O ring from lower piston rod. Inspect rack teeth and sealing surfaces and make sure oil passage is open.

20. Inspect piston for nicks and burrs and make sure all oil passages are open.

21. Start the disassembly of the steering-gear housing by removing the piston-rod bearing-support-pin snap ring with snap-ring

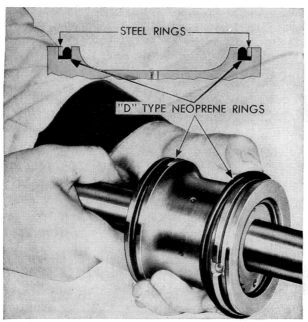

Fig. 13-7. Steel backup rings and neoprene piston rings on piston. (*De Soto Division of Chrysler Corporation*)

pliers. Then slide pin out of housing and remove roller support assembly. Remove two bearing-support-pin O rings, one from each side of the gear housing. Inspect roller and needle bearings and bearing-support pin for wear or other damage. Then inspect the steering-gear-shaft needle bearing in the gear housing for broken or rough needles. Do not remove the bearing unless inspection shows that it must be replaced. In such case, use a special driver and hammer to drive the bearing out. Remove lower piston-rod seal from housing.

[353]

REASSEMBLY AND ADJUSTMENT

New O rings and seals, lubricated with Lubriplate, should be used throughout the unit when it is reassembled.

1. *Assembly of steering-gear housing*

a. Remove garter spring from a new piston-rod seal (to prevent damage to seal during installation) and position seal over special driver, lip facing up or to inside of cylinder when installed. Insert seal-aligning pilot of tool in end of driver and drive seal into position. Then replace garter spring in seal.

b. If steering-gear-shaft needle bearing has been removed, install bearing with special driver. Drive in until marking on driver is even with side of housing. Always drive on letter side of bearing to avoid damaging it.

c. Install two piston-rod bearing-support-pin O rings after lubricating them with Lubriplate, and make sure they seal in housing. Start support pin through hole in cover side of housing. Put roller-support assembly in position in housing and push pin through roller support and opposite side of housing. Secure with snap ring.

2. *Assembly of piston and rods*

a. Lubricate the two valve-rod O rings with Lubriplate and install in ends of upper piston rod. Make sure rings seat. Lubricate two large O rings with Lubriplate and install one on each of the piston rods—upper and lower. Make sure they seat.

b. Install lower rod in lower end of piston (the end of the piston without a piston-pin hole), using snap ring. Note that a minimum gap of $^{25}/_{64}$ inch is specified. Gap must be located at the middle port of the five ports but must not obstruct the middle or adjacent ports. Snap ring must seat properly.

c. Lubricate valve assembly with Lubriplate and slide into piston. Then slide upper piston rod over valve rod, aligning piston-pin hole with hole in the piston rod. Lubricate O ring with Lubriplate and install on piston pin. Put pin, tapered end first, into piston-and-rod hole and tap down with a ¼-inch punch until pin is flush with bottom of ring groove.

d. Install upper piston-rod snap ring, using same precautions as noted in item b, above.

e. Install upper piston-rod seal in housing head as follows: take garter spring off seal, put seal on driver (lip of seal facing tool), and insert seal-aligning pilot in end of driver. Drive into housing head, replace garter spring, and lubricate seal with Lubriplate.

f. Install housing head (sealing lip first) onto upper piston rod. Use same precautions as during disassembly to protect the sealing surfaces on the housing head.

g. Slide connector nut onto upper piston rod, open end away from piston.

h. Lubricate valve-control-spacer seal with Lubriplate and install in center of spacer. Put protective tool over threaded end of upper piston rod. Install seal retainers in spacer and slide assembly into position over tool and onto piston rod. Install rod nut and tighten to 25 to 30 lb-ft. Lock in place with nut lock; tap outer diameter of lock into nut recess.

i. Slide valve-rod-adjusting disk retainer, large diameter first, over end of upper piston rod. Thread valve-rod disk (extended lock-thread section out) onto valve rod until about three threads show.

j. Place lock ring on worm connector (tang of ring toward threaded side). Slide worm connector—without ball bearings and worm shaft—over valve-control spacer and screw worm-connector nut on to connector. Hold worm connector stationary and tighten nut with special tools as shown in Fig. 13-6. Stake lock ring with punch.

k. Lubricate D rings with Lubriplate and install on piston (Fig. 13-7). Then install steel backup rings.

3. *Installation of piston-and-rod assembly in housing*

a. Lubricate lower piston rod, teeth, and installing tool with Lubriplate. Put installing tool on teeth and ring-compressing tool on housing. Make sure rack teeth will align with sector teeth on steering-gear shaft and install assembly in housing.

> **Caution:** Be extremely careful to avoid damaging oil seal or rings.

b. Remove tools. Lubricate large O ring with Lubriplate and install it on side of housing head facing the piston assembly.

c. Carefully slide special tool (dummy housing) over worm connector, make sure housing head seats in gear housing, and secure special tool to gear housing with three screws (tighten to 25 to 30 lb-ft). See Fig. 13-8.

d. Install thrust washer on gear-shaft adjusting screw. Position tool over threaded end of screw. Lubricate adjusting-screw O ring with Lubriplate and slide it over tool and into position on screw. Remove tool and insert thrust washer into recess in steering-gear shaft. Then insert end of screw and lock into position with snap ring. Screw adjusting screw (gear attached) into cover assembly as far as possible. Center the second tooth of the rack over the bearing-support pin. Lubricate new cover

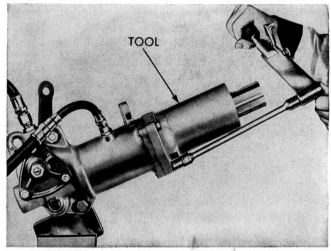

TOOL

Fig. 13-8. Attaching dummy housing (a special tool) to gear housing. (*De Soto Division of Chrysler Corporation*)

gasket with Lubriplate (to hold it in place) and put it on cover.

e. Center the middle tooth on the gear shaft with the second tooth space from end of rack. Insert gear-shaft assembly (with cover) into gear housing and tap into position with plastic hammer. Put lock washers and new seals on screws (concave side of washers toward housing) and tighten screws to 25 to 30 lb-ft.

f. Lubricate gear-housing-cover O ring with Lubriplate and install on housing cover. Push assembly, seal end first, into housing and install snap ring.

g. Install new steering-gear-shaft seal by first cleaning the sealing surfaces on the gear shaft and the counterbore in the steering-gear housing. Then lubricate seal with Lubriplate and put it, lip down, on a clean piece of paper. Carefully insert tapered end of sleeve (part of special tool) in seal and slide seal up about one-half inch on sleeve. Install sleeve over steering-gear shaft until seal contacts counterbore in housing. Install adapter (part of tool) over sleeve and push seal into

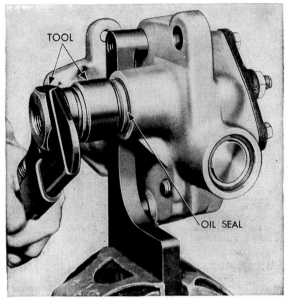

Fig. 13-9. Installing steering-gear-shaft seal with special sleeve and adapter. (*De Soto Division of Chrysler Corporation*)

position by turning coupling nut onto shaft threads (Fig. 13-9). Tighten until shoulder of adapter contacts housing. Remove nut and adapter. Wrap a piece of friction tape around sleeve so you can get a good grip on it and then, with a twisting motion, remove the sleeve. Install seal lock ring.

h. Install gear-shaft-adjusting-screw lock nut, but do not tighten it.

i. Make preliminary adjustment of adjusting screw as follows. Install steering-gear arm on shaft with lock washer and nut and tighten nut to 30 to 40 lb-ft. Work arm back and forth

[357]

so piston is moved from one extreme to the other. Turn adjusting screw if necessary so there is backlash.

4. *Centering the steering gear.* With car close to bench where steering gear is mounted in vise, connect pump in car to steering gear with special hoses. Pressure gauge should be connected in pressure line. Then proceed as follows:

a. Add oil to pump reservoir so proper oil level will be attained when extra hoses and gear assembly are filled. Open shutoff valve at gauge and start engine. Allow engine to operate long enough to fill hoses and gear assembly.

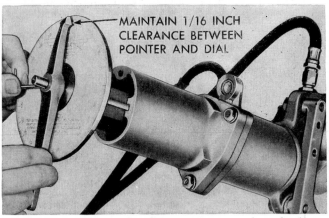

MAINTAIN 1/16 INCH CLEARANCE BETWEEN POINTER AND DIAL

Fig. 13-10. Installing adjusting handle on extension rod to check steering-gear centering. (*De Soto Division of Chrysler Corporation*)

b. Put alignment cap and dial over worm connector and lock into position with thumbscrew. Insert extension rod through alignment cap and over the valve-adjusting rod in the bottom of the worm connector. Tap the extension rod lightly so it is a tight fit on the valve-adjusting rod. Position the adjusting handle on the extension rod so there is about one-sixteenth inch clearance between it and the dial. Tighten set screw in handle (Fig. 13-10). Now turn the handle to adjust valve so pressure in hydraulic system is at a minimum. This is the center position.

Caution: Do not apply heavy pressure to adjusting handle as this could twist off the valve-adjusting rod.

c. Rotate handle slowly until piston moves to one extreme position. Then turn handle in the other direction until piston moves to other extreme. This purges air from system. Repeat several times. Then check pump reservoir and add more oil if necessary.

d. With engine idling, close shutoff valve momentarily to check pump pressure. It should be about 750 psi. Open valve.

e. Turn adjusting handle until the steering-gear arm reaches its center of travel and minimum pressure is noted on the gauge. Slowly turn the handle in one direction until the arm just starts to move. Note the position, in degrees, of the handle pointer on the dial. Turn handle in the opposite direction until arm starts to move, at same speed, in the other direction. Again note the position, in degrees, of the handle pointer on the dial. Set the handle in centered position between the two degree readings. This is the centered position of the valve. Repeat the check two or three times to make sure the centering is correct. Then leave the valve in the centered position. Stop engine, remove adjusting handle, extension, and alignment cap.

> **Caution:** Do not change position of valve-adjusting rod when removing tools.

f. Take dummy housing off by removing the three screws (see Fig. 13-8).

5. *Assembly of worm connector*

a. Insert worm into connector and align upper part of spiral grooves with ball-guide holes. Insert 30 balls into lower hole by tapping them in gently (using eraser end of pencil or similar object). Turn worm back and forth a few degrees to help. With 30 balls in, one should be visible at the other hole.

> **Caution:** Balls are a select fit with each other. If one ball is damaged or lost, use a complete new set.

b. Put remaining 10 balls in either half of the worm-connector ball guide, holding the end balls in with grease. Put other half of guide in place. Insert ends of guide into holes in worm connector and push guide down into place. Secure with clamp, two lock washers, and two screws, tightened to 10 to 12 lb-ft.

c. Check operation of worm to make sure it is free by turning it first one way and then the other.

[359]

Caution: Do not bottom worm since this could damage the guide.

6. *Installation of worm housing*

a. If bearing cups were removed, cups should be installed as shown in Fig. 13-5.

b. Lubricate worm-housing inner-bearing race and slide it over threaded end of worm until it seats.

c. Lubricate worm-connector guide rails with Lubriplate. Lubricate upper-housing O ring with Lubriplate and install on housing-head pilot.

d. Drop inner bearing into housing and hold it into place. Rotate worm connector so ball guide is in downward position. Pilot the worm housing over the guide rails on the worm connector. Attach housing with three screws and lock washers, tightening screws to 20-30 lb-ft.

e. Lubricate outer bearing and race with Lubriplate and install them. Slide thrust washer and lock washer against outer race.

f. Turn worm shaft out until lower race seats in bearing. Then install worm-housing-bearing adjusting nut, tapered end first.

g. Adjust the adjusting nut as follows. Put special tools over shaft. The inner tool fits over the adjusting nut, and the outer tool fits over the worm-shaft serrations. Use two torque wrenches as shown in Fig. 13-11. First, turn the worm shaft clockwise to 20 lb-ft torque (this seats the inner bearing) and hold it at this tension. Then with second torque wrench, tighten the adjusting nut to 15 lb-ft. Now, rotate the worm shaft back and forth several turns to assure proper seating of bearings. Loosen the adjusting nut. Hold the worm shaft at 5 lb-ft tension (clockwise) and tighten nut *to 5 pound-inches* (*not* lb-ft). Lock adjusting nut in position by bending tang of lock washer to index with slot in the nut. Note that only one tang is needed to lock the nut.

h. Install worm-housing oil seal, lip in, with special driver.

i. Add 18 ounces of SAE 10-W oil to worm housing through filler hole; install filler plug and tighten to 50 pound-inches.

7. *Gear backlash adjustment.* During this adjustment, the backlash between the sector on the steering-gear shaft and the rack on the lower piston rod is adjusted by turning the adjusting screw.

a. Start engine and then use special tool that fits serrations on end of worm shaft to turn the worm shaft. Turn worm shaft from one extreme of its travel to the other and count the number of turns. It should be approximately three and three-fourths turns. Then turn back from one extreme one and seven-eighths turns. This is approximate center. Now, remove the tool and install the tube coupling with the slot vertical (vertical when

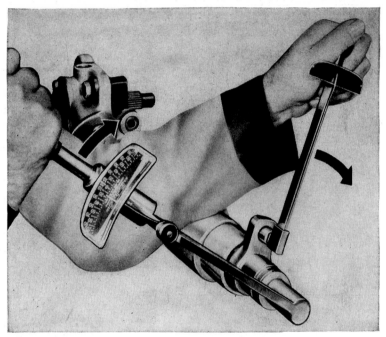

Fig. 13-11. Adjusting worm-housing-bearing adjusting nut. (*De Soto Division of Chrysler Corporation*)

the steering gear is installed on the car). Do not install screw and washer.

b. Rather than refer to the coupling positions in terms of degrees, it is easier to refer to them in terms of a clock. For instance, 90 degrees from vertical would be either three o'clock or nine o'clock, depending on whether it was clockwise or counterclockwise from vertical. Likewise, 150 degrees clockwise from vertical would be five o'clock, and 150 degrees counterclockwise from vertical would be seven o'clock.

c. Turn coupling from centered position to five o'clock and adjust the steering-gear-shaft adjusting screw, if necessary, to get some backlash. (This is backlash between the rack on the piston rod and the shaft sector.) Then, using the steering-gear arm to check backlash, readjust to reduce backlash to zero.

NOTE: When checking backlash, use a very light touch—a feather touch. Greater effort will cause other parts in the assembly to move and give a false sense of backlash.

d. Now, recenter the steering gear and turn the coupling counterclockwise past seven o'clock. Keep turning and testing for backlash. When you detect backlash, turn coupling back toward center, continuing to check for backlash. It should disappear as the coupling passes through seven o'clock.

NOTE: The no-backlash arc should be a total of 300 degrees, or 150 degrees on each side of center.

e. Suppose the backlash does not disappear until the coupling passes through nine o'clock. This means the adjustment is too loose (by a 60-degree arc, or from seven to nine o'clock). Also, the coupling is not centered. To correct the adjustment, return the coupling to the original centered position. Then divide in half the number of degrees that the adjustment is too loose (in this case 60 degrees divided by 2, or 30 degrees). Now, remove the coupling, turn it clockwise 30 degrees (or to one o'clock) and reinstall it on the worm shaft. Now, when it—and the worm shaft—is turned back to twelve o'clock, the gear will be centered in the no-backlash arc. That is, the backlash will appear at the same number of degrees either clockwise or counterclockwise.

f. Now, again turn the coupling to five o'clock and adjust the backlash to zero, as in item c, above. Recenter the coupling and turn counterclockwise past seven o'clock. Then check for backlash as in item d, above. Backlash now should disappear as coupling is moved through seven o'clock toward center.

Caution: Coupling slot must be centered in the no-backlash arc and not at center of over-all travel.

g. With adjustments complete, stop engine and tighten adjusting-screw lock nut to 40 lb-ft.

h. Install coupling screw and lock washer, tightening to 15 to 20 lb-ft.

i. Remove special hoses and adapters.

j. Install pressure hose connector and gasket on steering gear, tightening to 18 to 22 lb-ft. Install return hose connector and copper gasket, tightening to 25 to 30 lb-ft.

k. Cap fittings to prevent loss of oil. Remove steering-gear arm and take assembly from holding fixture in preparation for installing it on vehicle.

§172. Installation and alignment

1. Center gear to center of no-backlash arc (coupling slot vertical). Put tube insulator on tube and position tube and insulator on coupling. Master serration on steering-wheel end of tube should be up. Install pin.

2. When the jacket and shroud are installed, the horn-connector contact point will have to be raised. This provides clearance between it and the contact ring on the steering tube. Raise the contact point with a wire bent into a hook. Bend other end of wire over shroud to hold it.

   NOTE: It may be necessary to remove lower half of shroud from jacket and remove horn connector from jacket. Then, after the jacket is installed over the steering-gear tube, the horn connector can be reinstalled.

3. Put gearshift-rod-spring seats in spring (flanges facing inside of spring) and slide spring and seats over rod.

4. Slide jacket-and-shroud assembly over tube, guiding gearshift rod into bushing on gear housing.

5. Tighten two nuts on jacket-clamp assembly and remove the wire holding the horn contact point.

6. Install steering-gear assembly through toe-board opening. Push column-and-jacket assembly slightly toward passenger side of car to allow gear shaft to clear frame bracket.

7. Install front upper and rear gear-housing-to-bracket convex spacers, screws, and washers through opening in floor pan. Tighten to snug and back off one turn. Position insulator collar on upper shroud and align jacket-and-shroud assembly with instrument panel. Secure with two screws. Now, tighten the front upper and rear gear-housing-to-bracket screws to 70 lb-ft.

[363]

8. Install the front lower steering-gear-housing-to-bracket spacer, washer, and screw but leave screw loose. Tap wedge into position at this screw between bracket and gear housing (Fig. 13-12). Make sure wedge is properly positioned, as shown. Tighten screw to 70 lb-ft.

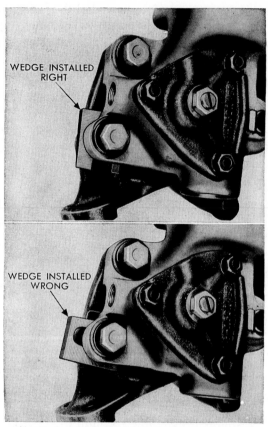

Fig. 13-12. Installing steering-gear-housing-bracket wedge. (*De Soto Division of Chrysler Corporation*)

9. Replace access cover in left-front fender shield.
10. Install steering-gear arm and drag link, tighten arm nut to 100 to 120 lb-ft.
11. Connect direction-signal indicator, horn, and selector-lever indicator light wires.

12. Install steering-column-jacket-bearing spacer (cone-shaped) and spring.

13. Install steering wheel and connect horn wire. Install horn control spring, cushion, and ornament.

14. Check clearance between steering-wheel hub and direction-signal housing. If it is not ⅛ inch, loosen the two column-jacket-to-instrument-panel screws slightly, loosen the two nuts on the jacket-clamp assembly (at top of worm housing), and slide jacket up or down as necessary to get ⅛ inch clearance. Retighten screws and nuts.

15. Slide gearshift-rod-lever spacer and lever on rod. Position selector lever in low or reverse, hold gearshift-rod lever and spacer flush against gear housing, and tighten nut. Make sure selector lever remains in low or reverse while tightening nut. Check operation by shifting selector lever to all positions. Connect gearshift control rod to lever and install cotter pin.

16. Remove protective caps from fittings in gear housing and connect hoses. Remove reservoir cover or filler cap and fill reservoir to proper level. Start engine and turn steering wheel from one extreme to the other several times to purge air from system. Note operation of steering gear.

17. Install floor-pan pedal-opening cover, steering-column toe pad, floor mat, and the accelerator and brake pedal pads. Put cover on shroud and install three screws.

18. Recheck oil level and add oil if necessary.

19. Adjust gearshift control rod, if necessary, as follows. Disconnect rod at bell crank on transmission. Make sure manual control lever at transmission is in neutral (second detent position from rear). Now, with selector-lever pointer still in neutral, adjust gearshift control rod to the required length to fit freely into the lever of the bell crank. Then reinstall rod. Operate selector lever through all indicator positions and road-test the car.

§173. Constant-control power-steering service   This section describes the servicing of the power-steering unit described and illustrated in §71.

1. Removal. Disconnect battery ground cable and horn wire. Remove horn button and steering wheel. Disconnect direction-signal

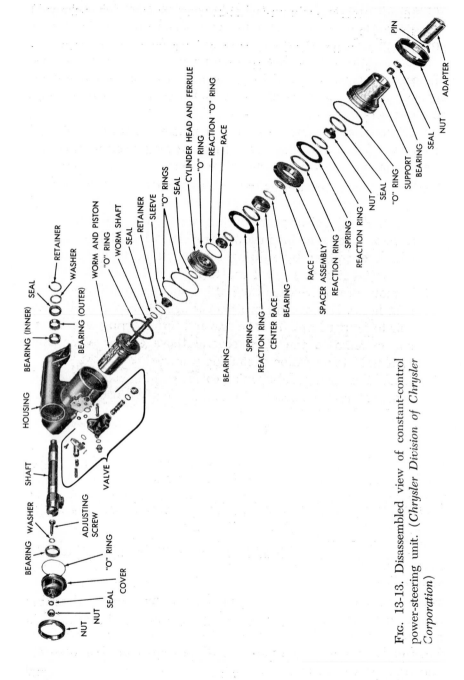

Fig. 13-13. Disassembled view of constant-control power-steering unit. (*Chrysler Division of Chrysler Corporation*)

wires at connectors. Remove jacket-tube-support bracket and loosen two bolts attaching jacket tube to steering housing so jacket can be pushed upward and steering-tube coupling pin can be removed.

Remove cotter key and nut at steering-arm ball joint. Disconnect oil hoses and cap hoses and fittings on steering gear. Remove steering-arm nut and use special tool to pull arm from shaft. Remove bolts and steering gear.

2. *Disassembly*. Figure 13-13 is a completely disassembled view of the unit. To disassemble, drain oil by turning steering-tube coupling from one extreme to the other. Remove coupling pin and coupling, valve body (and three O rings), and valve lever (pry

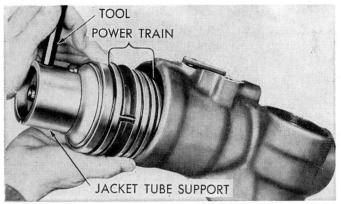

Fig. 13-14. Removing power train. (*Chrysler Division of Chrysler Corporation*)

under spherical head but do not use pliers). Loosen gear-shaft adjusting-screw lock nut and remove cover nut. Rotate worm shaft to full right turn; then return worm shaft and piston to center of travel and remove gear shaft and cover. Remove steering-column support nut and tanged washer.

Put a drift or pin through holes in jacket support and worm shaft and pull power train as a unit from housing (Fig. 13-14). Put power train in soft jaws of vise and remove jacket-support assembly, reaction spring and ring, spacer, O ring, and spacer. Keep worm from turning and turn nut to left to shear staked part of nut. Pick out bit of metal from notch in worm shaft. Then remove thrust-bearing nut, thrust-bearing race (thin), lower thrust bearing, lower race (thick), reaction ring, and spring.

The oil seal and reaction seal can be removed from the column jacket-support assembly, if necessary. Apply air pressure to the ferrule chamber to blow out reaction seal (after removing O ring). Likewise, air pressure is used to remove reaction ring from the cylinder head (applied to oil hole between the two O-ring grooves). O rings must be removed first.

Figure 13-15 is a disassembled view of the control valve. Follow

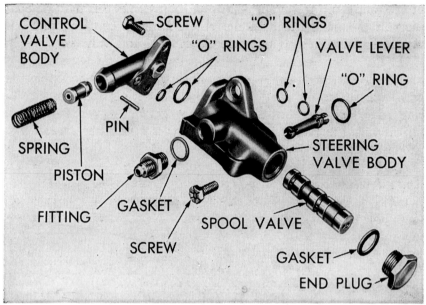

FIG. 13-15. Disassembled view of control-valve assembly. (*Chrysler Division of Chrysler Corporation*)

this illustration when disassembling the valve. Seals can be replaced in the steering gear housing by use of special tools.

3. *Reassembly.* Reassembly procedures on most components have already been indicated or are obvious. All new O rings and seals must be used on reassembly, and all parts should be lubricated with petrolatum during reassembly.

To reassemble the power train, first put piston assembly on bench, worm shaft up. Put cylinder head, ferrule up, on worm shaft and against piston flange. Make sure gap on worm-shaft ring is closed to avoid breaking shaft seal ring. Then install lower bearing race (thick), bearing, reaction spring and ring (flange up), and center bearing race (index lever holes). Install outer spacer, upper thrust bearing, race (thin), and a new worm-shaft thrust-bearing nut. Tighten nut by turning worm shaft counterclockwise one-half turn, hold shaft, and tighten nut to 10 lb-ft torque. (Do not turn worm shaft more than one-half turn!) Rotate worm center bearing race several turns to position parts, loosen adjusting nut, and retighten to give a bearing torque of 8 to 16 ounces. Check this by wrapping cord around the center bearing race and measure pull required to turn the race with a spring scale. Stake nut into slot in worm shaft.

Install center bearing spacer, engaging dowel pin with slot. Put reaction rings over center spacer and install upper reaction spring with cylinder-head ferrule through hole in spring. Install a new O ring in ferrule groove. Install jacket support, engaging cylinder-head ferrule and O rings, making sure reaction rings enter groove in jacket support. Align parts so valve-lever hole in center bearing spacer is 90 degrees from piston-rack teeth. Lock parts to worm shaft with a drill rod through jacket support and worm-shaft holes.

Install power train in housing with center-bearing-spacer valve-lever hole up. Align hole with clearance hole in housing with aligning tool. Install column support spanner nut and tighten to 150 lb-ft. Set piston at center of travel and install gear shaft and cover. Install cover spanner nut and tighten to 100 lb-ft. Install valve lever and valve body. Be sure three O rings are in place.

4. Adjustments. Back off gear-shaft adjusting screw. With steering unit in test fixture, connect test hoses to hydraulic pump on car with pressure gauge to check pressures. With pressure applied, position steering valve by tapping lightly on one of the pressure-control valve screws or on valve end plug. This should give equal gear-shaft torque (within 5 lb-ft and not to exceed 20 lb-ft in either direction) when shaft is slowly turned.

With gear shaft on center, tighten the adjusting screw until backlash just disappears. Tighten screw 1¼ turns; then hold it and tighten lock nut. Check operation of unit and oil pressure.

Readjust gear-shaft backlash by loosening adjusting screw until backlash is evident. Retighten until backlash disappears and then tighten further ⅜ to ½ turn. Tighten lock nut to 50 lb-ft.

Steering valve must be positioned to give equal torque. Test torque by turning worm shaft one turn either side of center and checking torque required to turn shaft through center. If it varies more than 5 lb-ft from left to right, shift the steering valve to get equal torque and tighten attaching screws to 15 lb-ft.

5. *Adding oil.* Installation of the unit is essentially the reverse of removal. After installation, fill oil reservoir in pump, start engine, and let it idle until the steering gear is up to operating temperature. Turn steering wheel to right and left to expel air. Refill reservoir.

CHAPTER CHECKUP

The chapter you have just finished completes the discussion in the book of the different steering systems used on modern automobiles. No doubt there will be still different power-steering mechanisms brought out on future cars. However, if you know the fundamentals discussed in the last few chapters, you will have no difficulty in understanding how the new steering gears operate and how they are to be serviced. In order for you to check up on yourself and find out how well you remember what you have just been studying, the following test has been included.

Correcting Trouble Lists

The purpose of this exercise is to help you spot related and unrelated troubles on a list. Refer to the test instructions at the end of Chap. 10 for an explanation of how to take this test.

Write down the lists in your notebook, but do not write down the item that does not belong.

1. Hard steering in both directions: front alignment off, bind in steering column or gear, oil pressure low, tire pressure low, fluid level high.
2. Low oil pressure: belt loose, coupling broken, pump valve stuck, mechanical trouble in pump, engine idle excessive, pressure loss in steering gear.
3. Hard steering in one direction: low tire pressure, control valve out of adjustment, bind in steering column or gear, front alignment off, excessive oil pressure.
4. Poor centering or recovery from turns: low tire pressure, balls in worm connector binding, bind in steering column or gear, bind in steering knuckles, worm-bearing adjustment too tight, front alignment off, pump valve stuck, gear-shaft adjustment too tight.

5. Car attempts to turn unless pressure is maintained on steering wheel: uneven tire pressure, control valve out of adjustment, gear-shaft adjustment too tight.

Completing the Sentences

The sentences below are incomplete. After each sentence there are several words or phrases, only one of which will correctly complete the sentence. Write down each sentence in your notebook, selecting the proper word or phrase to complete it correctly.

1. The worm housing is lubricated   *from the hydraulic system   separately   with long-fiber grease*
2. The gear housing is lubricated   *from the hydraulic system   from the worm housing   through a high-pressure grease fitting*
3. During disassembly of the steering gear, the old O rings and seals should be   *cleaned and reused   greased and reused   thrown away*
4. When centering the steering gear, it must be   *on the car   connected to pump   completely assembled   connected to steering linkage*
5. The worm bearings are adjusted by   *installing shims   turning an adjusting screw   turning an adjusting nut*
6. In the gear backlash adjustment, the backlash is set between the sector on the steering-gear shaft and the   *rack on lower piston rod   steering-gear arm   control-valve rod   upper piston-rod rack*
7. When the gear-backlash adjustment is complete, the coupling slot must be centered in the   *center of overall travel   center of piston travel   center of the no-backlash arc*
8. The no-backlash arc should be a total of   *130 degrees   150 degrees   300 degrees   600 degrees*

Servicing Procedures

Write down in your notebook the procedures that are asked for. Do not copy from the book, but write the procedures in your own words just as you might explain them to a friend. This will help you to remember them.

1. Describe the procedure for removing the coaxial power-steering unit from a car.
2. Explain how to drain and refill the hydraulic system.
3. Explain how to lubricate the worm housing.

[371]

4. List the main steps in disassembling the coaxial power-steering unit.
5. List the main steps in assembling the unit.
6. Explain how to center the steering gear (that is, center the valve).
7. Explain how to adjust the gear backlash.
8. List the major steps in installing the steering gear on a car.

SUGGESTIONS FOR FURTHER STUDY

If you can, examine the complete assembly and the parts that go into it. Your local school or automotive service shop may have an assembly, or parts of one, that you can examine. If possible, be on hand when the unit is being serviced. Notice carefully how the job is done. Study the repair manual issued by the manufacturer if you can locate one. Be sure to write down in your notebook any important facts you learn.

14: Automotive brakes

THIS CHAPTER describes the construction and operation of the various types of brakes used on automobiles. The chapters that follow explain how to service brakes. Since the great majority of brakes in use today are hydraulically actuated, the chapter reviews hydraulic principles and explains their application to brakes.

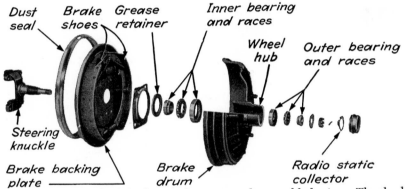

Dust seal

Brake shoes

Grease retainer

Inner bearing and races

Wheel hub

Outer bearing and races

Steering knuckle

Brake backing plate

Brake drum

Radio static collector

FIG. 14-1. Front-wheel brake mechanism in disassembled view. The brake drum and wheel hub are partly cut away. (*Cadillac Motor Car Division of General Motors Corporation*)

§174. Function and types of brakes   Brakes are devices for slowing and stopping the car. They may be operated by mechanical, hydraulic, air-pressure, or electrical devices. Essentially, however, all function in the same manner. The operating device forces brake shoes against the rotating brake drums at the wheels when the driver operates the brake pedal (§33). Friction between the brake shoes and the brake drums then slows or stops the wheels so that the car is braked. You should reread §§16 to 21 on friction if you do not remember the details of frictional action.

Figure 14-1 shows a front-wheel brake mechanism in disassembled view so that the relationship of the parts can be seen. When the mechanism is assembled, the brake drum fits around the brake

[373]

shoes as shown in Fig. 2-16. Figure 14-2 shows a rear-wheel brake mechanism in disassembled view.

The brake shoes are lined with an asbestos material that can withstand the heat and dragging effect imposed when the shoes are forced against the brake drum. During hard braking, the shoe may be pressed against the drum with a pressure of as much as 1,000 pounds. Since friction increases as the load, or pressure, increases (§17), a strong frictional drag is produced on the brake drum and a strong braking effect on the wheel.

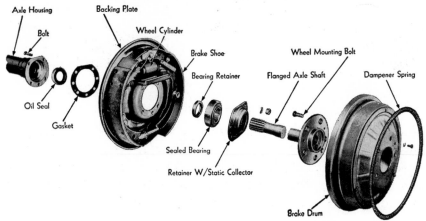

Fig. 14-2. Rear-wheel brake mechanism in disassembled view, showing attaching arrangement. (*Cadillac Motor Car Division of General Motors Corporation*)

A great deal of heat is produced, also, by the frictional effect between the brake shoes and drum. When you rub your hands together vigorously, they become warm. In a similar manner, when the drum rubs against the shoe, the drum and shoe get warm. In fact, under extreme braking conditions, temperatures may reach 500°F. Some of this heat goes through the brake linings to the shoes and backing plate where it is radiated to the surrounding air. But most of it is absorbed by the brake drum. Some brake drums have cooling fins to provide additional radiating surface for dispelling the heat more readily. Excessive temperature is not good for brakes since it may char the brake lining; also, with the lining and shoes hot, less effective braking action results. This is the reason that brakes "fade" when they are used continuously for relatively long periods, as they are, for instance, when coming down a mountain or long slope.

[374]

§175. Mechanical brakes Mechanical brakes are no longer widely used for braking or stopping the car, although almost all cars have a mechanically operated parking brake. Mechanical brakes incorpo-

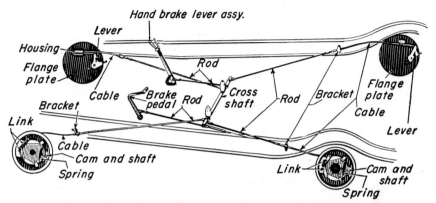

FIG. 14-3. Mechanically operated four-wheel brake system.

rate cables that link the brake pedal with the brake-shoe operating devices. Figure 14-3 illustrates a mechanically operated four-wheel brake system. Pressing down on the brake pedal pulls against cables attached to the brake-shoe expanding devices. The brake-shoe expanding device consists of a lever or cam that is actuated or

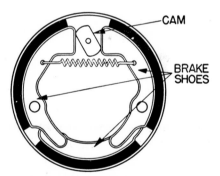

FIG. 14-4. Brake-shoe actuating device. Pull of a cable from the brake pedal rotates the cam. The cam, as it rotates, forces the ends of the shoes outward and into contact with the brake drum.

rotated to push one end of the brake shoe out. The other end of the brake shoe is attached to the brake backing plate by an anchor pin. Figure 14-4 illustrates one type of cam-operated brake shoe.

Mechanically operated parking brakes on most cars make use of a hand brake connected by cables to the rear-wheel brake shoes or to a separate brake that is part of the transmission shaft. Figure 14-5 illustrates the layout of a parking brake that makes use of the two rear-wheel brakes. The hand lever, when pulled, pulls cables that operate levers in the two rear-wheel brake mechanisms. The levers, as they operate, force the brake shoes apart and into contact with the brake drum.

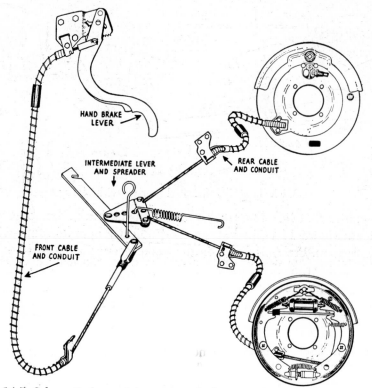

FIG. 14-5. Schematic layout of a parking-brake system. Operation of the hand-brake lever causes the intermediate lever to pivot forward. This pulls on the two rear cables so the rear brakes are mechanically applied. (*Pontiac Motor Division of General Motors Corporation*)

Figure 14-6 illustrates a transmission-shaft brake operated by a hand lever. Operation of the hand lever contracts the brake band so that it is compressed against the brake drum. The brake drum is mounted on the transmission shaft and, when it is held by the brake band, it prevents rotation of the rear wheels—which are mechanically coupled to the transmission shaft through the differential and propeller shaft. A variation of this design uses brake shoes that move out against a brake drum (Fig. 15-18).

[376]

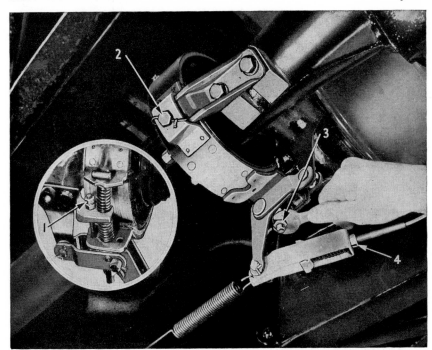

FIG. 14-6. Parking-brake system using auxiliary brake band and brake drum on the transmission shaft: 1, guide-bolt adjusting nut and lock nut; 2, anchor screw; 3, adjusting-bolt nut; 4, hand-brake-cable lock nut. (*Plymouth Division of Chrysler Corporation*)

§**176. Hydraulic principles** Since most brakes are hydraulically operated, we might review briefly the hydraulic principles that cause them to operate. Sections 12 to 15 describe the manner in which motion and pressure can be transmitted by liquid. Since liquid is not compressible, pressure on a liquid will force it through a tube and into chambers or cylinders where it can force pistons to move. This is shown graphically in Fig. 1-12 where a piston in a cylinder applies a pressure of 100 psi (pounds per square inch). In the illustration, liquid is shown being forced through lines or tubes to three other cylinders. The force the liquid applies to the pistons in the three cylinders is proportional to the size of the pistons. When the piston has an area of 1 square inch, there will be a force of 100 pounds on it (100 psi, in other words). If the piston has an area of 0.5 square inch, the force on it will be 50 lb (100 psi × 0.5 square inch). If the piston has an area of 2 square inches, the force on it

[377]

will be 200 lb (100 psi $\times$ 2 square inches). You might wish to review §§12 to 15 if these fundamentals are not clear in your mind.

§177. Hydraulic brake action Hydraulic brakes make use of the pressure of a liquid (hydraulic pressure) to force the brake shoes outward and against the brake drums. Figure 14-7 illustrates schematically a typical hydraulic braking system. The system consists essentially of two components: the brake pedal with master cylinder, and the wheel brake mechanisms, together with the connecting tubing or brake lines and the supporting arrangements.

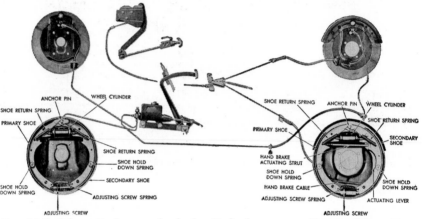

FIG. 14-7. Schematic layout of a hydraulic brake system. (*Pontiac Motor Division of General Motors Corporation*)

In operation, movement of the brake pedal forces a piston to move in the master cylinder. This applies pressure to liquid ahead of the piston, forcing the liquid—under pressure—through the brake lines to the wheel cylinders (Fig. 14-8). Each wheel cylinder has two pistons, as shown. Each piston is linked to one of the brake shoes by an actuating pin. Thus, when the liquid is forced into the wheel cylinders, the two wheel-cylinder pistons are pushed outward. This outward movement forces the brake shoes outward and into contact with the brake drum.

Note that, in Fig. 14-8, piston sizes and hydraulic pressures are given as examples of the pressures involved. The piston in the master cylinder has an area of 0.8 square inch. A push of 800 pounds is being applied to the piston. This gives a pressure of 1,000 psi in the system. This pressure at the rear wheels gives an outward

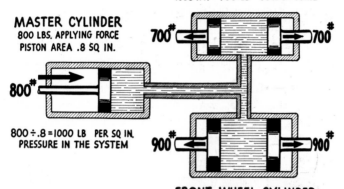

Fig. 14-8. As the brake pedal is moved, the piston in the master cylinder applies pressure to the liquid, forcing it, under pressure, into the wheel cylinders. (*Pontiac Motor Division of General Motors Corporation*)

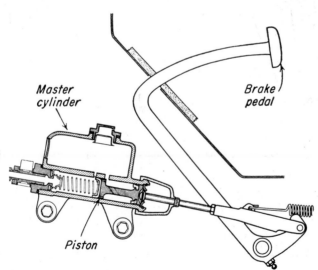

Fig. 14-9. Relationship between brake pedal and master cylinder. (*Pontiac Motor Division of General Motors Corporation*)

force of 700 pounds on each piston. The pistons are 0.7 square inch in area. At the front wheels, the piston area is shown to be 0.9 square inch, so that a pressure of 900 pounds is applied by the pistons to the front brake shoes.

The pistons are usually larger at the front wheels because, when the brakes are applied, the forward momentum of the car throws

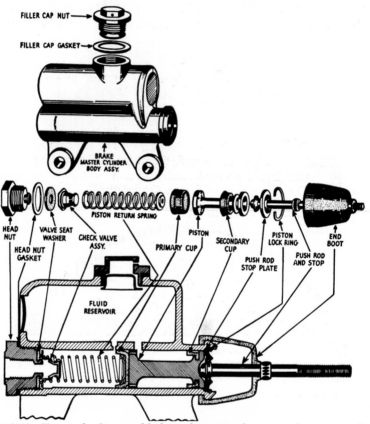

FILLER CAP NUT

FILLER CAP GASKET

BRAKE MASTER CYLINDER BODY ASSY.

HEAD NUT
VALVE SEAT WASHER
HEAD NUT GASKET
CHECK VALVE ASSY.
PISTON RETURN SPRING
PRIMARY CUP
PISTON
SECONDARY CUP
PUSH ROD STOP PLATE
PISTON LOCK RING
PUSH ROD AND STOP
END BOOT

FLUID RESERVOIR

Fig. 14-10. External, disassembled, and sectional views of master cylinder. (*Pontiac Motor Division of General Motors Corporation*)

more of the weight on the front wheels. A stronger braking effort at the front wheels is therefore necessary to achieve balanced braking effort.

§178. Master cylinder   Figures 14-9 and 14-10 show sectional and disassembled views of the master cylinder. The piston in the master cylinder is linked to the brake pedal through a lever arrangement

[380]

which provides a considerable mechanical advantage. That is, the push on the brake pedal is multiplied several times by the lever arrangement. For example, in the arrangement shown in Fig. 14-9, a push of 100 pounds on the brake pedal will produce a push of 750 pounds at the piston—when brakes are first applied.

As the piston in the master cylinder moves in (from the position shown in Fig. 14-9 to the position shown in Fig. 14-11), it moves past the compensating port. This traps the liquid in the cylinder that

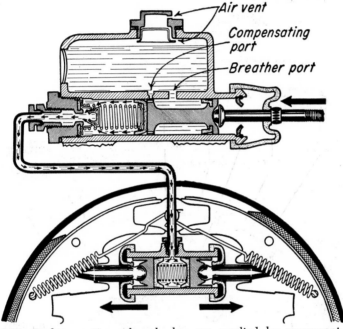

Fig. 14-11. Braking action when brakes are applied by movement of the master-cylinder piston. (*Pontiac Motor Division of General Motors Corporation*)

is ahead of the piston. Pressure rises rapidly, liquid is forced through the brake lines to the wheel cylinders. This action is shown in Fig. 14-11.

§**179. Wheel cylinders** Figure 14-12 shows the construction of a wheel cylinder. Hydraulic pressure applied between the two piston cups forces the pistons out. Thus, the brake-shoe actuating pins force the brake shoes into contact with the brake drums. The piston cups are so formed that the hydraulic pressure forces them tightly against the cylinder wall of the wheel cylinder. This produces a good sealing action that holds the liquid in the cylinder.

§180. Return stroke On the return stroke, spring tension on the brake linkage and spring pressure against the master-cylinder piston force the piston to move back in its cylinder. Liquid now flows from the wheel cylinders to the master cylinder as shown in Fig. 14-13.

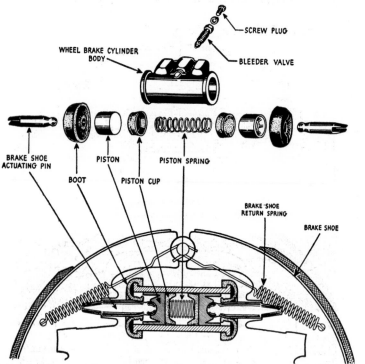

Fig. 14-12. Disassembled and sectional views of wheel cylinder. (*Pontiac Motor Division of General Motors Corporation*)

The tension of the brake-shoe springs forces the brake shoes away from the brake drums and thus pushes the wheel-cylinder pistons inward. Liquid is thus returned from the wheel cylinders to the master cylinder as shown by the arrows. However, some pressure is trapped in the lines by the check valve at the end of the master cylinder (see Fig. 14-10). As the pressure drops, the check valve closes, trapping a few pounds of pressure in the lines and wheel cylinders. This pressure serves the purpose of keeping the wheel cylinders

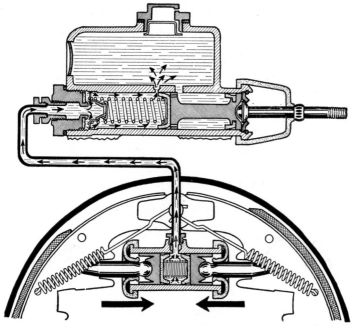

Fɪɢ. 14-13. Action in the hydraulic system when the brakes are released. (*Pontiac Motor Division of General Motors Corporation*)

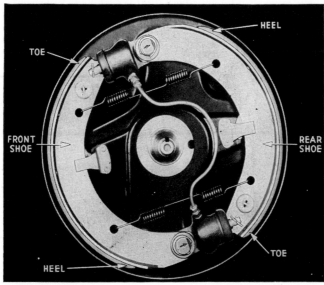

Fɪɢ. 14-14. Hydraulic brake using two wheel cylinders—one for each brake shoe. (*Chrysler Sales Division of Chrysler Corporation*)

[383]

from leaking and also of reducing the chances of air leaking into the system.

§181. Two wheel-cylinder arrangement   Figure 14-14 shows an arrangement which makes use of two wheel cylinders at the wheel. Each cylinder has a single piston, operating only one of the brake shoes.

§182. Disk brakes   Disk brakes have a different construction and operate in a somewhat different manner from the shoe type of brake described above. The principle of the disk brake can be illustrated by two disks mounted on a shaft (Fig. 14-15). One of the

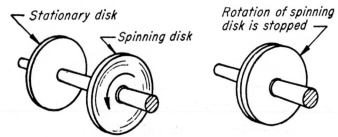

Fɪɢ. 14-15. The principle of the disk brake: when a spinning disk is brought into frictional contact with a stationary disk, the spinning disk will be brought to a stop. (*Chrysler Sales Division of Chrysler Corporation*)

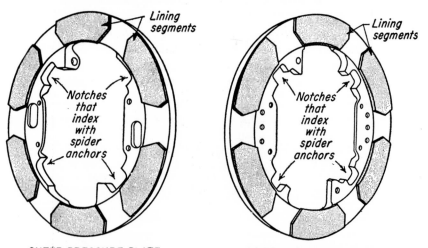

OUTER PRESSURE PLATE   INNER PRESSURE PLATE

Fɪɢ. 14-16. The two pressure plates used in the disk brake. (*Chrysler Sales Division of Chrysler Corporation*)

disks is held stationary so it cannot rotate. The other disk can rotate freely. However, if the two disks are brought together, the friction between them will bring the rotating disk to a stop.

The disk brake contains two pressure plates on which lining segments are bonded (Fig. 14-16). These pressure plates are semi-stationary and are positioned between an inner and an outer housing. Figure 14-17 is a sectional view of the assembly while Fig. 14-18 shows the outer-housing-and-hub assembly being removed. They are held in position—so they do not rotate—by a spider (Fig. 14-19) which is rigidly attached to the steering knuckle (at front wheels) or to the axle housing (at rear wheels). Notches in the pressure plates index with anchors on the spider to prevent rotation of the pressure plates.

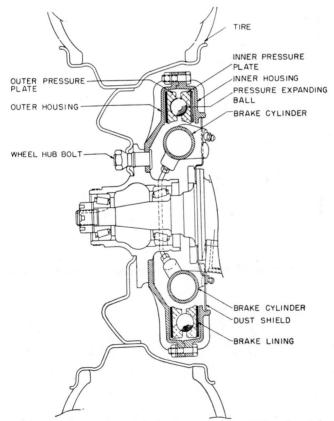

FIG. 14-17. Sectional view of disk brake assembly. (*Chrysler Sales Division of Chrysler Corporation*)

Fig. 14-18. Removing the outer-brake-housing-and-hub assembly. It is attached to the inner brake housing by a series of attaching bolts. (*Chrysler Sales Division of Chrysler Corporation*)

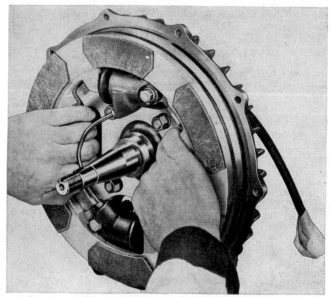

Fig. 14-19. Removing the pressure-plate assembly. (*Chrysler Sales Division of Chrysler Corporation*)

1. Operation when braking. Braking occurs when the two pressure plates are pushed away from each other and forced into contact with the inside faces of the inner and outer brake housings. A series of steel balls located between the two pressure plates causes the plates to push away from each other when the brakes are applied. This action is illustrated in Fig. 14-20, which shows one

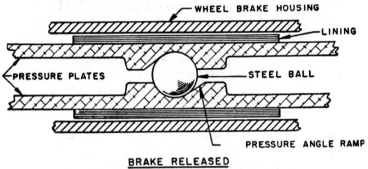

BRAKE RELEASED

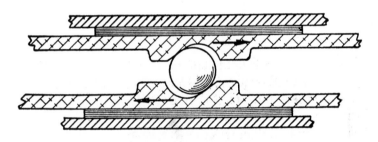

BRAKE ENERGIZED

Fig. 14-20. Action of steel ball as brakes are applied. Relative rotation of pressure plates as shown by arrows in lower illustration causes ball to roll up ramps, forcing the pressure plates apart and into contact with the brake housing. (*Chrysler Sales Division of Chrysler Corporation*)

of the steel balls in position. When the brakes are released, the steel ball is in the bottom of the ramps in the two pressure plates. The pressure plates are held in the released position by a series of short coil springs that tend to pull the plates toward each other.

When the brakes are applied, the wheel cylinders (there are two at each wheel) force the two pressure plates to rotate a few degrees in opposing directions, as shown in the lower illustration in Fig. 14-20. As this happens, the steel ball rides up both ramps and forces the two pressure plates away from each other. They move out and into contact with the inner faces of the brake housing, thus producing the braking action.

2. *Wheel cylinders.* There are two wheel cylinders mounted on the inner pressure plate (Fig. 14-21). The piston push rods bear against sockets in the outer plate. Thus, when the brakes are applied and the piston moves outward in the wheel cylinder, the two pressure plates are forced to rotate a few degrees in opposing directions as noted in the previous paragraph.

3. *Self-energizing effect.* The brakes have a self-energizing effect and this is an aid when they are applied. During forward car motion,

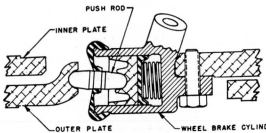

FIG. 14-21. One of the wheel brake cylinders in the pressure-plate assembly. (*Chrysler Sales Division of Chrysler Corporation*)

the inner pressure plate is held stationary so it cannot rotate. However, the notches in the outer pressure plate that index with the spider anchors are wider. Since they are wider, the outer pressure plate can rotate a few degrees. It does rotate these few degrees as the brakes are applied. The friction between the plate lining and the rotating brake housing causes the rotation to occur. As the outer pressure plate rotates in this manner, the steel balls ride further up on their ramps and brake application is increased. The energy needed to produce this additional braking action comes from the forward motion of the car—that is, from the rotation of the brake housing.

4. *Automatic brake adjuster.* There are automatic brake adjusters at each wheel. These devices automatically adjust for lining wear so as to maintain full brake-pedal effectiveness. Figure 14-22 is a sectional view of the automatic brake adjuster. There are two of these at each wheel. Let us examine one of them to see how it operates. The adjuster is mounted on the inner pressure plate and contains a rod positioned between two lugs on the outer pressure plate. In

operation, when the brakes are applied, the two pressure plates move in opposite directions. This carries the rod toward lug *B*. If the linings have worn, the rod contacts the lug before the linings contact the brake housing. As this happens, the rod is pushed back through the bracket plate of the adjuster. That is, the rod is repositioned. When the brakes are released, the two pressure plates move back toward the released position. However, the rod now contacts lug *A* and keeps the pressure plates from moving all the way back into their original positions. They are now held in a slightly advanced position. This compensates for any lining wear that has taken place. As additional wear takes place, the rod in the adjuster

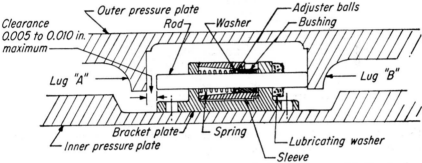

Fig. 14-22. Sectional view of the automatic brake adjuster with the brakes applied. (*Chrysler Sales Division of Chrysler Corporation*)

is further advanced. The pressure plates are therefore held at a more or less constant distance from the contacting faces of the brake housing when they are released. This means that the brake pedal stroke will not have to be increased for effective braking even though the linings have worn.

§183. Brake fluid The liquid used in the hydraulic braking system is called brake fluid. Brake fluid must have very definite characteristics. It must be chemically inert, it must be little affected by high or low temperatures, it must provide lubrication for the master-cylinder and wheel-cylinder pistons, and it must not attack the metallic and rubber parts in the braking system. Therefore, only the brake fluid recommended by the car manufacturer must be used when the addition of brake fluid becomes necessary.

Caution: Mineral oil must never be put into the brake system. Mineral oil will cause the rubber parts in the system, including the piston cups, to swell and disintegrate. This would, of course, cause faulty braking action and possibly complete brake failure. Nothing except the fluid recommended by the manufacturer must be put into the hydraulic brake system.

§184. Brake lines   Steel pipe is used between the master cylinder and the frame connections, and between the rear-axle T fitting and the rear-wheel cylinders. Flexible hose connects the brake pipe to the front-wheel cylinders and to the rear-axle fitting. These various hoses and pipes can be seen in Fig. 14-7. If a section of pipe or a hose becomes damaged, be sure to replace it with the proper pipe or hose as specified by the manufacturer. Since these lines are required to withstand considerable pressure, they are special. Ordinary copper tubing, for example, would not be satisfactory. The steel pipe, or tubing, must be double-flared (as explained in the following chapter) when it is installed.

§185. Hill-holder   When a car is braked to a stop on an upgrade and then put into forward motion again, the driver must operate the clutch, brake, and accelerator almost simultaneously. This series of actions may become, at times, somewhat complicated, and, to simplify stopping and starting on upgrades, some cars incorporate a hill-holder in the hydraulic braking system. The hill-holder functions to hold the car on an upgrade, preventing it from rolling down the hill backward, even though the brake pedal has been released. The device incorporates a special cylinder with a combination mechanical and ball balve (Fig. 14-23). The valve, in the hydraulic system, is between the master cylinder and the wheel cylinders. After the brakes have been applied and the car brought to a halt on an upgrade, depressing the clutch pedal forces the operating lever and camshaft in the hill-holder to move the ball-cage and valve assembly to the left (Fig. 14-23). Since the car is on an upgrade, the steel ball has rolled to the left against the rubber seal, closing off the hole through the center of the rubber seal. In this position, the passageway between the wheel-operating cylinders and the master cylinder is sealed off, preventing the return of the brake fluid from the wheel cylinders to the master cylinder, even though the brake pedal has been released. Then, when the clutch pedal is released to put the car in forward motion again, the oper-

[390]

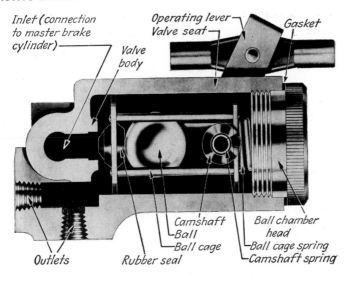

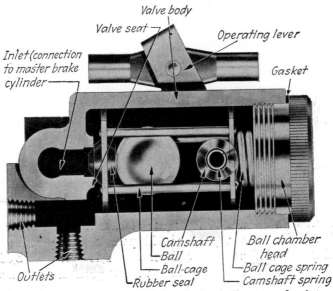

Fig. 14-23. Hill-holder. Two positions of the ball-cage-and-valve assembly. *Top,* running position with the passageway between the master and operating cylinders open. *Bottom,* sealed position, with the ball cage moved to the left by the clutch-operated lever and the ball having rolled against the rubber seal. (*Studebaker-Packard Corporation*)

ating lever moves the ball cage and the valve assembly to the right, opening the passageway between the wheel cylinders and the master cylinder. Thus, releasing the clutch pedal not only engages the clutch so that the car moves forward, but also releases the brakes. When the car is on level ground or on a downgrade, the hill-holder will be inoperative, since the ball will have rolled away from the rubber seal.

CHECK YOUR PROGRESS

Progress Quiz 5

Before you continue your study of automotive brake systems and start reading about power brakes, let us stop here and check up on the progress you have been making. There are two good reasons for the quizzes and the chapter checkups, as we have mentioned. First, they help you to review and thus to remember important points discussed in the book. Second, they give you a chance to check yourself on the progress you have been making. If you don't do as well as you would like, you can reread the previous pages and take the quiz again. This helps you to remember the important details you have been studying.

Completing the Sentences

The sentences below are incomplete. After each sentence there are several words or phrases, only one of which will correctly complete the sentence. Write down each sentence in your notebook, selecting the proper word or phrase to complete it correctly.

1. The most widely used brakes are operated   *electrically*
   hydraulically   *by air pressure*   *by vacuum*
2. During braking, the brake shoe is moved outward to press against the   *wheel cylinder*   *brake lining*   *brake drum*
   wheel rim
3. A piston with an area of 2.5 square inches is forced into a liquid-filled cylinder with a push of 500 pounds. The pressure on the liquid is   *200 psi*   *500 psi*   *1,250 psi*   *5,000 psi*
4. With a pressure of 800 psi acting on it, the push on a piston with an area of 0.4 square inch would be   *200 pounds*   *320 pounds*
   500 pounds   *5,000 pounds*
5. If the piston in the master cylinder has an area of 0.8 square inch and the push applied on it is 800 pounds, the hydraulic pressure in the brake fluid is   *100 psi*   *640 psi*   *1,000 psi*

6. In most models, each wheel cylinder contains   *one piston*
   two pistons   *three pistons*
7. As a rule, when comparing the front and rear wheel-cylinder pistons, it will be found that the pistons in the front wheel cylinders are *larger in diameter*   *smaller in diameter*   *the same size*
8. The piston in the master cylinder is connected by mechanical linkage to the   *wheel cylinders*   *brake shoes*   *brake pedal*   *wheel pedal*
9. In the wheel cylinder, movement of the pistons is carried to the brake shoes by   *cables*   *actuating pins*   *trunnion joints*   *springs*
10. The hill-holder described in the text is brought into operation on an upgrade by depressing the   *clutch pedal*   *brake pedal*   *accelerator pedal*

§186. Power brakes   For hard braking and fast stops, a considerable pressure must be exerted on the brake pedal with the braking system described above. Also, the heavier the vehicle, the greater the braking effort required. For many years, buses and trucks have used special equipment that assists the driver to brake the vehicle. This equipment may use either compressed air or vacuum. When the driver applies the brake, the compressed air or vacuum then supplies most of the effort required for braking. There is another system that uses an electrical means of braking.

In recent years, passenger cars have been supplied with vacuum-assisted braking systems, called *power brakes*. Essentially, they all operate in a similar manner. When the brake pedal is moved to apply the brakes, a valving arrangement is actuated. The valves admit atmospheric pressure on one side of a piston or diaphragm and apply vacuum to the other side. The piston or diaphragm then moves toward the vacuum side; this movement transmits most of the hydraulic pressure, through the brake fluid, to the wheel cylinders.

§187. Atmospheric pressure and vacuum   You will recall that, as noted in §§4 to 7, the atmospheric pressure is about fifteen psi at sea level. Vacuum is an absence of air. If we arranged a simple cylinder and piston (as shown in Fig. 14-24) and then applied atmospheric pressure to one side and vacuum to the other, the piston would move toward the vacuum side, as shown. If we held the piston stationary, we could calculate the pressure, or push, being

[393]

exerted on it, provided we knew the area of the piston, the atmospheric pressure, and amount of vacuum. Suppose the piston had an area of 50 square inches (about 8 inches in diameter). We'll assume also that the atmospheric pressure is 15 psi and the vacuum is great enough to have brought the pressure down to only 5 psi. With 15 psi on one side, and only 5 psi on the other, the difference in pressure is 10 psi—that is, there is an effective pressure of 10 pounds on every square inch of the piston area. Since there are 50 square inches of piston area, the push on the piston, urging it to the vacuum side, is 500 pounds (50 × 10). It is this effective pressure,

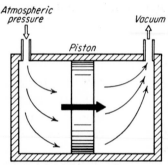

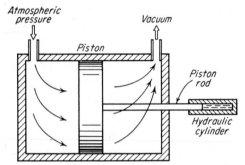

FIG. 14-24. If atmospheric pressure is applied on one side of a piston, and vacuum on the other side, the piston will move toward the vacuum side, as shown.

FIG. 14-25. If the piston rod is placed in a hydraulic cylinder, the pressure on the piston in the atmospheric-pressure cylinder will be translated into hydraulic pressure.

or push, that is utilized in power brakes. The vacuum is supplied by the automobile engine. We learned, in §7, that the engine is a vacuum pump in one sense of the word. With every intake stroke, the downward moving piston produces a partial vacuum in the cylinder and thus in the intake manifold. The vacuum side of the power-brake cylinder (Fig. 14-24) is connected to the intake manifold so it can utilize intake-manifold vacuum.

§188. Putting the vacuum to work   If we add a hydraulic cylinder to the cylinder and piston of Fig. 14-24 as shown in Fig. 14-25, we can utilize the push on the piston to produce hydraulic pressure. All the pressure on the piston is carried through the piston rod and into the hydraulic cylinder. Thus, in the example described above, the piston rod would push into the hydraulic cylinder with a 500-pound force.

If the end of the piston rod had an area of 0.5 square inch, then the pressure in the hydraulic fluid would be 1,000 psi (or 500 pounds divided by the area, 0.5 square inch). The hydraulic pressure can be altered by changing the size of either the piston or the rod (with same pressure differential acting on piston). For instance, a piston with an area of 100 square inches, and a rod of 0.2 square inch area, would produce a hydraulic pressure of 5,000 psi (or 1,000 pounds divided by 0.2 square inch).

If the hydraulic cylinder is connected to the wheel cylinders (as shown in Fig. 14-26), the hydraulic pressure produced will result in braking action. Note that even though the hydraulic cylinder has

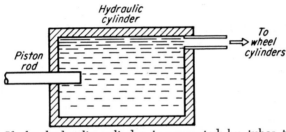

Fig. 14-26. If the hydraulic cylinder is connected by tubes to the wheel cylinders, movement of the piston rod into the hydraulic cylinder will produce braking action.

been increased in diameter, the piston rod entering it (Fig. 14-26) still displaces liquid; and it still produces the same pressure increase as it would if the cylinder were the same size as the rod (as shown in Fig. 14-25).

§189. **Bendix Treadle-Vac** This power-brake system is used on many General Motors and Ford Motor Company cars, and on others as well. Figure 14-27 show a schematic layout of this unit as installed on a car, while Figs. 14-28 and 14-29 are cutaway and sectional views of the unit. Vacuum is supplied by the engine intake manifold, and a special reservoir tank is used for vacuum reserve in case brakes are applied with the engine off. The vacuum reserve is, however, limited. Vacuum assistance will not continue indefinitely if brakes are applied, released, and reapplied repeatedly with the engine off. However, braking can still be achieved although the brake-pedal pressure will have to be considerably increased—since no vacuum assistance will take place. In the following

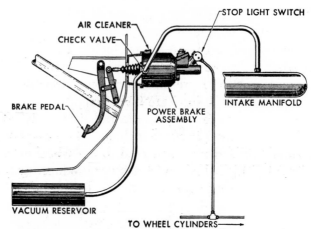

Fig. 14-27. Schematic layout of power-brake installation. Application of brake pedal causes power-brake unit to utilize engine vacuum to apply brakes. (*Lincoln-Mercury Division of Ford Motor Company*)

Fig. 14-28. Cutaway view of power-brake unit. (*Lincoln-Mercury Division of Ford Motor Company*)

discussion, refer to Fig. 14-29 for the names of parts and to Figs. 14-30 to 14-32 for illustrations of the actions taking place.

1. Operation—brakes off. Figure 14-30 is a sectional view of the power-brake assembly with the brakes released. In this position, the slide valve shuts off the vacuum port and opens the atmospheric port. Atmospheric pressure is admitted through the atmos-

[396]

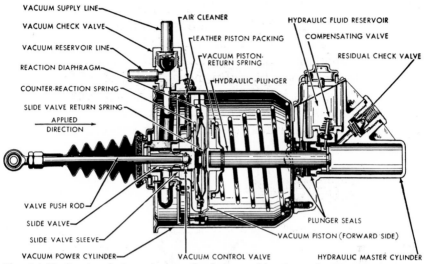

FIG. 14-29. Sectional view of power-brake assembly. (*Lincoln-Mercury Division of Ford Motor Company*)

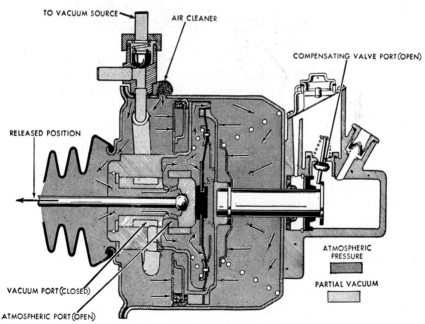

FIG. 14-30. Sectional view of power-brake assembly with brakes released. (*Lincoln-Mercury Division of Ford Motor Company*)

pheric port and through the piston to the forward side of the vacuum piston. Atmospheric pressure is shown by the dark shading in the illustration; the movement of the air is shown by the arrows. With atmospheric pressure acting on both sides of the piston, there is no tendency for the piston to move. A ring on the end of the hydraulic plunger is in contact with the stem of the compensating valve, holding this valve open. With the compensating-valve port open, hydraulic brake fluid can flow freely between the reservoir

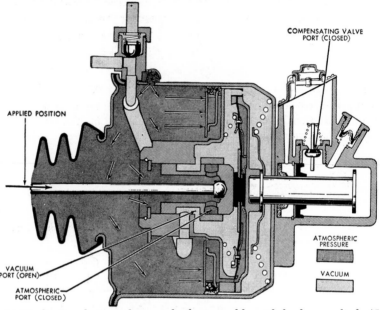

Fig. 14-31. Sectional view of power-brake assembly with brakes applied. (*Lincoln-Mercury Division of Ford Motor Company*)

and the hydraulic master cylinder. No pressure develops in the brake system and the brakes are not applied.

2. *Operation—brakes applied.* As the brake pedal is depressed to apply the brakes, the valve push rod moves inward, forcing the slide valve to move (Fig. 14-31). This movement of the slide valve closes off the atmospheric port and opens the vacuum port, as shown. Now, vacuum is connected to the forward side of the vacuum piston (and also to the rear side of the reaction diaphragm). Atmospheric pressure is still being applied to the rear side of the vacuum piston. The difference in pressure on the two sides of the

vacuum piston forces it to move forward as shown in Fig. 14-31. Atmospheric pressure is shown by the dark shading and vacuum by the light shading. As the vacuum piston is forced forward, the hydraulic plunger is forced into the master cylinder. The compensating valve therefore closes, and a high hydraulic pressure develops in the master cylinder. This forces brake fluid through the brake lines to the wheel cylinders; the brakes are therefore applied.

3. Brake feel. The driver should be able to apply the brakes by pedal-resistance feel—that is, he should be able to relate the amount of braking to the amount of pedal pressure he applies. The driver wants light braking when he applies the brake pedal lightly, and he wants heavy braking when he applies the brake pedal hard. To give this brake feel, the reaction diaphragm is included in the vacuum piston. There is atmospheric pressure between the forward part of the reaction diaphragm and the front plate of the vacuum piston (see dark shading in Figs. 14-30 and 14-31). This gives a reaction through the valve push rod to the brake pedal. When the driver brakes lightly, the push rod does not move the slide very far. Thus, only a small amount of vacuum is produced at the forward end of the vacuum piston—because the vacuum valve is opened only slightly. This means that the vacuum piston is not pushed forward very hard; the pressure differential between the two sides of the piston is not very large. Only light braking will result. Since there is not much vacuum produced, the vacuum back of the reaction diaphragm will be small. Thus, the backward push of the reaction diaphragm will be small. On the other hand, if the vacuum is high, due to strong braking, then the backward push of the reaction diaphragm will be high. This is because there is a large pressure differential on the two sides of the reaction diaphragm.

4. Operation—brakes holding or poised. As the brakes are applied, the forward motion of the brake pedal causes a forward motion of the slide valve. The amount that the slide valve advances is determined by the brake-pedal pressure. As the brake-pedal pressure is increased, the slide valve moves further, the vacuum piston moves further, and the hydraulic plunger therefore moves further into the hydraulic master cylinder to produce a further increase of braking effort. There may come a time in the braking cycle, however, when the driver may stop increasing the pressure and, instead, simply holds the brake pedal in a poised position—

neither increasing nor decreasing the pressure. At this point, the vacuum piston and slide-valve sleeve (which is attached to the piston) assumes the position shown in Fig. 14-32 with relation to the slide valve. Note that both the vacuum port and the atmospheric port are closed. The brakes are therefore held in the position shown, with the amount of braking effort selected by the driver being maintained. This holding action continues until the brake-pedal pressure is increased or decreased.

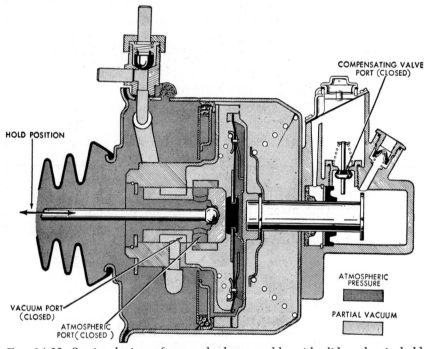

FIG. 14-32. Sectional view of power-brake assembly with slide valve in hold position. (*Lincoln-Mercury Division of Ford Motor Company*)

5. *Operation—brakes released.* When the brakes are released, the slide valve is returned to its released position as shown in Fig. 14-30. This closes the vacuum port and opens the atmospheric port. Now, with atmospheric pressure on both sides of the vacuum piston, there is no pressure differential. The vacuum-piston return spring moves the vacuum piston into the released position (Fig. 14-30). As the hydraulic plunger follows this movement, the hydraulic pressure in the brake lines and wheel cylinders is

[400]

relieved so that the brakes are released. Then, when the hydraulic plunger nears the end of its return travel, it opens the compensating valve, any remaining pressure is released, and brake fluid
can flow—as required—between the reservoir and hydraulic cylinder.

§190. **Kelsey-Hayes power brake** This power brake system is used
on Buick, and other cars. It is similar, in many ways, to the unit

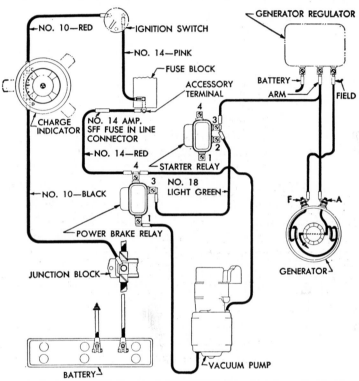

Fig. 14-33. Wiring circuit of power-brake vacuum pump and relay. (*Buick Motor Division of General Motors Corporation*)

covered in the previous section. This unit, however, is the "vacuum-
suspended" type—that is, when the brakes are not applied, vacuum
is being applied to both sides of the power piston. In other words,
the piston is suspended in vacuum (vacuum on both sides of it).
When the brakes are applied, atmospheric pressure is admitted to
one side of the piston. This is the reverse of the action in the unit
discussed previously. In that unit (Bendix Treadle-Vac), there is
atmospheric pressure on both sides of the piston. When the brakes

[401]

are applied, vacuum is admitted to the one side of the piston. In both, however, the end results are the same. Application of the brakes produces a pressure differential between the two sides of the piston so that the piston moves, causing a plunger to move into the hydraulic master cylinder. This movement displaces brake fluid and forces it, under pressure, into the wheel cylinders so that braking results. A description of the Kelsey-Hayes unit follows.

On certain late-model power-brake systems, there is a vane-type vacuum pump in the line between the power-brake cylinder and the engine intake manifold. This vacuum pump furnishes vacuum for power braking at times when the engine is not operating. The pump is operated by an electric motor which is turned on and off by a relay. Figure 14-33 shows a wiring diagram of the system. The winding of the power-brake relay is connected to the generator. When the engine is not running, the generator is not operating and can furnish no voltage. Thus, the contact points of the power-brake relay are closed. When the ignition switch is turned on, the electric motor in the vacuum pump will be connected to the battery through the relay contact points and the ignition switch. The vacuum pump will now start and will immediately furnish vacuum for braking. However, as soon as the engine starts, generator voltage builds up; this voltage actuates the power-brake relay and causes the relay contact points to separate. The circuit between the vacuum-pump motor and the battery is thereby broken and the vacuum pump stops operating.

1. Operation—brakes off. Figure 14-34 is a cutaway view of the power brake assembly. Figure 14-35 is a sectional view of the unit with the parts positioned in the unapplied, or brakes-off, position. You will note that this unit has no brake-fluid reservoir. The reservoir is mounted separately in a convenient place and connected by tubing to the hydraulic cylinder of the brake assembly. No separate vacuum reservoir is used since the vacuum chamber itself serves as a vacuum reservoir; the vacuum chamber is connected directly to the intake manifold of the engine.

When the engine is running with the brakes off, the vacuum valve is open and vacuum is maintained on both sides of the power piston. With vacuum on both sides of the piston, there is no tendency for the piston to move. The air valve is closed. Note that there is a common floating valve-seat ring against which one or the other valve seats (or both seat at times). The piston remains in the position shown in Fig. 14-35. The hydraulic plunger is in the position shown. The compensating port in the end of the plunger sleeve is positioned inside the seal so that the hydraulic cylinder

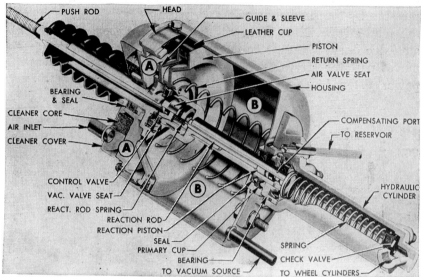

FIG. 14-34. Cutaway view of power-brake assembly. (*Buick Motor Division of General Motors Corporation*)

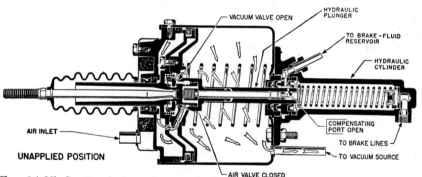

FIG. 14-35. Sectional view of power-brake assembly with brakes in unapplied position. Open arrows indicate vacuum. (*Kelsey-Hayes Wheel Company*)

is open to the brake-fluid reservoir. No pressure is being applied to the brake fluid and the brakes are off.

2. *Operation—brakes applied.* Figure 14-36 shows the actions taking place when the brakes are applied. Pressure on the brake

pedal causes the push rod to move into the unit as shown by the heavy arrow at the left. The push-rod movement (after the first few thousandths of an inch) closes the vacuum valve and opens the air valve. This admits air into the rear of the cylinder. In the illustration (Fig. 14-36), vacuum is indicated by the open arrows, air pressure by the shaded arrows, and hydraulic pressure is shown by the solid arrows. Note that, with the vacuum valve closed and the air valve open, air pressure enters the space around the push rod, moves past the air valve, and applies against the rear side of the power piston. Since vacuum is maintained on the front side of the

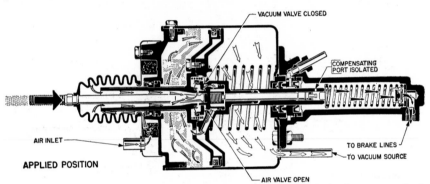

Fig. 14-36. Sectional view of power-brake assembly with brakes in applied position. Open arrows indicate vacuum, shaded arrows indicate atmospheric pressure, and solid arrows indicate brake-fluid hydraulic pressure. (*Kelsey-Hayes Wheel Company*)

piston, the pressure differential forces the piston to move (from the shaded position shown in the illustration to the solid position shown). This movement forces the hydraulic plunger into the hydraulic cylinder. As the plunger moves in, the compensating port is moved past the seal and isolated. Now, further plunger movement builds up hydraulic pressure and forces brake fluid to flow from the hydraulic cylinder through the brake lines to the wheel cylinders as indicated by the solid arrows. The brakes are applied.

3. *Brake feel.* As noted in §189, 3, the driver should be able to apply the brakes by pedal-resistance feel. Light pedal pressure should give light braking, heavy pressure hard braking. To provide brake feel, there is a reaction rod in the hydraulic-plunger sleeve (this rod is named in Fig. 14-34). One end of the reaction rod is exposed to the hydraulic pressure of the brake fluid in the hydraulic

cylinder. This hydraulic pressure is therefore applied to the end of the rod and attempts to force the reaction rod away from the hydraulic cylinder. The push is carried through the rod to the floating valve seat, from the seat to the push rod, and thence to the brake pedal. Thus, the greater the hydraulic pressure, the greater the reaction that the driver gets at the brake pedal. Since the reaction is proportional to the hydraulic pressure, the driver has an accurate feel of the amount of braking effort being made.

4. *Operation—brakes holding or poised.* There is an intermediate position in brake application at which the brakes are poised, or held. This occurs when the driver holds the brake pedal at a constant

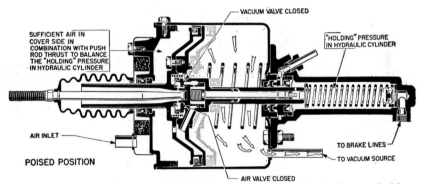

VACUUM VALVE CLOSED

SUFFICIENT AIR IN
COVER SIDE IN
COMBINATION WITH PUSH
ROD THRUST TO BALANCE
THE "HOLDING" PRESSURE
IN HYDRAULIC CYLINDER

"HOLDING" PRESSURE
IN HYDRAULIC CYLINDER

AIR INLET

TO BRAKE LINES

POISED POSITION

TO VACUUM SOURCE

AIR VALVE CLOSED

Fig. 14-37. Sectional view of power-brake assembly with brakes in hold, or poised, position. (*Kelsey-Hayes Wheel Company*)

pressure, for example. With this condition, the air valve seats, and the situation shown in Fig. 14-37 results. Here, both the vacuum valve and the air valve are closed. Air trapped in the rear, or cover side, of the cylinder, combined with the push-rod thrust furnished by the driver's foot, just balances the holding pressure in the hydraulic cylinder. This amount of pressure will continue so long as the brake pedal and push rod are not moved. But if the driver applies further pressure, then the air valve will again be opened to produce a further power-piston movement. On the other hand, if the driver releases pressure, the push rod will move back to close the air valve and open the vacuum valve. This reduces the pressure on the rear, or cover side, of the piston so the piston moves back to reduce the pressure.

5. *Operation—brakes released.* When the brakes are released, the push rod returns to its released position as shown in Fig. 14-35.

[405]

The air valve is closed; the vacuum valve is opened. Vacuum is introduced to both sides of the power piston so the piston moves to the position shown, because of the piston-spring pressure. This pulls the hydraulic plunger out of the hydraulic cylinder. The compensating port in the plunger sleeve moves past the seal and thereby opens the hydraulic cylinder to the reservoir. Now brake fluid can flow to or from the reservoir as required. Pressure in the hydraulic cylinder is released and the brakes are off.

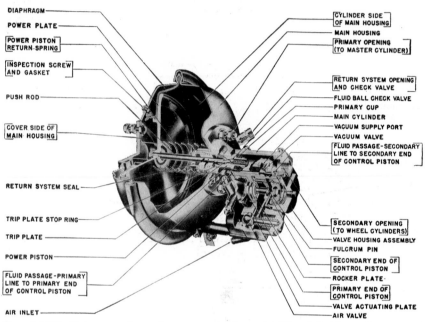

Fig. 14-38. Cutaway view of a power-brake assembly. (*De Soto Division of Chrysler Corporation*)

§191. Kelsey-Hayes Vacdraulic booster brake

This unit, shown in Fig. 14-38, is used on De soto and other cars. It is a vacuum-suspended unit, as is the unit described in the previous section—that is, in the unapplied position, there is vacuum on both sides of the power plate. The construction of this unit, however, is somewhat different from the power-brake assemblies previously described. Instead of a power (or vacuum) piston, it uses a power plate attached to a sealed diaphragm. Furthermore, its operation is controlled by the hydraulic pressure in the brake master cylinder. Operation of the unit is as follows:

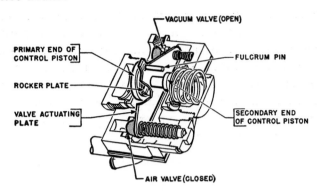

**UNAPPLIED POSITION
OR AS PRESSURE IS RELEASED**

FIG. 14-39. Cutaway view of the control piston and valve assembly, showing location of parts in the unapplied position. (*Kelsey-Hayes Wheel Company*)

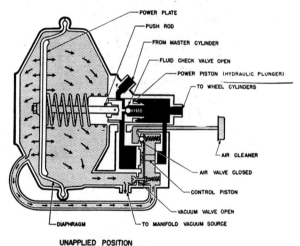

**UNAPPLIED POSITION
OR
AS PRESSURE IS RELEASED**

FIG. 14-40. Sectional view of power-brake assembly with brakes unapplied. (*Kelsey-Hayes Wheel Company*)

1. Operation—brakes off. Figure 14-39 shows the position of the valves, and Fig. 14-40, the position of the other parts, in the assembly when the brakes are released. In this position, the vacuum valve is open and the air valve is closed. Vacuum from the engine intake manifold is introduced to both sides of the power plate; the power plate assumes the position shown with the return spring fully extended. The power piston, or hydraulic plunger, is in the

[407]

retracted position and no hydraulic pressure is being exerted on the
brake fluid; so no braking is taking place. Note that the power-
piston cylinder is connected by a tube to the master cylinder of the
hydraulic braking system. In the unapplied position, brake fluid
can flow from the master cylinder past the fluid check valve, through
the main cylinder, and to the wheel cylinders. The fluid check
valve—a ball-check valve—is held off its seat by a trip-plate assembly in the end of the push-rod assembly. The brake fluid is also
free to flow to both ends of the control piston.

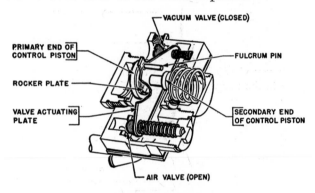

FIG. 14-41. Cutaway view of control piston and valve assembly, showing position of parts as brakes are applied. (*Kelsey-Hayes Wheel Company*)

   2. *Operation—brakes applied.* When the brakes are applied,
hydraulic pressure is increased in the master cylinder. The master
cylinder is of the type shown in Fig. 14-10. The increasing pressure
is not applied to the wheel cylinders. Instead, it is applied to the big
end of the control piston as shown in Fig. 14-42. This pressure
causes the control piston to move and the actuating plate to close
the vacuum valve and open the air valve (Fig. 14-41). As these
valves close and open, the condition shown in Fig. 14-42 results.
Atmospheric pressure is admitted past the air valve to the cover
side of the power plate. Vacuum is still being introduced to the
other side of the power plate. The pressure differential therefore
causes the power plate to move (to the right in Fig. 14-42). This
forces the push rod to move and the power piston moves ahead
of it. The fluid check valve closes and, consequently, brake fluid
ahead of the power piston is trapped. Further power-plate and

power-piston movement therefore produces a high pressure in the main cylinder and this high pressure is carried to the wheel cylinders to produce braking. The same high pressure is also applied to the small end of the control piston, and it opposes the control-piston movement which originally opened the air valve and closed the vacuum valve. However, since the big end of the control piston

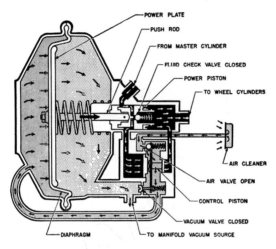

POWER PLATE
PUSH ROD
FROM MASTER CYLINDER
FLUID CHECK VALVE CLOSED
POWER PISTON
TO WHEEL CYLINDERS
AIR CLEANER
AIR VALVE OPEN
CONTROL PISTON
VACUUM VALVE CLOSED
TO MANIFOLD VACUUM SOURCE
DIAPHRAGM

APPLYING POSITION
AS PRESSURE IS INCREASED

FIG. 14-42. Sectional view of power-brake assembly with brakes applied. (*Kelsey-Hayes Wheel Company*)

is several times the area of the small piston, the pressure (in psi) at the small end would have to be several times that at the big end to equalize the push. For instance, if the big end had an area of 1 square inch, and the small end an area of ¼ square inch, then it would take 1,000 psi at the small end to equalize the push from 250 psi at the big end.

Note that the pressure in the master cylinder is boosted or increased several times by the action of the power-brake mechanism. The increase is actually proportional to the difference in area of the two ends of the control piston, as noted above. In the example mentioned, a pressure of 250 psi in the master cylinder would produce a pressure of 1,000 psi in the wheel cylinders.

3. Operation—brakes poised or holding. When the driver, after having applied the brakes, holds the brake pedal constant—neither increasing nor decreasing the pedal pressure—the control piston

[409]

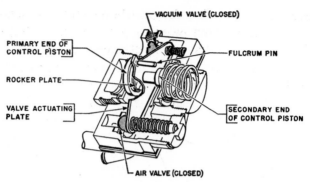

POISED IN APPLIED POSITION
AS PRESSURE IS MAINTAINED

Fig. 14-43. Cutaway view of control piston and valve assembly, showing position of parts as pressure is maintained after brakes have been applied. (*Kelsey-Hayes Wheel Company*)

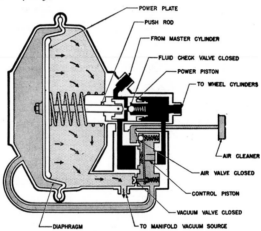

POISED POSITION
AS PRESSURE IS MAINTAINED

Fig. 14-44. Sectional view of power-brake assembly in poised position. (*Kelsey-Hayes Wheel Company*)

moves back a little so as to close both valves (Fig. 14-43). With both the vacuum valve and the air valve closed, the pressure against the power plate is maintained at a constant value. This maintains a constant pressure on the hydraulic fluid in the main cylinder so that the hydraulic pressure in the wheel cylinders is maintained (Fig. 14-44). If the driver moves the brake pedal one way or the other to apply more or less pressure, then there is a change in pres-

[410]

sure against the big end of the control piston. This causes the control piston to move, thereby opening one or the other of the two valves. If the pressure has increased, then the air valve is opened to admit more air back of the power plate for increased braking action. If the pressure is reduced, then the vacuum valve is opened to introduce vacuum back of the power plate for reduced braking.

4. *Operation—brakes released.* When the pedal pressure is reduced or pedal released and the pressure in the master cylinder is reduced, the control piston moves as mentioned in the previous paragraph. This opens the vacuum valve so that pressure on both sides of the power plate is the same. The plate therefore moves into the position shown in Fig. 14-40. This movement pulls the push rod back. The power piston moves back with it, thus reducing the pressure in the system and at the wheel cylinders. As the push rod reaches the fully released position, the trip plate causes the fluid check valve to open. This releases any hydraulic pressure left in the system causing the brakes to be fully released.

§192. **Vacuum-cylinder booster brake**   A sectional view of a vacuum-cylinder type of booster brake is shown in Fig. 14-45. In this unit there is a mechanical linkage between the vacuum piston and the master cylinder. When the brake pedal is depressed, pressure is applied to the hydraulic fluid in the master cylinder. Pressure is also applied, through the linkage, to the valve shaft leading to the vacuum cylinder. This pressure opens valve *C* so that the portion of the cylinder to the left of the piston is opened to atmospheric pressure. Since the right side is opened to the engine intake manifold so that manifold vacuum is introduced to this side, a pressure differential develops. This forces the piston to the right, the movement applying a powerful force through the piston hollow shaft and linkage to the master-cylinder push rod. The amount of pressure applied is determined by the amount the brake pedal is depressed. This device acts as a follow-up to the brake-pedal movement, providing most of the pressure against the master-cylinder piston; therefore it is responsible for most of the braking effort.

§193. **Air brake**   The air brake makes use of compressed air to apply the braking force to the brake shoes. A typical air-brake-system layout is illustrated in Fig. 14-46; the compressor unit, air-reservoir tank, brake chamber, and wheel mechanism are shown

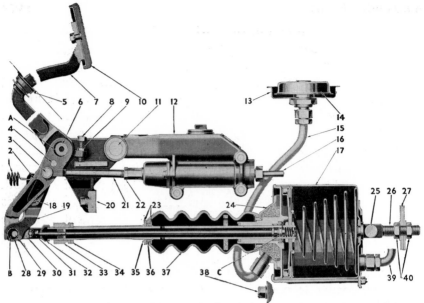

FIG. 14-45. Sectional view of booster brake. (*Chrysler Sales Division of Chrysler Corporation*)

1. Brake-pedal pull-back spring
2. Brake-master-cylinder operating lever
3. Brake-master-cylinder-piston push-rod end pin
4. Brake-master-cylinder operating-lever pin
5. Brake-pedal draft pad
6. Clutch-and-brake-pedal shaft
7. Brake pedal and bushing
8. Brake-pedal stop screw
9. Brake-pedal-stop-screw lock nut
10. Brake-pedal pad
11. Pedal-bracket-and-brake-master-cylinder adapter shaft
12. Master-cylinder assembly
13. Air-cleaner bracket
14. Air cleaner
15. Air-cleaner tube, or hose
16. Master-cylinder-to-frame T tube
17. Brake-operating-cylinder assembly
18. Lever screw
19. Lever
20. Pedal-bracket and brake-master-cylinder adapter

21. Piston push rod
22. Push-rod-end check nut
23. Piston-rod-guard retainers
24. Dust cover
25. Frame-bracket clevis pin
26. Frame-bracket clevis
27. Bracket
28. Valve-rod-yoke-end bushing
29. Piston-rod-yoke-end pin
30. Valve-rod-yoke end
31. Valve-rod adjusting nut
32. Valve-rod guard
33. Piston-rod yoke end
34. Piston-rod yoke-end adjusting nut
35. Piston-rod guard-retainer lock ring
36. Piston-rod guard washer
37. Piston-rod guard, or boot
38. Lubricant plug
39. Manifold tube, or hose
40. Frame-bracket-clevis check nuts
A. Clearance between operating lever and pedal shaft
B. Clearance between operating-cylinder-valve-rod yoke and pin
C. Brake-operating cylinder valve

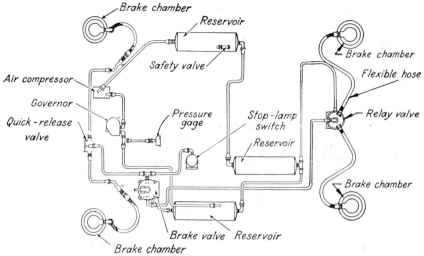

FIG. 14-46. Layout of a typical air-brake system. (*International Harvester Company*)

FIG. 14-47. Installation of an air-brake system on a heavy-duty truck. (*International Harvester Company*)

in Fig. 14-47. Air-reservoir tanks are necessary in order to have adequate braking power at all times, even when the engine is not running. The air compressor, which is a small air pump, operates to maintain air pressure in the tanks. When the air pressure is applied to the brake chambers by operation of the treadle pedal, the brake chamber causes the brake shoes to push outward against the brake drum.

§194. Electric brakes Electric brakes make use of electromagnets to provide the braking force against the brake shoes. Each wheel

FIG. 14-48. Construction of electric-brake mechanism. Left, controller. Right, wheel-braking mechanism. (*Warner Electric Brake Manufacturing Company*)

contains a semistationary circular electromagnet and an armature disk that revolves with the wheel (Fig. 14-48). The electromagnet operates from battery current. A controller in the driver's compartment enables the driver to connect the electromagnets to the battery and to vary the amount of current flowing from the battery to the electromagnets, in order to vary the amount of braking action. When the brakes are not applied, there is no magnetic attraction between the electromagnet and the armature disk in the wheel. When the driver applies the brakes, current begins to flow through the electromagnets. This builds up a magnetic field, causing mag-

[414]

netic attraction between the semistationary electromagnet and the rotating armature disk. The electromagnet is thus forced to shift through a limited arc in the direction of the wheel rotation. There is a lug on the electromagnet that is connected to a cam; movement of the electromagnet and the lug causes the cam to press against the end of the brake shoes and forces the brake shoes outward against the brake drum. The greater the current flowing through the electromagnet, the greater the braking effect.

CHECK YOUR PROGRESS

Progress Quiz 6

Here is your progress quiz on the last half of the chapter on power brakes. Power brakes increased in importance in recent years since many cars have been supplied with them. Thus, you will want to know all you can about them. The quiz that follows will help you to remember the explanations of the power brakes given in the past few pages. It will also check your memory on the facts about this subject. If your memory does not "check out" very well, it simply means that you should review the material again.

Completing the Sentences

The sentences below are incomplete. After each sentence there are several words or phrases, only one of which will correctly complete the sentence. Write down each sentence in your notebook, selecting the proper word or phrase to complete it correctly.

1. The type of braking system referred to as power brakes makes use of   *compressed air   vacuum   electromagnets*
2. With a pressure differential of 9 psi between the two sides of the piston in a power-brake assembly, and a piston area of 45 square inches, the effective push on the piston is   *50 pounds 405 pounds   455 pounds*
3. When the brakes are off in the Bendix Treadle-Vac, on both sides of the vacuum piston there is   *atmospheric pressure vacuum   about 100 psi   about 150 psi*
4. The Bendix Treadle-Vac contains a   *flapper valve   poppet valve   slide valve*
5. The atmospheric port is closed and the vacuum port opened, in the Bendix Treadle-Vac, by forward movement of the   *slide valve release lever   vacuum valve*

[415]

6. On both sides of the piston in the Kelsey-Hayes power-brake unit, with the engine running and the brakes off, there is   *compressed air*   *vacuum*   *atmospheric pressure*

7. In the Kelsey-Hayes power-brake unit, push-rod movement—as the brakes are applied—causes the   *vacuum valve to open*   *air valve to open*   *air valve to close*

8. Operation of the booster brake used on De Soto is controlled by   *master cylinder hydraulic pressure*   *movement of a slide valve*   *rotation of the power plate*

9. Opening and closing of the vacuum valve and air valve in the booster brake used on De Soto is produced by movement of the   *slide valve*   *control piston*   *valve lifter*   *cam*

10. In the electric braking system, each wheel contains a semistationary, circular   *wheel cylinder*   *armature disk*   *electromagnet*

CHAPTER CHECKUP

NOTE: Since the following is a chapter review test, you should review the chapter before taking it.

You have been moving along very well in your studies of the automobile chassis and have completed most of the book. This book may be somewhat more difficult to study than other books in the McGraw-Hill Automotive Mechanics Series since it discusses several more-or-less independent mechanisms. These mechanisms have little in common except for the fact that they are all used on the automobile. Thus, the steering system has a different purpose and different operating principles than the brake system, for example. Yet all of the mechanisms are important to the automobile, and it is important for you to understand them all—and understand them well. The chapter checkup that follows gives you the chance to review the important details of brake systems covered in the chapter. Be sure to write the answers to the questions down in your notebook. You'll be glad you've kept a notebook when you have finished the book: you can go to the notebook to refresh your memory whenever you are hazy about some point. Further, writing down the facts in your notebook helps you remember them.

Correcting Parts Lists

The purpose of this exercise is to give you practice in spotting unrelated parts in a list. In each list below, there is one item that does not belong. Write down each list in your notebook, but do not write down the item that does not belong.

1. Hydraulic brake system: master cylinder, brake pedal, brake fluid, brake lines, cable linkage, wheel cylinders.

[416]

2. Master cylinder: body, check valve assembly, activating pin, piston return spring, piston, push rod, fluid reservoir.
3. Wheel cylinder: body, piston spring, push rod, piston, piston cup, actuating pin.
4. Bendix Treadle-Vac: valve push rod, slide valve, vacuum piston, rocker plate, hydraulic plunger, hydraulic master cylinder, hydraulic fluid reservoir, compensating valve.
5. Kelsey-Hayes power brake: push rod, piston, hydraulic cylinder, vacuum reservoir, hydraulic plunger, reaction rod.

Completing the Sentences

The sentences below are incomplete. After each sentence there are several words or phrases, only one of which will correctly complete the sentence. Write down each sentence in your notebook, selecting the proper word or phrase to complete it correctly.

1. In the hydraulic brake system, movement of a piston in the master cylinder produces hydraulic pressure which causes movement of the   *wheel-cylinder pistons   brake pedal   brake cam*
2. Braking is produced by the frictional effect between the brake drum and the   *wheel-cylinder pistons   brake shoes   wheel studs   wheel rim*
3. Rubber parts in the hydraulic braking system will swell and disintegrate from the effects, in the system, of   *brake fluid   low pressure   mineral oil*
4. To operate, power brakes make use of pressure differential between vacuum from the intake manifold and   *venturi vacuum   compressed air   atmospheric pressure*
5. In the Bendix Treadle-Vac, the brake feel is achieved by use of a   *reaction rod   reaction diaphragm   vacuum piston   hydraulic valve*
6. In the Kelsey-Hayes power brake, brake feel is achieved by use of a   *reaction rod   reaction diaphragm   vacuum piston   hydraulic valve*
7. In the booster brake used on De Soto, brake feel is achieved by   *hydraulic pressure in master cylinder   a reaction rod   a reaction valve*
8. In a vacuum-suspended unit, when the brakes are off, the piston or diaphragm has, on both sides of it,   *atmospheric pressure   a vacuum   hydraulic pressure*

Purpose and Operation of Components

In the following, you are asked to write down the purpose of certain parts, or the operation of various components in the brake systems de-

[417]

scribed in the chapter. If you have any difficulty in writing down your explanations, turn back to the chapter and reread the pages that will make the explanations clear. Don't copy, try to tell it in your own words just as you would explain it to a friend. Write in your notebook.

1. Describe the operation of a mechanical braking system.
2. Describe the operation of a hydraulic braking system.
3. Why are the wheel-cylinder pistons usually larger in the front-wheel cylinders?
4. Describe the construction of a master cylinder.
5. Describe the construction of a wheel cylinder.
6. Describe the construction of the Bendix Treadle-Vac unit.
7. Describe the operation of the Bendix Treadle-Vac unit when the brakes are applied; when they are held, or poised; when they are released.
8. Describe the operation of the Kelsey-Hayes power brake when the brakes are applied; when they are held, or poised; when they are released.
9. Describe the operation of the booster brake used on De Soto when the brakes are applied; when they are held, or poised; when they are released.
10. Explain the way in which brake feel is achieved in the brake units mentioned in the three previous questions.

SUGGESTIONS FOR FURTHER STUDY

If you can obtain shop manuals issued by the car or equipment manufacturers which describe the various power-brake or booster-brake systems, be sure to study them very carefully. Also, if you can examine these units, assembled or disassembled, in your local school or service shop, it will help you to understand how these units operate. Be sure to write down everything you learn of importance in your notebook. Later, you will be glad that you did this, because your notebook will become a valuable reference source for you.

15: Brake service

THIS CHAPTER discusses the trouble-shooting, adjusting, removal, repair, and reinstallation of the various hydraulic-brake-system components. The chapter that follows (Chap. 16) discusses these same operations on power brakes.

§195. Trouble-shooting chart—hydraulic brakes The chart that follows relates various braking troubles to their possible causes and corrections. This chart gives you a means of logically tracing down troubles to their actual causes. This permits quick location of causes and quick correction. Once you know the cause, the trouble is usually relatively easy to correct. Following the trouble-shooting chart are several sections that describe the adjusting and repair procedures on different types of hydraulic brakes.

NOTE: The troubles and possible causes are not listed in the chart in the order of frequency of occurrence. That is, item 1 does not necessarily occur more often than item 2, nor does item *a* under Possible Cause necessarily occur more often than item *b*.

HYDRAULIC BRAKE TROUBLE-SHOOTING CHART

(See §§196 to 213 for details of checks and corrections listed.)

Complaint	Possible Cause	Check or Correction
1. Brake pedal goes to floor board	*a.* Brake shoes out of adjustment	Adjust
	b. Brake pedal out of adjustment	Adjust
	c. Brake linings worn	Replace linings
	d. Lack of brake fluid	Add fluid, bleed system (see also, item 10, below)
	e. Air in system	Add fluid, bleed system (see also item 9, below)

Complaint	Possible Cause	Check or Correction
	f. Worn master cylinder	Repair
2. One brake drags	*a.* Brake shoes out of adjustment	Adjust
	b. Clogged brake line	Clear or replace line
	c. Wheel cylinder defective	Repair or replace
	d. Weak or broken return spring	Replace spring
	e. Loose wheel bearing	Adjust bearing
3. All brakes drag	*a.* Incorrect brake pedal adjustment	Adjust
	b. Reservoir filler vent clogged	Clear vent
	c. Mineral oil in system	Replace damaged rubber parts. Use only recommended brake fluid in system
4. Car pulls to one side when braking	*a.* Brake linings soaked with oil	Replace linings and oil seals, avoid overlubrication
	b. Brake linings soaked with brake fluid	Replace linings, repair or replace wheel cylinders
	c. Brake shoes out of adjustment	Adjust
	d. Tires not uniformly inflated	Inflate tires correctly
	e. Brake line clogged	Clear or replace line
	f. Defective wheel cylinder	Repair or replace
	g. Brake backing plate loose	Tighten
	h. Mismatched linings	Use same linings all around
5. Soft or spongy pedal	*a.* Air in system	Add brake fluid, bleed system (see also item 9, below)

Complaint	Possible Cause	Check or Correction
	b. Brake shoes out of adjustment	Adjust
6. Poor braking action requiring excessive pedal pressure	*a.* Brake linings soaked with oil	Replace linings and oil seals, avoid overlubrication
	b. Brake linings soaked with brake fluid	Replace linings, repair or replace wheel cylinders
	c. Brake shoes out of adjustment	Adjust
	d. Brake linings water-soaked	Will be all right when dried out
	e. Brake linings hot	Allow to cool
	f. Glazed brake drum	Turn or grind drum to remove glaze
7. Brakes too sensitive or brakes grab	*a.* Brake shoes out of adjustment	Adjust
	b. Wrong brake lining	Replace with correct lining
	c. Brake linings greasy	Replace, check oil seals, avoid overlubrication
	d. Brake drums scored	Turn or grind drums
	e. Backing plates loose	Tighten, adjust brakes
8. Noisy brakes	*a.* Brake linings worn	Replace linings
	b. Shoes warped	Replace shoes
	c. Shoe rivets loose	Tighten, replace rivets or linings as necessary
	d. Brake drum rough or worn	Turn or grind drums
	e. Loose parts	Tighten
9. Air in system	*a.* Plugged filler vent	Clear
	b. Leaky valve in master cylinder	Repair or replace
	c. Loose line connections, damaged tube	Tighten connections, replace damaged line

[421]

Complaint	Possible Cause	Check or Correction
10. Loss of brake fluid	a. Master cylinder leaks	Repair, replace defective parts
	b. Wheel cylinder leaks	Repair, install actuating pins correctly
	c. Loose line connections, damaged tube	Tighten connections, replace damaged line

§196. Trouble diagnosis The chart above gives you a good idea of the types of troubles that might be found in hydraulic braking systems, their causes, and corrections. Let us discuss these troubles in more detail. Later sections will explain how to make corrections.

1. Brake pedal goes to floor board. When this happens, it means that there is no pedal reserve, since full pedal movement does not provide adequate braking. This may be due to pedal or linkage that is out of adjustment, to brake shoes that are out of adjustment, or to worn linings. It could also be due to lack of brake fluid or to air in the system. Air prevents normal braking since it will compress when hydraulic pressure is applied, and the hydraulic pressure will not be carried to the wheel cylinders. Another condition that would allow the brake pedal to go to the floor board without normal brake application is a defective master cylinder. For example, the piston cup might be cracked and thus allow the brake fluid to bypass instead of building up hydraulic pressure.

2. One brake drags. This means that the brake shoes are not moving away from the brake drum when the brakes are released. The condition could be due to incorrect shoe adjustment, to a clogged brake line which does not release pressure from the wheel cylinder, to sticking pistons in the wheel cylinder, to weak or broken brake-shoe return springs, or to a loose wheel bearing which permits the wheel to wobble so that the brake drum comes in contact with the brake shoes even though they are retracted.

3. All brakes drag. When all brakes drag, it may be that the brake pedal does not have sufficient play to allow the piston in the master cylinder to retract fully. This would prevent the lip of the piston cup from clearing the compensating port so that hydraulic pressure would not be relieved as it should be (see Figs. 14-11 and 14-13). As a result, the wheel cylinders would not release the brake shoes. A similar condition could result if mineral oil had been added

[422]

to the system since this would be apt to cause the piston cup to swell. If it swells enough, it would not clear the compensating port even with the piston in the fully retracted position (Fig. 15-1). A clogged compensating port would have the same result. Do not use a wire or drill to clear the port; this might produce a burr that would cut the piston cup. Instead, clear it with alcohol and compressed

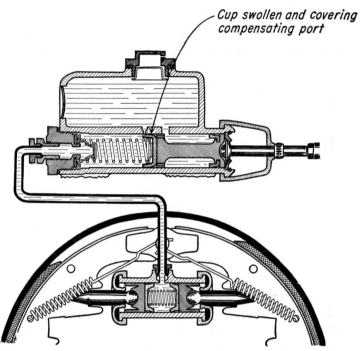

Cup swollen and covering compensating port

Fig. 15-1. If the primary piston cup swells badly, it can close off the compensating port to the reservoir with the piston fully retracted, as shown. This causes dragging or locked brakes since hydraulic pressure will not release. (*Pontiac Motor Division of General Motors Corporation*)

air. Clogging of the reservoir vent might cause dragging brakes since this could trap pressure in the reservoir which would prevent release of pressure. This might be just as likely to cause leakage of air into the system (see item 9a in chart).

4. Car pulls to one side. If the car pulls to one side when the brakes are applied, it means that more braking pressure is being applied on one side than on the other. This happens if some of the brake linings have become soaked in oil or brake fluid (so they lose

[423]

braking effectiveness), if brake shoes are unevenly or improperly adjusted, if tires are not evenly inflated, or if defective wheel cylinders or clogged brake lines are preventing uniform braking action at all wheels. In addition, a loose brake backing plate or the use of two different types of brake lining will cause the car to pull to one side when the brakes are applied.

Linings will become soaked with oil if the lubricant level in the differential and rear axle is too high since this usually results in leakage past the oil seal (Fig. 15-2). The oil leaks onto the brake linings and soaks them. At the front wheel, brake linings may

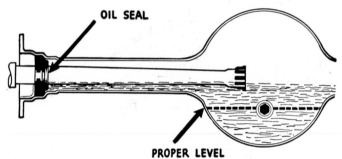

OIL SEAL

PROPER LEVEL

FIG. 15-2. A high lubricant level in the differential and rear-axle housing may cause leakage past the oil seal. This would result in soaked brake linings. (*Pontiac Motor Division of General Motors Corporation*)

become oil-soaked if the front-wheel bearings are improperly lubricated or if the oil seal is defective or not properly installed. Wheel cylinders will leak brake fluid onto the brake linings if they are defective, or if an actuating pin has been improperly installed (see item 10, below). If the linings at a left wheel become soaked with brake fluid or oil, for example, the car will tend to pull to the right. This is because the brakes will be more effective on the right side.

5. *Soft or spongy pedal.* If the pedal action is soft or spongy, it is likely that there is air in the system, although out-of-adjustment brake shoes could also cause this. Refer to item 9, below, for conditions that could allow air to get into the system.

6. *Poor braking action requiring excessive pedal pressure.* If the brake linings are soaked with oil or brake fluid, they will not hold well and excessive pedal pressure will be required for braking action. Improper brake-shoe adjustment or the use of the wrong brake lining could cause the same trouble. Sometimes, when brake

linings have become wet after a hard rain or after driving through deep water puddles, they will not hold very well. In this case, normal braking action will be restored after the brake linings have dried out. But if the linings are soaked with oil or brake-fluid, they must be replaced since it is not feasible to rid the linings of these contaminants. Another possible cause of poor braking action is excessive temperature. After the brakes have been applied for long

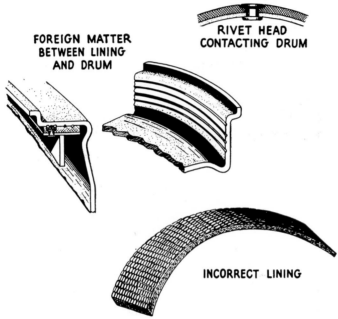

FOREIGN MATTER BETWEEN LINING AND DRUM

RIVET HEAD CONTACTING DRUM

INCORRECT LINING

FIG. 15-3. Brake drums can be scored by foreign matter—such as dirt particles—between the lining and drum, by worn linings that permit the rivet head to contact the drum, or by use of very harsh linings, especially on steel drums. (*Pontiac Motor Division of General Motors Corporation*)

periods, as when coming down a long hill, they begin to overheat. This overheating reduces braking effectiveness so that the brakes "fade." Often, if the brakes are allowed to cool, braking efficiency will be restored. However, excessively long periods of braking at high temperature may char the brake linings so that they must be replaced. Further, the brake drum may become glazed so that it is too smooth for effective braking action. In this case, the drum must be ground or turned to remove the glaze. Glazing may also take place even though the brakes are not overheated.

7. *Brakes too sensitive or brakes grab.* When the brakes are too sensitive and they brake hard, or grab, with slight brake-pedal pressure, it may be that the linings have become greasy (if linings are greasy, the brakes are apt to grab, but if they are soaked with oil, they will not produce much braking effect at all). If the brake shoes are out of adjustment, if the wrong lining is being used, or if drums are scored or rough (Fig. 15-3), grabbing may result as the linings come into contact with the drum. A loose backing plate may cause the same condition; as the linings come into contact with the drum, the backing plate shifts to give hard braking.

8. *Noisy brakes.* If the brake linings wear so much that the rivets come into contact with the brake drum (see Fig. 15-3), if the shoes become warped so pressure on the drum is not uniform, if shoe

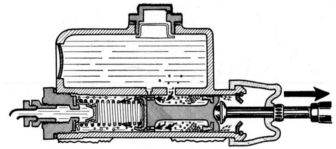

Fɪɢ. 15-4. If the filler vent becomes plugged, air may be drawn into the system on the return stroke of the piston, past the rear piston cup, as shown by the small arrows and bubbles. (*Pontiac Motor Division of General Motors Corporation*)

rivets become loose so they contact the drum, or if the drum becomes rough or worn, brakes will become noisy. Any of these conditions is apt to cause a squeak or squeal when the brakes are applied. Also, loose parts, such as the brake backing plate, may rattle.

9. *Air in system.* If air gets into the hydraulic system, poor braking and a spongy pedal will result. Air can get into the system if the filler vent becomes plugged (Fig. 15-4), since this might tend to create a partial vacuum in the system on the return stroke of the piston. Air could then bypass the rear piston cup (as shown by the arrows) and enter the system. It is possible to accidentally plug the vent (by wrench action) when the filler plug is removed. Always check the vent and clean it when the plug is removed and replaced.

[426]

Air can also get into the system if the master-cylinder valve is leaky and does not hold pressure in the system. This could allow air to seep in around the wheel-cylinder piston cups since there would be no pressure holding the cups tight against the cylinder walls. Probably the most common cause of air in the braking system is low brake fluid in the master cylinder. If the brake fluid drops below the compensating port, then the hydraulic system will draw air in as the piston moves forward on the braking stroke. Air in the system must be removed by adding brake fluid and bleeding the system as described in a later section.

10. *Loss of brake fluid.* Brake fluid can be lost if the master cylinder leaks, if the wheel cylinder leaks, if the line connections are

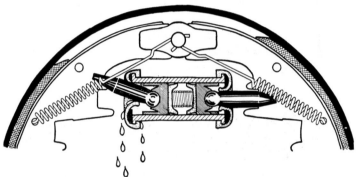

Fɪɢ. 15-5. Incorrect installation of the actuating pin will cause a side thrust on the piston which will permit leakage of brake fluid from the wheel cylinder. Pin must always align in the notch in the brake-shoe. (*Pontiac Motor Division of General Motors Corporation*)

loose, or if the line is damaged. One possible cause of wheel-cylinder leakage is incorrect installation of the actuating pin (Fig. 15-5). If the pin is cocked, as shown, then the side thrust on the piston may permit leakage past the piston. Leakage from other causes at the master cylinder or wheel cylinder requires removal and repair, or replacement, of the defective parts.

§**197. Brake service**   Whenever you encounter a complaint of faulty braking action, always try to analyze it and determine its cause, as noted in the previous section. In many cases, a minor adjustment of the brakes is all that will be required. However, at times the brakes must have a major adjustment—addition of brake fluid, bleeding of the system, repair or replacement of the master or wheel cylinders, or replacement of the brake linings. Also, brake drums may require grinding or turning. The following sections describe these various services.

§198. Adjustment of brakes Brake adjustments are divided into two classes, minor adjustments and major adjustments. Minor adjustments compensate for brake-lining wear and are made without removing the car wheels (Figs. 15-7 and 15-12). Major adjustments require aligning of the brake shoes by moving both toe and heel ends of the shoes. The latter adjustment is required after removal and installation of brake shoes or drums, or when the anchors have been otherwise disturbed. The minor and major brake adjustments detailed below are typical but vary somewhat from car to car. In addition to these adjustments, the brake pedal must be adjusted after the brake shoes have been correctly aligned. The brake pedal is usually adjusted by turning the rod linking the brake pedal and the piston in the master cylinder. Before brake adjustment is attempted on any particular car, the car manufacturer's shop manual should be consulted.

Before any adjustment is attempted, the fluid level in the master cylinder, the brake-pedal toe-board clearance, and brake-lining and brake-drum condition should be checked. Fluid should be added (§212) and the brake-pedal linkage adjusted, as necessary. For minor brake adjustments, it is not necessary to remove all four wheels to check the brake-lining condition, since similar conditions should be found at each wheel. Thus, as a rule, only one drum and wheel need be removed. Remove a front wheel since front-wheel linings wear faster than rear-wheel linings. However, for a major adjustment, all four wheels will be removed, so that all brake linings and drums can be checked. Linings should be inspected for wear or contamination with grease or oil. Drums should be inspected for roughness or scoring. See §§208 and 209 for lining and drum service.

Caution: Handle brake linings with care to avoid getting grease on them. Even slight amounts of grease—from greasy fingers—may cause uneven brake action.

Before the major brake adjustment is made, wheel-cylinder clamps should be installed, if specified, and the shoe return springs and shoes should be removed, so that all dirt and rust can be cleaned from metal parts. Then all metal contact points should be lubricated with special lubricant (keep lubricant from brake linings) and the shoes and springs reinstalled. Make sure that the return springs have normal tension. Replace weak springs.

CHECK YOUR PROGRESS
Progress Quiz 7

Here is another progress quiz—another chance for you to check yourself on the progress you are making in the book. The quiz below covers the first half of the chapter. As you take the quiz, you will find it helps you to review what you have learned. It will also give you a tip-off if you haven't learned the important details well enough. This gives you a chance to review the important points so you will remember them.

Correcting Trouble Lists

The purpose of this exercise is to help you spot related and unrelated troubles on a list. For example, in the list, *All brakes drag; incorrect brake pedal adjustment, reservoir filler vent clogged, air in lines, mineral oil in system,* you can see that *air in lines* does not belong because that condition could hardly cause all brakes to drag. Any of the other conditions in the list could. In each list, you will find one item that does not belong. Write down each list in your notebook, but *do not write down* the item that does not belong.

1. Brake pedal goes to floorboard: brake shoes out of adjustment, brake pedal out of adjustment, brake linings worn, lack of brake fluid, brake line clogged, air in system, worn master cylinder.
2. One brake drags: brake shoes out of adjustment, clogged brake line, wheel cylinder defective, master cylinder defective, weak return spring.
3. All brakes drag: incorrect brake pedal adjustment, filler vent clogged, mineral oil in system, brake lining soaked with oil.
4. Car pulls to one side when braking: brake linings soaked with oil or brake fluid, shoes out of adjustment, tires not uniformly inflated, brake line clogged, master cylinder defective, defective wheel cylinder, backing plate loose, mismatched linings.
5. Soft or spongy pedal: air in system, brake lining water-soaked, shoes out of adjustment.
6. Poor braking action requiring excessive pedal pressure: brake linings hot, brake linings wet, brake linings soaked with oil or brake

[429]

fluid, shoes out of adjustment, glazed brake drums, brake drums scored.

7. Brakes too sensitive or brakes grab: shoes out of adjustment, backing plates loose, linings greasy, drums scored, linings soaked with oil, wrong linings.

8. Brakes noisy: linings worn, shoes warped, shoe rivets loose, brake drum rough or worn, air in lines, loose parts.

9. Air in system: plugged filler vent, leaky valve in master cylinder, high fluid level in reservoir, low fluid level in reservoir.

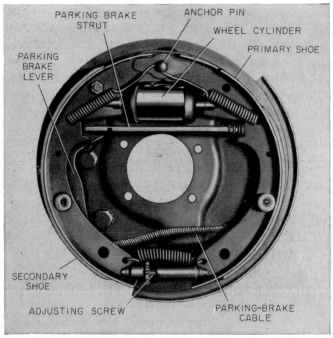

FIG. 15-6. Details of a Bendix rear-wheel brake mechanism. (*Oldsmobile Division of General Motors Corporation*)

10. Loss of brake fluid: master cylinder leaks, wheel cylinder leaks, mismatched linings, loose line connections, damaged brake tube.

§199. Bendix brake adjustments The Bendix brake shown in Fig. 2-16 and 15-6 has been used on later-model General Motors and Ford Motor Company automobiles (and others). In this assembly, the brake shoes are held in position by hold-down cups and springs. There is an expanding adjusting screw (star-shaped) at the bottom (see Fig. 15-6) that can be turned to move the brake shoes outward toward the brake drum and can thus compensate for brake-lining wear. In addition, the anchor pin is either eccentric or assembled in a slotted hole. This arrangement makes it possible to shift the upper ends of the brake shoes to the front or back, or up or down, so that the clearances between the linings and drum will be equalized when the brakes are released. Normally, the anchor pin will not require adjustment unless parts have been replaced or repaired.

1. Bendix brake minor adjustment. To make a minor adjustment, jack up the car until all four wheels clear the floor. Loosen or disconnect the parking-brake cables at the parking-brake equalizer,

BRAKE SHOE
ADJUSTER

TO EXPAND SHOES

Fig. 15-7. Adjusting brakes with brake-adjustment tool inserted through adjusting-hole cover. (*Buick Motor Division of General Motors Corporation*)

and remove the adjusting-hole covers at all wheels. Expand brake shoes by turning the star adjusting screw (Fig. 15-7). This is done by moving the outer end of the tool upward (as shown) repeatedly until a heavy drag is felt on the wheel as it is turned. Then back off the adjusting screw approximately 14 to 16 notches. Brake adjustment should then be correct. If a heavy drag is still felt at the wheel, it will be necessary to readjust the anchor pin as explained under major adjustments, below. If this is not necessary, replace adjusting-hole covers and then adjust the parking-brake cables.

2. Parking-brake adjustment. In adjusting the parking brakes, the objective is to tighten them sufficiently to assure adequate braking when the brake handle is pulled most of the way out. There should be some reserve—that is, it should not be necessary to pull the handle all the way out to secure full braking. On the other hand, the adjustment should not be so tight as to cause the brake shoes to be shifted toward the brake drum with the brake handle all the way in (retracted). Parking brakes are adjusted in different ways depending on the type of linkage used between the brake handle and the cables leading to the parking-brake levers at the wheels. Chevrolet, for instance, specifies that, first, the parking-brake handle should be pulled out for seven clicks of the pawl (not seven notches). Then, check nuts at cable ends should be loosened, forward check nuts should be turned against the clevis plates to draw each brake cable up until a moderate drag is felt when wheel is rotated, and the check nuts should be tightened securely. To check, set parking-brake handle back two clicks from full release; no brake-shoe drag should be felt.

On Ford, the parking brake is adjusted by first checking the position of the equalizer lever pin with the handle in the released position. The lever pin should align horizontally with the frame cross member. If it does not, adjust equalizer lever nut until it is correctly positioned. Then remove the slack from the brake cables by turning the adjusting nuts on the equalizer rod. But do not tighten the cables too much or the shoes will be pulled off their anchors.

§200. Bendix brake major adjustment   To make a major adjustment, jack up the car and remove the wheels, wheel hubs, and brake drums. Check the brake linings for wear and the brake-drum braking surfaces for smoothness. Worn brake linings should be replaced (§208) and excessively rough drums should be turned or ground (§209). Disconnect brake-shoe return springs, and remove brake-shoe hold-down cups, springs, and brake shoes. Examine shoes for defects as noted in §208. Clean all parts that are dirty or rusty, taking extreme care to avoid getting grease on the brake linings. Even slight traces of grease—from greasy fingers—might be sufficient to cause eccentric braking action and might require brake-lining replacement. If wheel cylinders give any indication of leakage or other defect, they should be removed for servicing or replacement (§210).

Lubricate all metal contact points with special lubricant (Fig. 15-8). Reinstall brake shoes and brake-drum assemblies. Adjust front-wheel bearings as required (§§96, 108, and 114). Add brake fluid to master cylinder and adjust brake-pedal toe-board clearance as already noted (§198). With these preliminaries out of the way, the anchor pin is adjusted as necessary. The procedure for making these adjustments varies to some extent. Typical procedures follow:

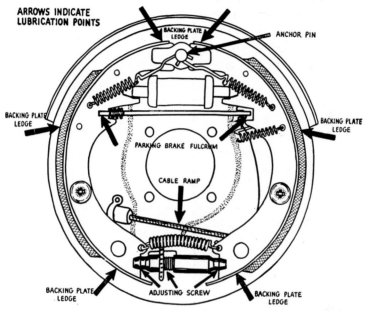

Fig. 15-8. Lubrication points in wheel-brake mechanism indicated by arrows. The backing-plate ledges are areas on which the brake shoes ride as they move toward or away from the brake drum. (*Pontiac Motor Division of General Motors Corporation*)

1. Chevrolet (slotted anchor-pin hole). Loosen the anchor-pin nut (Fig. 15-9) just enough to permit pin to shift in slotted hole—but no more than this or pin will tilt. Turn brake adjusting screw (star screw) to expand shoes so a heavy drag is felt as drum is turned (Fig. 15-7). Tap pin and backing plate lightly to center shoes in drum. If drag on drum is reduced, tighten star screw a few notches to restore drag. Again tap pin and backing plate. Repeat if necessary until drag remains constant. This means shoes are now centered. Tighten anchor nut just enough to hold without shifting.

Back off adjusting screw 10 notches and check clearance at toe and heel of secondary (rear) shoe with a 0.010-inch feeler (Fig. 15-10). If clearances at ends of shoe are not equal, tap anchor pin up or down to equalize clearance. Then tighten nut to 60 to 80 lb-ft torque. Finally, replace wheels and then make minor adjustment, as above (§199), backing off each star adjusting screw 14 notches from the light-drag position. Replace hole covers, adjust parking brakes, and then road-test brakes.

Fig. 15-9. Loosening anchor-pin nut in preparation for pin adjustment. (*Buick Motor Division of General Motors Corporation*)

Fig. 15-10. Checking clearance between shoe and brake drum by inserting feeler gauge through checking slot in drum. (*Buick Motor Division of General Motors Corporation*)

2. Ford (slotted anchor-pin hole). The anchor pin adjustment is similar to Chevrolet, and Ford suggests this procedure: Insert 0.010-inch feeler gauge between lower end of secondary (rear) shoe and move gauge up until the shoe is wedged forward. Expand shoes by turning star adjusting screw and then back off until 0.010 inch clearance is established 1½ inches from ends of secondary shoe. If this clearance cannot be obtained, loosen the anchor-pin nut just enough to let pin slip—but do not loosen too much or pin will tilt.

[434]

Tap nut with soft hammer to position shoe. Tap up to increase clearance at adjusting-screw end of shoe. Tighten nut, make minor adjustment to establish correct shoe clearance, adjust parking brakes, and road-test car.

3. *Cadillac-Oldsmobile (eccentric anchor pin)*. Loosen handbrake cable so levers are free at rear wheels. Then insert 0.015-inch

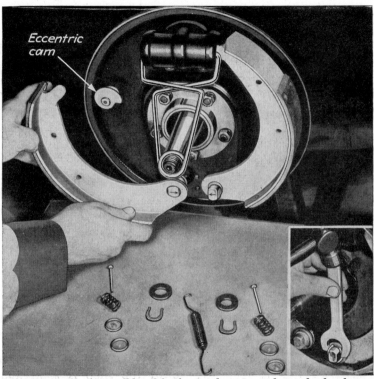

Fig. 15-11. Details of a Lockheed brake mechanism with one brake shoe partly removed. Minor adjustment is made by turning the eccentric cam. (*Plymouth Division of Chrysler Corporation*)

feeler gauge at lower end of secondary (rear shoe) and wedge shoe forward by moving gauge up. Expand shoes by turning star adjusting screw until primary shoe is tight against the drum and secondary shoe is snug on feeler. Back off just enough to establish 0.015 inch clearance 1½ inches from each end of secondary shoe. If 0.015 inch clearance cannot be obtained, loosen anchor-pin lock nut and turn eccentric anchor pin as required to equalize clearances. For instance, if clearance is excessive at the top, turn the anchor pin in

[435]

the direction that the wheel rotates as the car moves forward. Tighten lock nut, recheck clearances, and road-test brakes.

§201. Lockheed brake adjustments The Lockheed brake (shown partly disassembled in Fig. 15-11) is used on Chrysler Corporation cars (Plymouth, Dodge, De Soto, and Chrysler) and has been used on many other cars (Ford prior to 1949, for example). In this

assembly, the lower ends of the brake shoes are attached by anchor bolts and there is a pair of cams near the middle of the brake shoes to provide for clearance adjustments. The upper ends of the shoes rest against the pistons in the wheel cylinders. Normally, the only adjustment required is to turn the two eccentric cams so as to compensate for lining wear and maintain proper clearance between the brake shoes and brake drum.

§202. Lockheed minor brake adjustment To make a minor adjustment, jack up the wheels, and turn the front brake-shoe adjusting cam (eccentric cam) until the shoe is solid against the brake drum. Then back off cam until the wheel may be

Fig. 15-12. Adjusting brake-shoe clearances by turning cams (1). (*Plymouth Division of Chrysler Corporation*)

spun without interference (Fig. 15-12). Turn the rear brake-shoe adjusting cam until the shoe lining is solid against the brake drum. Then back off until the wheel may be spun freely. Road-test the car.

§203. Lockheed major brake adjustment After removing the wheels, hub assemblies, brake-shoe return springs and brake shoes, clean all parts. Figure 15-11 shows a brake shoe being removed. Note the use of the special brake-shoe-clip removing tool in the lower right-hand corner of the illustration. Note also the use of the wheel-cylinder clamp. This is important on the Lockheed brake to prevent the wheel-cylinder pistons from pushing out of the cylinder when the brake shoes are removed.

When handling the brake shoes, be very careful to avoid getting grease or oil on the linings. New linings should be installed and the brake drum rebored, if necessary (see §§208 and 209).

After the brake shoes are reinstalled, a special tool should be used to centralize the shoes with respect to the drum (Figs. 15-13

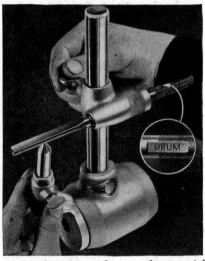

Fig. 15-13. Checking brake-drum alignment with special gauge. (*Plymouth Division of Chrysler Corporation*)

Fig. 15-14. Transferring the special gauge setting—from drum—to the brake-shoe gauge. (*Plymouth Division of Chrysler Corporation*)

to 15-16). As a first step in the procedure, the drum-gauge part of the tool is used to check drum alignment (Fig. 15-13). The gauge is then set to indicate accurately the inside diameter of the brake drum. Next, this measurement is transferred to the shoe gauge as shown in Fig. 15-14. This is done by setting the gauge so that the edge of the finger marked "drum" just touches the point of the brake-drum gauge as shown in the illustration.

Check the positions of the arrows on the brake-shoe anchor bolts and make sure that each arrow points *away from* the heel of the shoe that the bolt controls. See Figs. 15-15 and 15-16.

The adapter bushing is then installed on the steering knuckle

[437]

(for front-wheel-brake adjustment) or on the rear-axle shaft (for rear-wheel-brake adjustment). The finger of the brake-shoe gauge should be turned from "drum" to "heel" and the gauge should then be slid into position over the adapter as shown in Fig. 15-15 or 15-16. The "heel" setting will give the correct clearance of 0.006 inch for *both the heel and the toe* of the shoe.

NOTE: On earlier models (prior to 1946 on Plymouth), the "toe" edge of the gauge was used to set toe of single-wheel-cylinder brakes. But on later models, the "heel" edge is used to check both the heel and toe of the shoe.

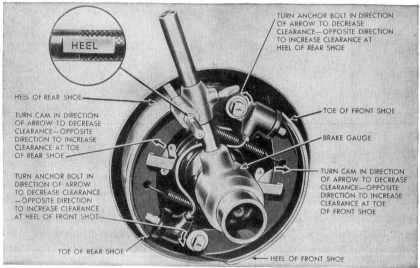

FIG. 15-15. Adjusting front-wheel brake shoes. (*Plymouth Division of Chrysler Corporation*)

Swing the brake-shoe gauge around until the finger is over the toe of the shoe. Then turn the adjusting cam until the lining is in contact with the gauge finger. See Figs. 15-15 and 15-16.

Next, swing the gauge around until the finger is over the heel of the brake shoe. Turn the anchor bolt until the lining is in contact with the gauge finger. See Figs. 15-15 and 15-16.

Recheck the toe clearance. Readjust it if necessary. Then recheck and readjust the heel clearance as needed. It may be necessary to repeat this procedure a couple of times to achieve uniform clearance of the shoe.

Repeat the procedure outlined for each shoe. When the shoes are adjusted, tighten locking nuts, install wheel and hub assemblies, and road-test the car.

§204. Transmission-shaft hand brake Figure 14-6 shows a hand brake which operates on a drum assembled on the transmission shaft. Figure 15-17 shows a disassembled view of the same hand brake. This is an external-contracting type of brake—that is, the brake band surrounds the brake drum and contracts as the hand brake is applied. An internal-expanding type of transmission-shaft hand brake is shown in Figs. 15-18 and 15-19. In this unit, there

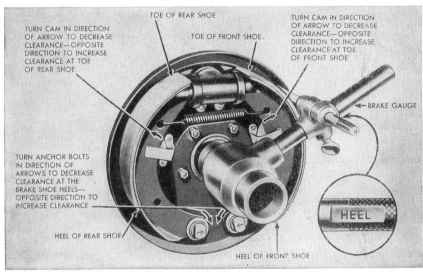

Fig. 15-16. Adjusting rear-wheel brake shoes. (*Plymouth Division of Chrysler Corporation*)

are two brake shoes that expand, or move out, against the brake drum. In both types the brake drum is assembled onto the end of the transmission shaft; when the brake is applied, the shaft is held stationary by the brake band or brake shoes. Adjustment and repair procedures for these two hand brakes are given below.

1. External contracting adjustment. Adjust anchor bolt (No. 2 in Fig. 14-6) so the clearance between the drum and lining at the anchor bracket on the brake band is 0.020 inch. Lock anchor bolt securely. But do not draw up the lock wire on the anchor bolt tightly; this would restrict brake action. Then turn adjusting nut

[439]

(No. 1 in Fig. 14-6) until clearance between band and bottom of drum is 0.020 inch. Finally, turn the adjusting-bolt nut (No. 3 in Fig. 14-6) to get 0.020 inch clearance between band and top of drum. Adjust hand-brake cable by loosening the lock nut (No. 4 in Fig. 14-6) and removing the clevis pin from the yoke. Then turn yoke until cable slack is removed with the actuating cam flat against the end bracket on the band. With proper adjustment, the

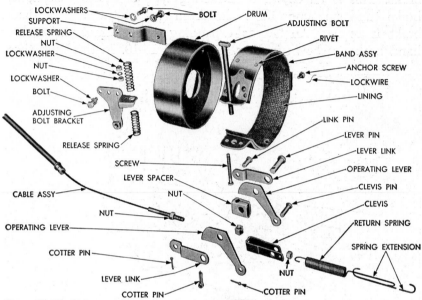

Fig. 15-17. Disassembled view of transmission-shaft hand brake. (*Dodge Division of Chrysler Corporation*)

hand brake should lock when the lever is pulled back four to six notches.

2. *External-contracting band replacement.* There is very little involved in replacement of the brake band. Refer to Fig. 15-17. To remove the band, take off the anchor screw, and remove upper and lower adjusting nuts, screw, and bolt. Band can then be slipped off drum and over propeller shaft. Refer to Fig. 15-17 if other parts must be removed; it shows the proper relationship of the various parts.

3. *Internal expanding adjustment.* The numbers in parentheses below refer to numbered parts in Fig. 15-19 unless otherwise noted. With transmission in neutral and the hand brake released, discon-

nect front end of propeller shaft. Remove adjusting-screw cover plate (No. 24). Loosen cable clamp bolt (No. 33) and back off cable adjusting nut (No. 15). Turn brake-shoe adjusting nut (No. 6) until a slight drag is felt when the drum is turned. Back off nut at least one full notch (use special spanner). The two raised shoulders on the adjusting nut must be seated in the grooves on the adjusting

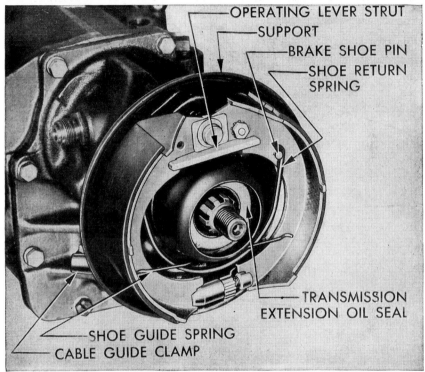

Fig. 15-18. Internal-expanding type of transmission-shaft hand brake assembled on transmission. Drum is not shown. (*Dodge Division of Chrysler Corporation*)

sleeve (No. 7). Position cable adjusting nut (No. 15) against cable housing so there is 0.005 to 0.010 inch clearance between the operating lever and the brake-shoe table. Lock adjustment by tightening clamp bolt and turning the adjusting nut tight against housing. Hand brake should now apply when handle is pulled out four to six clicks. Install adjusting-screw cover plate and connect propeller shaft.

4. *Internal expanding disassembly and assembly.* Figures 15-18 and 15-19 show the relationship of the various parts in the brake

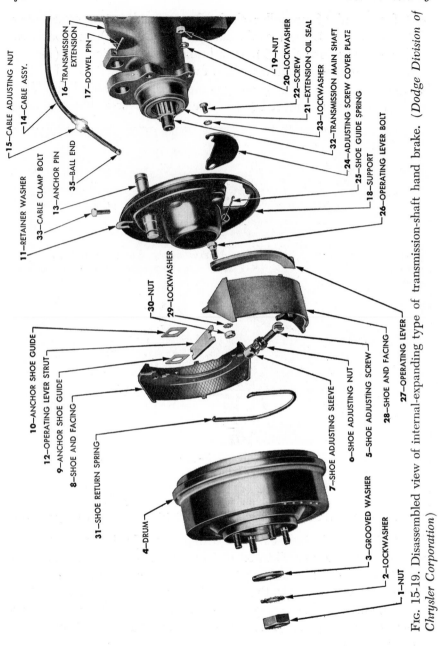

FIG. 15-19. Disassembled view of internal-expanding type of transmission-shaft hand brake. (*Dodge Division of Chrysler Corporation*)

15—CABLE ADJUSTING NUT
14—CABLE ASSY.
16—TRANSMISSION EXTENSION
17—DOWEL PIN
19—NUT
20—LOCKWASHER
22—SCREW
21—EXTENSION OIL SEAL
23—LOCKWASHER
32—TRANSMISSION MAIN SHAFT
24—ADJUSTING SCREW COVER PLATE
25—SHOE GUIDE SPRING
18—SUPPORT
26—OPERATING LEVER BOLT
11—RETAINER WASHER
33—CABLE CLAMP BOLT
13—ANCHOR PIN
35—BALL END
30—NUT
29—LOCKWASHER
10—ANCHOR SHOE GUIDE
12—OPERATING LEVER STRUT
9—ANCHOR SHOE GUIDE
8—SHOE AND FACING
31—SHOE RETURN SPRING
7—SHOE ADJUSTING SLEEVE
6—SHOE ADJUSTING NUT
5—SHOE ADJUSTING SCREW
28—SHOE AND FACING
27—OPERATING LEVER
4—DRUM
3—GROOVED WASHER
2—LOCKWASHER
1—NUT

assembly and should serve as a satisfactory guide in case the brake must be disassembled for replacement of linings (or other parts). The linings are of the bonded, or cemented, type. Replacement of linings on brake shoes is covered in a later section.

§205. Lockheed self-adjusting brakes Figures 15-20 to 15-22 show the details of this type of brake. The brake shoes are self-centering

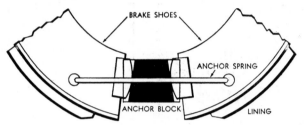

Fig. 15-20. Self-centering device on brake. Curved flanges on the ends of the shoes can ride up or down on anchor block to center shoes. (*Studebaker-Packard Corporation*)

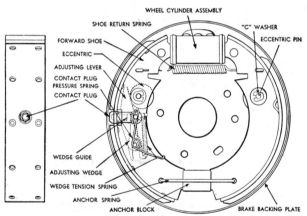

Fig. 15-21. Details of the self-adjusting device on brake. (*Studebaker-Packard Corporation*)

and, further, automatically adjust for lining wear. Thus, no minor adjustments are required. Adjustment is needed only when new linings are installed. Operation and adjustment procedures follow.

1. *Operation.* The self-centering device makes use of an anchor block which is rigidly attached to the backing plate (Fig. 15-20). The sides of the block are machined so they point toward the center of the axle. Rounded flanges on the ends of the shoes ride on these sides of the block. When the brakes are applied, the rounded flanges

[443]

will slide down along the sides of the anchor block. Thus, the shoes center themselves with respect to the drum.

The self-adjusting device is built into the shoes (Figs. 15-21 and 15-22). Numbers in parentheses below refer to numbered parts in Fig. 15-22. There is a contact plug (No. 4) which extends through a hole in the brake lining, as shown in Fig. 15-23, to contact the

Fig. 15-22. Assembly of the self-adjusting device on the brake shoe: 1, shoe return spring; 2, brake eccentric cam; 3, adjusting lever; 4, contact plug; 5, wedge guide; 6, plug-and-lever pin; 7, wedge; 8, wedge spring; 9, lower pivot pin. (*Studebaker-Packard Corporation*)

Fig. 15-23. Contact plug (1) held in position in shoe by actuating spring (2). (*Studebaker-Packard Corporation*)

brake drum. The inner end of the plug is pinned to the adjusting lever (No. 3) which, in turn, is pinned at its lower end to the brake shoe by the lower pivot pin (No. 9). The upper end of the lever bears against the brake eccentric cam (No. 2). There is a spring-actuated wedge (No. 7) between the plug-and-lever pin (No. 6) and the wedge guide (No. 5).

During brake application, the shoe carries the plug (No. 4) with it so the plug contacts the brake drum. As the brake lining wears (the plug does not wear appreciably), the plug is pushed inward when the brake shoe moves out to the brake drum. This inward movement of the plug widens the distance between the pin (No. 6) and the guide (No. 5) and allows the adjusting wedge (No. 7) to move upward. This movement takes up any play between the wedge guide and the pin (No. 6). Now, when the brakes are released, the shoe cannot move back as far as before. In other words, the brake shoe has been adjusted, or moved outward, to compensate for lining wear. The self-adjusting action continues, with the wedge gradually advancing upward, until the lining has worn to a point where it must be replaced. When this point is reached, the contact plug has reached its full limit of travel. Further lining wear then

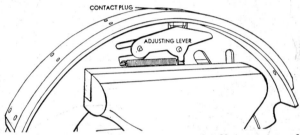

Fig. 15-24. Clamping shoe in vise in preparation for filing contact plug. (*Studebaker-Packard Corporation*)

causes increased brake-pedal travel; this warns the driver that lining replacement is due.

2. *Brake-shoe service.* The brake shoes are removed as already described. After the shoes are relined (see §208), the self-adjusting device must be reassembled in those shoes which use it. Refer to Fig. 15-22, which shows the relationships among the parts. The device is installed on the inner side (backing-plate side) of the shoe web. First, install the wedge guide (No. 5). Then position the wedge so its yoke straddles the pivot-pin hole in the web of the shoe. Insert the contact plug (No. 4) and put the plug damper spring between the plug and web. Install the adjusting lever (No. 3), the plug actuating spring, and wedge tension spring (No. 8). The contact plug must then be filed so it conforms to the curved contour of the lining. To file it, clamp the shoe in a vise so the jaws of the vise bear against the adjusting lever (Fig. 15-24). This prevents movement of the contact plug. The thickness gauge which is included in the brake-lining kit should be installed on the

lining so the lining will not be damaged while the contact plug is filed.

Check the action of the contact plug, after assembly, by completely depressing the plug, retracting the wedge, and noting if the plug is free to move. Then check the wedge action by releasing the

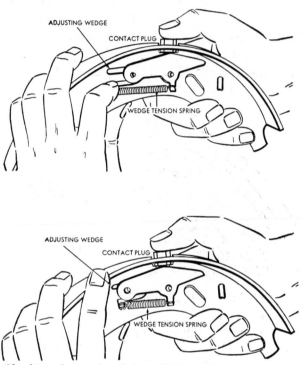

FIG. 15-25. Checking the action of the self-adjusting device on the brake shoe. *Top,* see if contact plug is free when the adjusting wedge is held in the fully retracted position. *Bottom,* see if wedge advances when plug is pushed in. (*Studebaker-Packard Corporation*)

wedge when the plug is all the way out. Press the plug in and note if the wedge advances as the plug moves in. Figure 15-25 shows how to make these checks.

§206. Brake adjustment   On the type of brake shown in Fig. 2-17, the adjustment for lining wear is made by turning an adjusting cover on the wheel cylinder. Jack up all four car wheels, and disconnect the emergency- or parking-brake cables at the idler lever. Remove the adjusting-hole covers, insert a screw driver through one of the adjusting holes, and turn the adjusting cover in a clockwise direction (when looking at the end of the cylinder) until the shoe causes a slight drag on the brake drum (Fig. 15-26). Then turn the adjusting cover back four notches to provide running clearance. Repeat for the other brake shoe. Repeat at all four wheels. Adjust the parking brake by fully releasing the brake lever, loosening the check nuts at the cable ends, and pulling the cables until a positive stop is felt. Hold the cable and adjust the check nuts against the clevis plates. Tighten the nuts securely. No other adjustments are provided on this type of brake.

Fig. 15-26. Adjusting brake shoes by turning adjusting cover on wheel cylinder. (*Chevrolet Motor Division of General Motors Corporation*)

§**207. Brake repair** Various brake parts may require repair. The brake linings may need to be replaced on the brake shoes, the brake drums may need reboring or grinding, brake tubing may require replacement, the wheel cylinders or master cylinder may need rebuilding, or the hydraulic system may require flushing or bleeding. The procedures for performing all of these operations are detailed below.

§**208. Brake lining** As a first step in replacing brake linings, the brake shoes must be removed (as already explained). Brake linings can be checked by removing one front wheel and noting their condition (brake drum can be checked at the same time). It can normally be assumed that the brake linings at the other three wheels will be in about the same condition. If the linings are oil-

or brake-fluid-soaked, or if they are worn down to the replacement point, then linings at all wheels should be replaced.

1. Shoe inspection. When the shoes have been removed, they should be cleaned and checked for distortion, cracks, or other defects (Fig. 15-27). You can check a shoe for distortion or warping by laying the web on a flat surface plate. Put it on the corner of the surface plate so you can see how snugly the web lies on the surface. If the web is twisted, the shoe is bent. It is somewhat difficult to

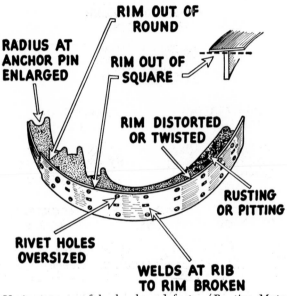

Fig. 15-27. Various types of brake-shoe defects. (*Pontiac Motor Division of General Motors Corporation*)

straighten accurately a bent or warped shoe. Such conditions, and other shoe defects, require installation of new shoes. Shoes may become distorted from high temperatures due to excessive braking or from improper lining installation.

2. Lining replacement. Brake linings are either riveted or cemented (bonded) to the brake shoes. Some manufacturers recommend that on the bonded type no attempt should be made to install new linings on the shoes. The shoes should be replaced when the linings have become worn. Other manufacturers supply information on the bonding procedure. Typical replacement procedures on both riveted and bonded types follow:

[448]

a. Riveted type. On the riveted type, drill out the rivets to remove the old lining. Do not punch them out since this may distort the shoe. Avoid using too large a drill because this would enlarge the rivet holes in the shoe and make it hard to do a good reinstallation job. Clean the shoe surfaces and file off any burrs or rough spots. Wash the shoe in degreasing compound and wipe dry. Then put the new lining in place and attach it with the two center rivets. Use a roll type of set to set the rivets. A pointed punch might

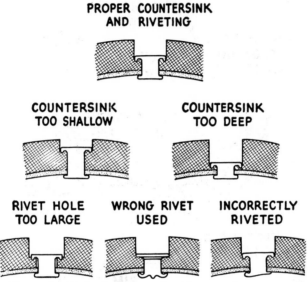

Fig. 15-28. The right method contrasted with several wrong methods of installing brake-shoe rivets. (*Pontiac Motor Division of General Motors Corporation*)

split the rivets. Figure 15-28 shows the right way contrasted with several wrong ways of installing rivets.

Caution: Be sure your hands are dry and free of grease or oil. Remember, even a slight trace of grease on a brake lining may cause erratic braking action that would require installation of another lining.

With the center rivets set, use a brake-lining clamp (Fig. 15-29), if necessary, to hold the lining against the shoe, and install the outer rivets. A special riveting press should be used (Fig. 15-30) if it is available.

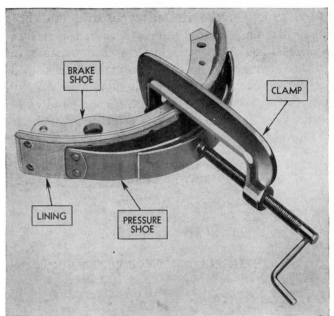

F‍IG. 15-29. Using brake-lining clamp to hold the brake lining tightly against the brake shoe during the riveting operation. (*Chevrolet Motor Division of General Motors Corporation*)

b. Bonded type. On the bonded type of shoe, the shoe should be put in a vise and a hammer and chisel used to chip off the old lining. Use care to avoid damaging or distorting the shoe. Next, the shoe should be cleaned in degreasing compound and the face sanded off smooth and bright. The new precemented lining should be put into position on the shoe and clamped into place with a special lining clamp (Fig. 15-31) as shown in Fig. 15-32.

N‍OTE: If the lining is old or of the type requiring cement, apply cement before the clamping operation.

Put the shoe, with the lining in place, into an oven at the specified temperature and leave it for the specified time. Then, using asbestos gloves, remove the shoe. Take off the clamp and allow the shoe to cool slowly. Do not dip the shoe in water or blow air on it. This might cause the shoe to become distorted.

A variation of the above procedure makes use of an anvil type of bonder. The anvil has an internal heating element and is curved to conform to the shape of the shoe. There is a slot in which the shoe web fits. To use the anvil type of bonder, the shoe is clamped

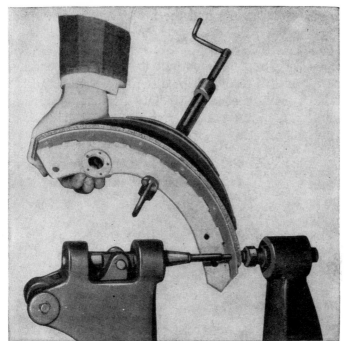

Fig. 15-30. Riveting the brake lining to the brake shoe. (*Chevrolet Motor Division of General Motors Corporation*)

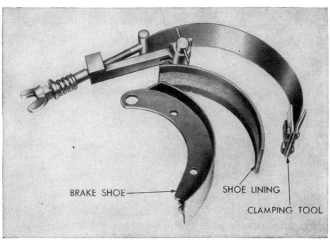

BRAKE SHOE

SHOE LINING

CLAMPING TOOL

Fig. 15-31. Special clamping tool for clamping bonded type of shoe lining to brake shoe. (*Dodge Division of Chrysler Corporation*)

[451]

on the anvil (web in slot) and the heating element turned on for the specified time.

Caution: It is extremely important to follow the bonding procedure exactly. Any trace of dirt or oil on the bonding surfaces will prevent the formation of a satisfactory bond. Also, if the curing time is incorrect, or the curing temperature too high or too low, a poor bond will result.

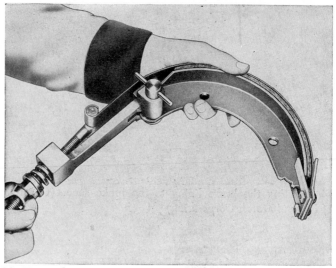

Fig. 15-32. Using clamping tool to clamp bonded type of shoe lining to brake shoe. (*Dodge Division of Chrysler Corporation*)

3. *Grinding linings.* To assure more perfect brake operation with new linings, some manufacturers recommend the use of a brake-lining grinder, such as shown in Fig. 15-33. The grinder shown is used after the brake shoes are reinstalled and adjusted. The grinding disk is adjusted to take a light cut on the linings. Then, when the grinder is rotated about the axle, it removes high spots or irregularities from the linings that would tend to cause poor braking action. Of course, if the brakes were used for a while, these high spots would be worn down so that good braking action would be attained. The grinder simply makes it certain that good braking will result immediately.

Another method of grinding new brake-shoe lining makes use of a special off-the-car fixture in which the shoe is assembled. The shoe is then brought into contact with a rotating grinding wheel so that high spots on the lining are eliminated. It is also possible, on this type of grinder, to take a slightly heavier cut at the toe and heel ends of the lining. The advantage of such a cut is that heavy toe or heel contact will be prevented during braking and consequently the center part of the lining can become effective. This assures good braking action.

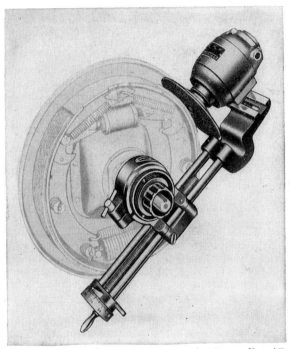

Fɪɢ. 15-33. Brake-lining grinder installed on wheel spindle. (*Barrett Equipment Company*)

§**209. Brake drum** Brake drums should be inspected for distortion, cracks, scores, roughness, or for excessive glaze or smoothness (glaze lowers friction and braking efficiency). Drums that are distorted or cracked should be discarded and new drums installed. Light score marks can be removed with fine emery cloth. All traces of emery must be removed after smoothing the drum. Deeper scores and roughness, as well as glaze, can be removed by turning or grinding the drum.

Caution: After grinding or turning a drum, be sure all traces of cuttings or abrasives are removed. Do not touch the finished surface or get any oil or grease on it. This would prevent normal braking action.

Cast-iron drums can be either turned or ground, but steel drums, because of their hardness, usually require grinding. Many automo-

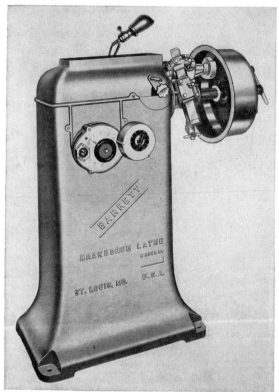

FIG. 15-34. Brake-drum lathe for reconditioning brake drums. (*Barrett Equipment Company*)

bile manufacturers recommend turning in preference to grinding, since a ground drum does not wear in as readily as a turned drum and is more apt to cause uneven braking when new. Figure 15-34 illustrates a typical drum lathe.

In the servicing of drums, only enough material should be removed to smooth up the braking surface. However, if it is necessary to take off considerable material, the drum should be turned oversize and oversized brake linings be installed. For instance, one car manufacturer recommends that, if the drum has to be turned to more than 0.010 inch oversize, it be turned to 0.030 inch oversize, so that the regularly supplied 0.030 inch oversize linings can be installed.

Caution: Removing excessive amounts of material will result in overheating of the drum during braking action, possible warping, and faulty brake action. Not more than about twenty-five per cent of the total thickness of the drum should be removed, in any event. If more than this amount must be removed to take out deep scores or roughness, new drums should be installed.

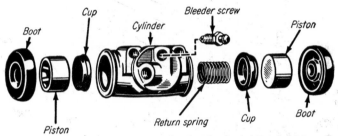

FIG. 15-35. Disassembled view of a wheel cylinder. (*Ford Motor Company*)

§**210. Wheel and master cylinder** Wheel and master cylinders must be disassembled and assembled with extreme care, in order to avoid getting the slightest trace of grease or dirt in them. Hands must be clean—washed with soap and water, not gasoline—since any trace of oil or gasoline on the cylinder parts may ruin them. Naturally, the bench and the tools must be clean.

To remove a wheel cylinder from the car, the wheel and the drum must be off and the brake pedal should be blocked up to prevent its operation. Then, the tube or hose should be disconnected from the cylinder and the cylinder removed by taking out the attaching bolts. The tube end at the wheel should be taped closed, to prevent entrance of dirt. The cylinder can be disassembled by rolling off the rubber boots or taking off the covers (see Fig. 15-35). All parts should be washed in brake-system cleaning fluid. Old boots and piston cups should be discarded if they are not in excellent condition. Some manufacturers recommend replacement of these parts every time the cylinder is disassembled. If the cylinder is scored, it should be polished with crocus cloth (not sandpaper or emery cloth).

[455]

Some manufacturers permit the use of a hone if the diameter of the cylinder is not increased more than a few thousandths of an inch. If scores do not come out, the cylinder should be replaced. Also, cylinder and pistons should be replaced if the clearance between them is excessive. When reassembling the cylinder, lubricate all parts with brake fluid.

Caution: Never allow any grease or oil to come in contact with rubber parts of the brake system, since this would cause them to swell and might destroy braking action.

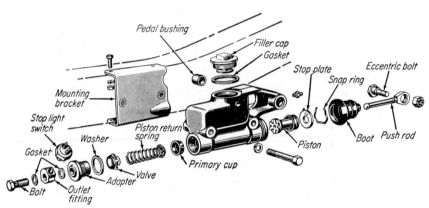

Fig. 15-36. Disassembled view of a brake master cylinder. (*Ford Motor Company*)

To remove a master cylinder, detach the brake pedal and brake line and take out the bolts holding the cylinder to the frame. Then, drain out the brake fluid and disassemble the cylinder by taking off the boot and removing the push rod and the snap ring or stop plate, so that piston, cup, spring, valve, and other parts will come out (see Fig. 15-36). Use extreme care to keep all parts clean and free of grease or oil. All old rubber parts that appear at all deteriorated should be discarded. Some manufacturers supply master-cylinder repair kits and recommend that the parts in such a kit be used to replace the old parts whenever a master cylinder is disassembled.

All parts should be washed in brake-system cleaning fluid. If the cylinder is scored, it should be polished with crocus cloth (not sandpaper or emery cloth). Some manufacturers permit the use of a hone provided the diameter of the cylinder is not increased more than a few thousandths of an inch. However, if light polishing or honing does not remove scores, the cylinder should be replaced.

Check the fit of the piston to the cylinder and, if the fit is not within specifications, replace the piston and cylinder.

On reassembly, lubricate the parts with brake fluid. Never allow grease or oil to come in contact with any rubber parts of the brake system.

§211. Preparing hydraulic-brake tubing for installation Special steel tubing must be used for hydraulic brakes since it is best able to withstand the high pressures developed in the system. Tubing must

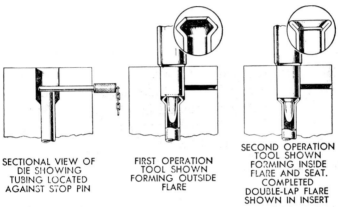

SECTIONAL VIEW OF DIE SHOWING TUBING LOCATED AGAINST STOP PIN

FIRST OPERATION TOOL SHOWN FORMING OUTSIDE FLARE

SECOND OPERATION TOOL SHOWN FORMING INSIDE FLARE AND SEAT. COMPLETED DOUBLE-LAP FLARE SHOWN IN INSERT

FIG. 15-37. The three steps in double-lap flaring hydraulic-brake tubing. (*Ford Motor Company*)

be cut off square with a special tube cutter. Tubing must not be cut with a jaw type of cutter or with a hack saw. Either of these methods may distort the tube and leave heavy burrs that would prevent normal flaring of the tube. After the tube has been cut off, a special flaring tool must be used to flare the tube. This is a three-step operation (Fig. 15-37): (1) The tubing is installed in the flaring fixtures after the new coupling nuts have been installed on the tubing and the end of the tubing has been dipped into brake fluid (for lubrication during flaring). Then the clamping nut or handle is tightened to hold the tubing at the proper depth in the fixture. (2) A forming tool is inserted and driven down with a few light hammer blows. This bows out the end of the tubing as shown at the center in Fig. 15-37. (3) The second forming tool is inserted and driven down with light hammer blows. This laps over the flare as the flare is final-formed (as shown to the right in Fig. 15-37).

§212. Flushing, filling, and bleeding the hydraulic system   *1. Flushing.* If dirt or damaging liquid has been introduced into the hydraulic system, it will be necessary to flush out the system. It must be repeated here that mineral oil should never be put into the system since it will cause the rubber parts to swell and deteriorate; braking action may be completely lost. When flushing the system only the special flushing compound recommended by the car manufacturer should be used. Anything else is apt to cause damage to the rubber, fabric, or metal parts in the system.

To flush the system, remove the bleeder-valve screws at all wheel cylinders and attach bleeder drains.

Caution: Clean away dirt and grease from around the valves so as to avoid getting any dirt into the cylinders. Any dirt at a valve or in a drain tube may get sucked into the cylinder on the brake-pedal return stroke. This could cause subsequent failure of the wheel cylinder and brakes at the wheel.

Put the lower ends of the drain tubes into clean glass jars (one tube in a jar is shown in Fig. 15-38). Unscrew the bleeder valves about three-fourths turn. Then operate the brake pedal with full strokes to force all fluid from the system. When all fluid is out, fill the master cylinder with brake-system cleaning fluid (use only recommended brake-system cleaning fluid). Use a master-cylinder filler such as is shown in place in Fig. 15-38, so that the reservoir will be replenished as the cleaning fluid passes through the system. Operate the brake pedal with full stokes until all the cleaning fluid in the reservoir and in the filler has passed through the system. Then use dry, clean air—applied through the master cylinder—to blow out all the liquid from the system. Do not apply too much air pressure. Finally, add new brake fluid and bleed the system as outlined in the following section.

2. Filling and bleeding the hydraulic brake system. Whenever a brake system has been flushed, when the fluid has become low, or when air has leaked into the system, the system must be bled to eliminate the air. Air in the system will cause a soft or spongy brake-pedal action; the air will compress when the brakes are applied and poor braking action will result. Air is eliminated by adding brake fluid and bleeding off a little of the fluid from each wheel cylinder. To add brake fluid, first make sure that the bleeder valves are closed at all cylinders. Then, either a master-cylinder reservoir filler such as shown in Fig. 15-38, or a pressure tank such as shown in Fig. 15-39, can be used. In either case, the reservoir filler or pressure tank should contain approved brake fluid.

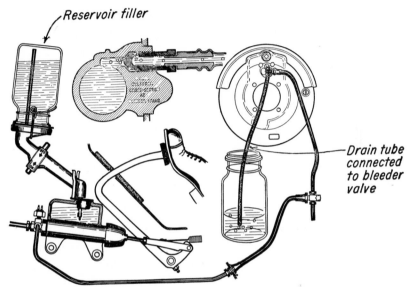

Fig. 15-38. Bleeding hydraulic system with a master-cylinder reservoir filler. (*Pontiac Motor Division of General Motors Corporation*)

When the reservoir is filled and the filler is in place (or pressure tank connected), install a bleeder drain and jar at one wheel cylinder (make sure dirt is cleaned from around the connection so that dirt will not get into wheel cylinder). Open the bleeder drain. When using the reservoir, have someone get into the car and pump the brake pedal with full strokes, allowing it to return slowly (Fig. 15-38). Continue until the fluid flows from the drain tube into the glass jar in a solid stream that is free of air bubbles. Make sure the end of the tube is below the liquid level in the jar, to prevent air from being sucked into the system on the brake-pedal return strokes. Tighten the bleeder valve, remove the drain tube, and replace the screw in the valve. Repeat the operation at the other wheel cylinders. Be sure to maintain proper fluid level in the master-cylinder

[459]

reservoir. When the bleeding operation is complete, remove the master-cylinder filler, make sure the fluid level in the reservoir is correct, and then install the filler plug and gasket. Make sure the vent is open.

When the pressure tank is used (Fig. 15-39), no assistant is needed. The pressure tank is first partly filled with brake fluid. Then, air is compressed in the tank by use of the tire-inflating equipment.

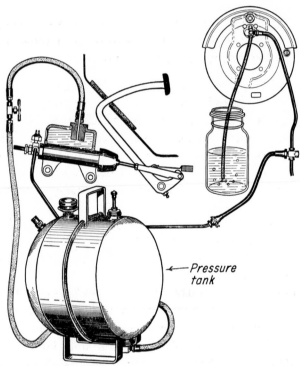

←—*Pressure tank*

FIG. 15-39. Bleeding hydraulic system with a pressure tank. (*Pontiac Motor Division of General Motors Corporation*)

The brake fluid is therefore under pressure in the tank. When the tank is connected to the master cylinder as shown in Fig. 15-39, and the valve is turned on, brake fluid flows from the tank, under pressure, to the master-cylinder reservoir. Brake fluid is forced through the brake line and wheel cylinder to which the drain tube has been connected, as shown. With the pressure tank, the valve in the line from the tank to the reservoir is turned on. Brake fluid is allowed to flow from the tank into the brake system, until the brake fluid runs from the drain tube in a solid stream without air bubbles. Then, the valve is tightened, the drain tube removed, and the screw replaced. The operation is repeated at each wheel cylinder.

Do not attempt to reuse the brake fluid in the glass jar. It is apt to be contaminated or dirty.

§**213. Servicing disk brakes** The disk brake described in §182 is serviced as follows:

Caution: Parts are not interchangeable between wheels. The parts in the brake assembly used at a wheel are matched and should be restored to the wheel from which they were taken.

1. *Disassembling front brake.* Remove damper springs and clips. Remove 10 attaching bolts. Note that there is a cutout cast in both the inner and outer housings; these should mate when the parts are assembled. Remove dust cap, cotter pin, nut, and washer. Then take off outer-housing-and-hub assembly (Fig. 14-18). Disconnect brake hose from frame connection and allow fluid to drain from it. On some models, the dust shield must be detached and slid off the brake hose.

Next, slide pressure plate assembly off (Fig. 14-19). Put assembly on a clean surface so linings will not be contaminated with oil, grease, or dirt. Lift off inner brake housing. Detach and remove spider and dust shield.

2. *Disassembling rear brake.* Remove damper springs and clips and 10 attaching bolts. Remove cotter pin, axle nut, and washer. Separate inner and outer housings. Then use a special puller and pull outer-housing-and-hub assembly from axle. Remove key from axle. Disconnect brake hose from tube at axle housing connection and allow fluid to drain. On some models, the dust shield must be detached and slid off the brake hose.

Next, slide the pressure-plate assembly off. One of the two buffer assemblies used in the rear pressure-plate assembly will drop out. Put assembly on a clean surface so linings will not be contaminated. Detach and remove spider and the grease seal assembly. Lift off the dust shield.

3. *Disassembling pressure-plate assembly.* Release automatic adjusters by inserting two thin-shank screw drivers between the release sleeves and the adjuster guides of the adjusters and twisting both

[461]

screw drivers at the same time. Remove four coil springs and separate the pressure plates. Figure 15-40 shows the pressure plates separated. Wheel cylinders can be removed from the inner pressure plate if they require replacement. If the adjusters need attention, they can be serviced without removing the adjuster bracket from the inner pressure plate.

4. Assembling pressure-plate assembly. With the wheel cylinders and adjusters in place, put the six steel balls on the inner pressure plate (Fig. 15-40) and place outer plate in position. It will be necessary to cock the wheel-cylinder push rods slightly. Secure with four retaining springs.

Fig. 15-40. Outer and inner pressure plates of disk brake separated. Note location of steel balls, wheel cylinders, and adjusters on the inner pressure plate. (*Chrysler Sales Division of Chrysler Corporation*)

5. Installing rear brake. Install dust shield. Wrap wax paper over axle shaft to protect seal lip. Install spider and seal assembly, aligning buffer loading-pin holes in spider with corresponding holes in dust shield. Install inner brake housing. Release both self-adjusters as noted in item 3, above. Insert the two buffer assemblies in the spider anchors, washer ends first. Make sure lock grooves in buffer face the dust shield. Use a pair of water-pump pliers and hold buffer in compressed position in spider leg while inserting a blunt-ended lock pin ($\frac{3}{16}$ inch in diameter by $1\frac{1}{2}$ inches long) through the hole in the dust shield. Lock both buffers in compressed position in this manner. Then install pressure-plate assembly and remove the two lock pins. Install brake-tube dust grommet (on models where it was removed) and connect brake hose to tube at axle housing. Put outer-housing-and-hub assembly into position, lining up keyways. Insert key and drive into position with fiber hammer. Install washer, axle nut, and cotter pin. Make sure outer housing and inner housing align according to markings or cast-in cutouts. Secure with 10 bolts, lock washers, and nuts. Install damper springs and clips and replace wheel.

6. *Installing front brake.* Install dust shield and spider. Make sure the pressure-plate antirattle pad-and-spring assembly is at a two-o'clock position on the right-front wheel and at a ten-o'clock position on the left-front wheel. Note that the two lower spider arms each contain an antirattle spring-and-pad assembly to reduce vertical movement of the inner pressure plate.

Install inner brake housing. Release both self-adjusters in the pressure-plate assembly as noted in item 3, above. Install the assembly. Install brake-tube dust grommet (on models where it was removed) and connect brake tube to frame connection. Install outer-housing-and-hub assembly. Be sure the two housings are aligned in accordance with markings or cast-in cutouts. Install outer wheel bearing, washer, and nut. Adjust bearing, install cotter pin, and replace dust cap. Install 10 housing bolts, lock washers, and nuts. Install damper springs and clips and replace wheel.

CHAPTER CHECKUP

NOTE: The following is a chapter test and you should review the chapter before taking it.

You are making fine progress in your study of the automotive chassis; a few more chapters and you will have completed the book. The test that follows covers the diagnosis and correction of various hydraulic-brake troubles as well as normal brake servicing. Brake adjustment and repair is an important part of automotive service and thus it will be important for you to know about such things. If you have any trouble with the questions below, it means you should reread the chapter so as to fix the facts more firmly in your mind. Don't be discouraged if you have to reread the chapter several times. Most good students reread their lessons several times since this is the best way to remember the facts. Write the answers in your notebook; this is a good aid to your memory.

Diagnosing Brake Complaints

Let's see how good a trouble-shooter you are. In the following, you assume that a customer has brought his car in with a complaint of

[463]

improper braking action. After each complaint there are listed several brake defects. Pick the defect that would be *most likely* to cause the complaint. Write the complaint, and the most likely cause, in your notebook.

1. A customer complains that the pedal goes to the floorboard with little or no braking action. This could be due to   *a clogged brake line   worn brake linings   reservoir vent clogged broken shoe-return spring*

2. The complaint is that one brake drags. This could be due to *lack of brake fluid   air in system   brake shoe out of adjust-ment*

3. The complaint is that all brakes drag. This could be due to *lack of brake fluid   air in system   incorrect pedal adjust-ment*

4. You are road-testing a car and find, when braking, that the car pulls sharply to the right. This could be due to   *linings soaked with oil or brake fluid   high fluid level in reservoir   brake pedal out of adjustment   master cylinder defective*

5. You find, when testing the brakes on a car, that the brake pedal feels spongy or soft. You know that this is most likely to be due to *tires not uniformly inflated   brake linings soaked with oil brake fluid in system   air in system*

6. You find, when testing the brakes on a car, that you have to exert a very heavy pedal pressure to get any braking action. Pedal travel seems normal. It is likely that the trouble is due to   *linings soaked with oil or brake fluid   air in system   brake drums scored   backing plates loose*

7. When testing the brakes on a car, you find that even with only a light pedal pressure, the brakes are apt to grab. Of the following, you would suspect the most probable cause to be   *plugged filler vent   low fluid level   shoes out of adjustment*

8. You notice, when testing the brakes on the road, that every time you apply the brakes they squeal. The most probable cause is   *low pedal pressure   low brake-fluid level   worn brake linings plugged filler vent*

Completing the Sentences

The sentences below are incomplete. After each sentence there are several words or phrases, only one of which will correctly complete the sentence. Write down each sentence in your notebook, selecting the proper word or phrase to complete it correctly.

[464]

Brake Service

1. Brake adjustments are divided into two classes, *on the car and off the car* *minor and major* *partial and full*
2. Minor brake adjustments are made *on the bench* *with wheels off* *without removing wheels*
3. To check the condition of the brake linings and drums, it is usually necessary to remove *all four wheels* *one front wheel* *both rear wheels*
4. Bendix brake minor adjustment is made by *turning eccentric cam* *turning adjusting screw* *shifting brake drum* *turning contact plug*
5. Bendix brake major adjustment is made by *turning eccentric cam* *turning adjusting screw* *turning or shifting anchor pin* *shifting drum*
6. Lockheed brake minor adjustment is made by *turning eccentric cam* *turing adjusting screw* *shifting brake drum* *turning contact plug*
7. When making a major adjustment on the Lockheed brake, it is necessary to turn the *brake band* *contact plug* *shoe anchor bolt* *adjusting screw*
8. An important part of the brake self-adjustment device is the *contact plug* *adjusting screw* *shift lever* *air vent*
9. Brake linings are attached to the brake shoes by either *rivets or screws* *rivets or bonding* *retainer springs or bolts*
10. Serious damage to rubber parts in the hydraulic brake system can result from the presence, in the system, of *air* *brake fluid* *mineral oil*

Servicing Procedures

Write down in your notebook the servicing procedures that are asked for. Don't copy from the book, but try to explain the procedure in your own words just as you would tell it to a friend.

1. What steps should be taken before any adjustment to the brake shoes is made?
2. Explain how to make a Bendix brake minor adjustment; major adjustment.
3. Explain how to make a Lockheed brake minor adjustment; major adjustment.
4. Explain how to adjust an external-contracting transmission-shaft hand brake.
5. Explain how to adjust an internal-expanding transmission-shaft hand brake.

[465]

6. Explain how the Lockheed self-centering, self-adjusting brake operates.
7. Explain how to replace riveted brake lining. Bonded brake lining.
8. Explain how to service a brake drum.
9. Explain how to service wheel and master cylinders.
10. Explain how to flush, fill, and bleed a hydraulic system.

SUGGESTIONS FOR FURTHER STUDY

Your local school automotive shop or friendly automotive repair shop probably has some discarded brake components such as wheel and master cylinders that you can examine. Possibly you will be able to disassemble and reassemble these units. Further, if you can watch an expert make brake adjustments, replace brake linings, and perform the other services described in the chapter, you will have a much clearer idea of how these jobs are done. Study every shop repair manual that you can. Be sure to write down in your notebook any interesting and important facts you learn in the shop or by studying the manuals.

16: Power-brake service

THIS CHAPTER discusses the trouble-shooting, adjusting, removal, repair, and reinstallation of the components in the power-brake system described in Chap. 14. The previous chapter describes the same operations on hydraulic brakes. Since that part of the system after the power cylinder is hydraulic, practically the entire previous chapter also applies to power-brake systems. Thus, the service operations required on wheel cylinders, brake shoes, brake drums, tubing, and the brake-shoe adjusting procedures are identical regardless of whether the car is or is not equipped with power brakes. The previous chapter, then, can be considered to apply to all braking systems employing hydraulic pressure. The present chapter applies only to power-brake units.

§214. Trouble-shooting chart—power brakes The chart, below, relates various power-braking troubles to their possible causes and corrections. This chart gives you a means of logically tracing down troubles to their actual causes and permits quick location of causes and their rapid correction. The chart and the sections that follow pertain to power-brake units only. Generally speaking, the trouble-shooting chart in §195, which covers hydraulic brakes, also applies to power-brake systems. Thus, the troubles listed in the chart in §195, as well as the trouble-corrections described in §§196 to 213, also apply to power brakes.

NOTE: The troubles and possible causes are not listed in the chart in the order of frequency of occurrence. That is, item 1 does not necessarily occur more often than item 2, nor does item *a* under Possible Cause necessarily occur more often than item *b*.

POWER-BRAKE TROUBLE-SHOOTING CHART

(See §§215 to 221 for details of checks and corrections listed. Not all of the possible causes and checks or corrections listed apply to all models of power brakes described in the chapter; this is due to individual variations among models.)

Complaint	Possible Cause	Check or Correction
1. Excessive brake-pedal pressure required	a. Defective vacuum check valve	Free or replace
	b. Hose collapsed	Replace
	c. Vacuum fitting plugged	Clear, replace
	d. Binding pedal linkage	Free up
	e. Air inlet clogged	Clear
	f. Faulty piston seal	Replace
	g. Stuck piston	Clear, replace damaged parts
	h. Faulty diaphragm	Replace (applies to diaphragm type only)
	i. Causes listed under item 6, Poor braking action, in chart in §195	
2. Brakes grab	a. Reaction, or "brake-feel," mechanism damaged	Replace damaged parts
	b. Air-vacuum valve sticking	Free up, replace damaged parts
	c. Causes listed under item 7, Brakes too sensitive or grab, in chart in §195	
3. Pedal goes to floor board	a. Hydraulic-plunger seal leaking	Replace
	b. Compensating valve not closing	Replace valve
	c. Causes listed under item 1, Brake pedal goes to floor board, in chart in §195	
4. Brakes fail to release	a. Pedal linkage binding	Free up
	b. Faulty check valve action	Free, replace damaged parts
	c. Compensator port plugged	Clean port
	d. Hydraulic-plunger seal sticking	Replace seal
	e. Piston sticking	Lubricate, replace damaged parts as necessary

Complaint	Possible Cause	Check or Correction
	f. Broken return spring	Replace
	g. Causes listed under item 3, All brakes drag, in §195	
5. Loss of brake fluid	*a.* Worn or damaged seals in hydraulic section	Replace, fill and bleed system
	b. Loose line connections	Tighten, replace seals
	c. Causes listed under item 10, Loss of brake fluid, in §195	

§215. Bendix Treadle-Vac power-brake removal, disassembly, and inspection To remove the assembly from the car, the vacuum and hydraulic lines as well as the pedal linkage must be disconnected. Then the cover plate (or bracket) attaching bolts must be removed so the power-brake unit can be taken off the car. The dip stick should be removed if it interferes. On some cars, the cover plate is removed with the power brake and taken off afterwards. When disassembling the unit, be very careful to avoid getting dirt on the operating parts since this could cause faulty braking action. Be especially careful to avoid getting mineral oil or grease on the hydraulic-system parts since the rubber parts will be damaged by oil or grease. *Do not handle the piston cups or seals with greasy hands!* Disassemble as follows:

NOTE: When overhauling the unit, always use a repair kit; the kit contains all new parts that should be replaced. If replacing the leather piston packing or reaction diaphragm, use a piston-packing-and-diaphragm kit.

1. Refer to Fig. 16-1. Put brake unit in holding fixture and remove dust boot (No. 1). Remove felt (No. 2), straighten retaining tangs (No. 3) and remove end plate (No. 4) and gasket (No. 5). Slide vacuum hose (No. 6) from tube attached to vacuum cylinder (No. 7). Remove air cleaner (No. 8).
2. Refer to Fig. 16-2. If piston must be removed, take out screw (No. 5), tube and plate (No. 6), and gasket (No. 7). Pull vacuum piston and valve assembly (No. 3) from cylinder (No. 1).

3. Refer to Fig. 16-3. Remove snap ring (No. 1) and pull out slide valve and push rod assembly (No. 3). Remove rubber stop (No. 4) and washer (No. 5) from sleeve end of piston plate (No. 10). Do not remove screw (No. 6), tube (No. 7), gasket

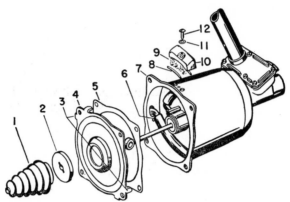

FIG. 16-1. Removal of end plate. Parts are identified in text. (*Oldsmobile Division of General Motors Corporation*)

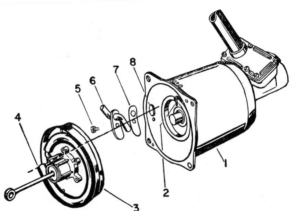

FIG. 16-2. Removal of vacuum piston and valve. Parts are identified in text. (*Oldsmobile Division of General Motors Corporation*)

(No. 8) and hose (No. 9) except when using a piston-packing-and diaphragm kit.

4. Refer to Fig. 16-4. Push in on retainer plate (No. 2) to release C washer (No. 1), and slide C washer out of groove in hydraulic plunger (No. 4). Remove plate (No. 2) and spring (No. 3).

5. Refer to Fig. 16-5. Scribe a line across vacuum cylinder (No.

3) and master cylinder (No. 8), as shown. Remove three attaching screws (No. 1) and lock washers (No. 2) and lift off vacuum cylinder. Remove gasket (No. 4) and rubber gasket (No. 5). Push plunger into master cylinder and remove leather seal (No. 6) from cylinder.

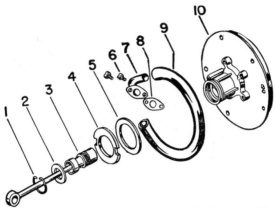

Fig. 16-3. Sleeve-valve and vacuum-hose removal. Parts are identified in text. (*Oldsmobile Division of General Motors Corporation*)

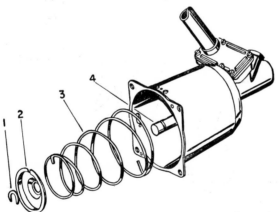

Fig. 16-4. Removing vacuum-piston return spring and retainer. Parts are identified in text. (*Oldsmobile Division of General Motors Corporation*)

6. Refer to Fig. 16-6. Scribe a line across master cylinder and cover. Remove six screws (No. 1), cover (No. 3), and gasket (No. 4). Remove compensating valve (No. 5) with 1⅛-inch thin-wall socket. Loosen outlet fitting (No. 6) with 1¼-inch wrench but do not remove. Remove retainer ring (No. 7). Remove hydraulic plunger (No. 12) from master cylinder and

[471]

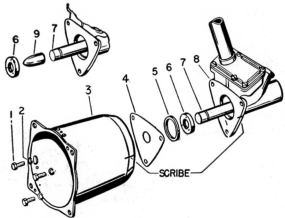

FIG. 16-5. Vacuum-cylinder and leather-seal removal. At upper left, using seal assembly tool (9) on end of plunger to protect seal (6) during assembly. Parts are identified in text. (*Oldsmobile Division of General Motors Corporation*)

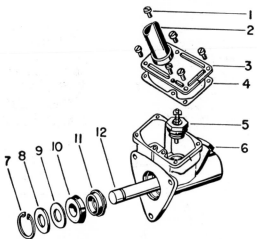

FIG. 16-6. Removal of cup seal (10), hydraulic plunger (12), and compensating valve (5). (*Oldsmobile Division of General Motors Corporation*)

remove steel washer (No. 8), fiber washer (No. 9), rubber cup (No. 10) and retainer (No. 11) from plunger.

7. Refer to Fig. 16-7. From hydraulic master cylinder (No. 5), take outlet fitting (No. 1), residual check valve spring (No. 4), valve cup (No. 3), and gasket (No. 2).

8. Refer to Fig. 16-8. Compensating valve (No. 5) may be removed from fitting (No. 3) by spreading and removing retainer (No. 1) and spring (No. 2).

[472]

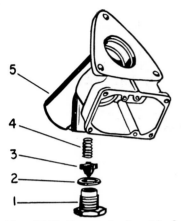

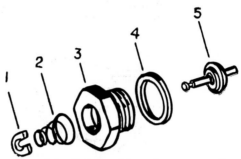

FIG. 16-7. Removal of residual check valve cup (3). (*Oldsmobile Division of General Motors Corporation*)

FIG. 16-8. Relationship of compensating valve (5) to the fitting (3). (*Oldsmobile Division of General Motors Corporation*)

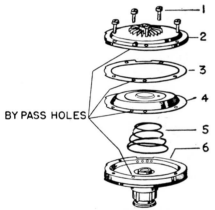

BY PASS HOLES

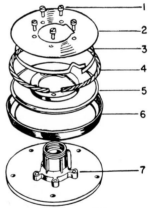

FIG. 16-9. Removal of diaphragm cover (2), diaphragm (4), and spring (5). (*Oldsmobile Division of General Motors Corporation*)

FIG. 16-10. Disassembling vacuum piston by removing retainer plate (2). Parts identified in text. (*Oldsmobile Division of General Motors Corporation*)

9. Do this step only if piston packing or diaphragm require replacement. Refer to Fig. 16-9. Loosen five screws (No. 1) on vacuum-piston-plate assembly, press down on diaphragm cover (No. 2), and take out screws. Then remove cover (No. 6), valve return spring (No. 5), diaphragm (No. 4), and gasket (No. 3).

[473]

10. Do this step only if piston packing or diaphragm require replacement. Refer to Fig. 16-10. With sleeve end of vacuum piston plate up, remove attaching screws (No. 1), retainer plate (No. 2), expander spring (No. 3), cotton wicking (No. 4), retainer plate (No. 5), and leather piston packing (No. 6).

11. Inspection. Clean all metal parts with Bendix Metalclene. Parts that will come into contact with hydraulic brake fluid should then be rewashed in clean alcohol. Handle all parts carefully to avoid getting them dirty or contaminating hydraulic parts with grease or mineral oil. When using a repair kit, discard all old rubber parts and use the new parts furnished. Replace other parts, such as the housings or hydraulic plunger, if rusted, scored, or worn. Slight corrosion on the inside of the power cylinder can be polished off with fine emery cloth (remove all abrasive after polishing).

§216. Bendix Treadle-Vac reassembly and installation   Essentially, reassembly is the reverse of disassembly. Detailed procedures follow. Dip hydraulic parts in clean alcohol and place in a clean pan or on a clean paper in readiness for assembly.

1. Refer to Fig. 16-8. Insert grooved stem of valve (No. 5) through fitting (No. 3), put large end of spring (No. 2) over stem, and secure with washer (No. 1). Squeeze end of washer together with pliers. Put new gasket (No. 4) on threads of fitting.

2. Refer to Fig. 16-7. Put new gasket (No. 2) over hydraulic outlet fitting (No. 1), hold fitting vertically, and insert cone end of cup and retainer (No. 3) into fitting. Put spring (No. 4) into place and thread outlet fitting into master cylinder finger tight.

3. Refer to Fig. 16-6. Push washer end of plunger (12) all the way into master cylinder and assemble, over end of plunger, cup retainer (No. 11) (flat side against washer), cup (No. 10) (after dipping cup in brake fluid), fiber washer (No. 9), and steel washer (No. 8). Slide parts into recess of cylinder and secure with retainer snap ring (No. 7). Install compensating valve (No. 5) and tighten it securely. Use new gasket (No. 4) and install cover (No. 3) with screws (No. 1). Align

scribe marks and tighten screws. Securely tighten fitting (No. 6).

4. Refer to Fig. 16-5. Pull out hydraulic plunger (No. 7), put seal assembly tool (No. 9) on end of plunger, and assemble leather seal (No. 6) over seal tool with lip of leather toward master cylinder. Press seal into recess of cylinder and then remove assembly tool. Put gasket (No. 5) in master-cylinder recess. Put lock-washers (No. 2) on screws (No. 1), and insert screws through holes in cylinder (No. 3) so gasket (No. 4) can be put into place and cylinder attached to master cylinder (No. 8). Wipe out vacuum cylinder after tightening screws, and pull plunger all the way out.

5. Refer to Fig. 16-4. Put large end of spring (No. 3) into cylinder. Make sure hook end of spring comes between a screw head and a raised projection in the end of the vacuum cylinder so that spring will not turn. Put retainer plate (No. 2) on end of plunger and secure with C washer. Make sure hook end of spring enters the notch of the retainer plate.

6. If the vacuum power piston has been disassembled, reassemble as follows. Refer to Fig. 16-11. Put piston plate (No. 7) in assembling ring (J-5406) (sleeve end up), put leather piston packing (No. 6) in ring (lip side up), retainer plate (No. 5) (concave side down). Then put cotton wicking (No. 4) inside of lip of leather. Coil the expander spring (No. 3) and assemble it against inner side of wicking with gripper points up and the loop end hooked under clip at opposite end of spring. Put retainer plate (No. 2) in place and secure with screws (No. 1). Saturate cotton wick with shock-absorber fluid.

7. Refer to Fig. 16-12. Make three guide pins (No. 7) by cutting off heads of No. 8–32 × 3-inch machine screws. Thread guide pins in piston plate (No. 6) and assemble parts as illustrated. Large diameter of spring (No. 5) should be centered on piston plate. Align holes in diaphragm (No. 4) and gasket (No. 3) with holes in piston plate, and assemble over guide pins. Align holes in cover (2) with holes in diaphragm and assemble cover over guide pins. Make sure bypass holes align. Remove guide pins one at a time and install screws (No. 1).

8. Refer to Fig. 16-3. Put steel washer (No. 5) on hub of piston assembly (No. 10), soften cement coating on the new piston

[475]

stop washer (No. 4) with gasoline, and assemble with cement side against steel washer and with inside diameter engaged in groove in hub. Make sure slide valve (No. 3) and screen are clean and dry. *Do not* lubricate slide valve or sleeve. Insert slide valve and push rod (No. 3) in sleeve of vacuum piston, and replace stop washer (No. 2) and snap ring (No. 1).

9. Refer to Fig. 16-2. Apply thin film of shock-absorber fluid to inside of cylinder (No. 1), and insert piston (No. 3) so free

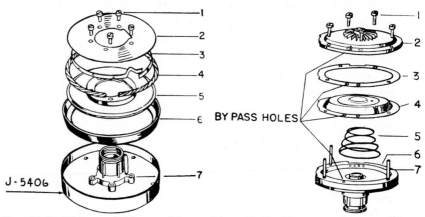

FIG. 16-11. Using special assembling ring (identified by Oldsmobile as J-5406) to assemble vacuum piston. (*Oldsmobile Division of General Motors Corporation*)

FIG. 16-12. Using guide pins (7) to assure proper alignment of parts as diaphragm (4) and cover (2) are re-attached to vacuum piston (7). (*Oldsmobile Division of General Motors Corporation*)

end of hose (No. 4) aligns with center of hole (No. 8). Push piston into cylinder until piston engages hook (No. 2) at end of piston return spring. Twist piston 20 to 25 degrees in both directions; then move piston through its full stroke several times so it will find its normal operating position. Attach new gasket (No. 7) and the tube and plate (No. 6) with screw (No. 5). Slide end of hose (No. 4) on end of tube about ⅝ inch. Operate piston through its full stroke several times to make sure the vacuum hose does not rub against cylinder or piston. If it does, remove and rotate piston to another position. Install air cleaner on cylinder.

10. Refer to Fig. 16-1. Put new end-plate gasket (No. 5) on end

plate, align holes, and attach end plate to cylinder shell by crimping down the tangs (No. 3). Assemble push-rod felt (No. 2) on push rod next to flange of end plate. Dip small end of boot (No. 1) in brake fluid and assemble over eye end of push rod. Then assemble large diameter of boot on groove of end plate (No. 4).

11. After assembly is complete, reinstall the unit on the car and road-test it. If brakes do not function normally, refer to §§195 and 214 for cause and correction. With engine stopped and transmission in neutral, apply brakes several times to exhaust all vacuum in the system. Depress the brake pedal, hold foot pressure on pedal, and start the engine. If the vacuum system is operating, the pedal will tend to fall away under foot pressure, and the pressure required to hold the pedal down will decrease. If this does not occur, the vacuum system is not functioning properly.

Stop the engine and again exhaust all vacuum by repeatedly applying brakes. Then depress brake pedal and hold foot pressure on it. If the pedal gradually falls away under foot pressure, the hydraulic system is leaking.

If the brake pedal travels to within an inch of the toe board (when the brakes are first applied), the brake shoes require readjustment or relining.

§217. Kelsey-Hayes power-brake removal and disassembly To remove the power-brake unit from the car, remove cranking-motor splash pan (which would interfere with removal). Then disconnect the return spring, remove clevis pin at front end, and then remove brake-pedal push rod with cylinder push rod attached. Disconnect breather tube which is clamped to inlet tube on air-cleaner cover. Disconnect and remove pipe and hose that connect vacuum check valve to power cylinder. Disconnect pipe between reservoir and hydraulic cylinder, allowing fluid to drain. Throw this fluid out; do not try to reuse it! Cover pipe end with tape so dirt won't get into it. Then take cylinder off car by removing nuts and lock washers attaching it. Disassemble as follows (see Fig. 16-13). Certain parts, such as the sealing O rings, piston cups and seals, push-rod boot, check valve assembly, and so on, should be replaced with new parts when the unit is overhauled. Overhaul kits, with all these parts, are

[477]

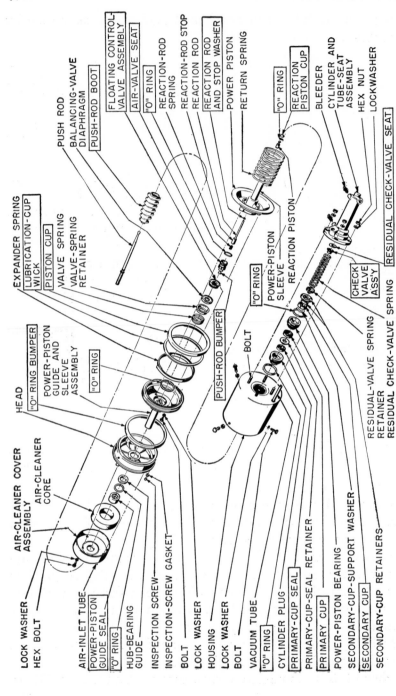

LOCK WASHER
HEX BOLT

EXPANDER SPRING
LUBRICATION-CUP
WICK
PISTON CUP
VALVE SPRING
VALVE-SPRING
RETAINER

PUSH ROD
BALANCING-VALVE
DIAPHRAGM
PUSH-ROD BOOT
FLOATING CONTROL-
VALVE ASSEMBLY
AIR-VALVE SEAT
"O" RING
REACTION-ROD
SPRING
REACTION-ROD STOP
REACTION ROD
REACTION ROD
AND STOP WASHER
POWER PISTON
RETURN SPRING

"O" RING
REACTION
PISTON CUP
BLEEDER
CYLINDER AND
TUBE-SEAT
ASSEMBLY
HEX NUT
LOCKWASHER
RESIDUAL CHECK-VALVE SEAT

HEAD
"O" RING BUMPER
POWER-PISTON
GUIDE AND
SLEEVE
ASSEMBLY

"O" RING

POWER-PISTON
SLEEVE
REACTION PISTON

CHECK
VALVE
ASS'Y

AIR-CLEANER COVER
ASSEMBLY
AIR-CLEANER
CORE

"O" RING

PUSH-ROD BUMPER

BOLT

BOLT

RESIDUAL-VALVE SPRING
RESIDUAL CHECK-VALVE SPRING
RESIDUAL-VALVE
RETAINER
RESIDUAL CHECK-VALVE

LOCK WASHER
HEX BOLT

AIR-INLET TUBE
POWER-PISTON
GUIDE SEAL
"O" RING
HUB-BEARING
GUIDE
INSPECTION SCREW
INSPECTION-SCREW GASKET
BOLT
LOCK WASHER
HOUSING
LOCK WASHER
BOLT
VACUUM TUBE
"O" RING
CYLINDER PLUG
PRIMARY-CUP SEAL
PRIMARY-CUP-SEAL RETAINER
PRIMARY CUP
POWER-PISTON BEARING
SECONDARY-CUP-SUPPORT WASHER
SECONDARY CUP
SECONDARY-CUP RETAINERS

Fig. 16-13. Completely disassembled view of Kelsey-Hayes power-brake unit. Boxed names are parts that should be discarded when unit is overhauled. (*Kelsey-Hayes Wheel Company*)

supplied. An overhaul should not be started unless the proper kit is available.

1. Remove push-rod boot and push rod. Mount power cylinder in bench vise (Fig. 16-14), but tighten vise jaws on hydraulic cylinder only enough to hold unit. Overtightening will damage or crack hydraulic cylinder. Remove four bolts with lock washers, pry air cleaner up with screw driver, and remove cover and cleaner core (Fig. 16-14). Remove the three bolts, with lock washers, that hold head to cylinder. Then loosen head by inserting screw driver tip in the three screw driver slots (Fig. 16-14) and twisting screw driver. Free head by tapping upward under head flange.

   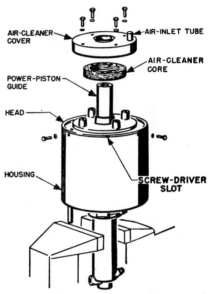

   FIG. 16-14. Removing air cleaner and cylinder head. (*Kelsey-Hayes Wheel Company*)

   Caution: Hold down on piston guide as head comes free. Otherwise the piston return spring will throw parts upward as head is freed.

2. Power piston and guide will come off with head. Take return spring from housing. Remove housing and hydraulic cylinder from vise and turn it upside down in a pan to allow old fluid to drain (Fig. 16-17). Discard old fluid.

3. Make a holding fixture from an 8-inch length of 4-inch pipe and mount piston and head assembly on it (Fig. 16-15). Lift head from piston, and remove O ring and bumper from head (Fig. 16-15). Then put head, with inside rim up, in arbor press, and press out bearing, O ring, and guide seal.

4. Bend back lip of leather piston cup and remove felt wick and expander spring (*A* in Fig. 16-16).

5. Remove three bolts, with lock washers, and take guide assembly and O ring from power piston (*B* in Fig. 16-16).

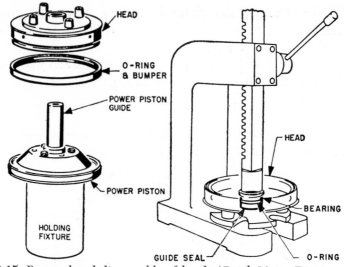

FIG. 16-15. Removal and disassembly of head. (*Buick Motor Division of General Motors Corporation*)

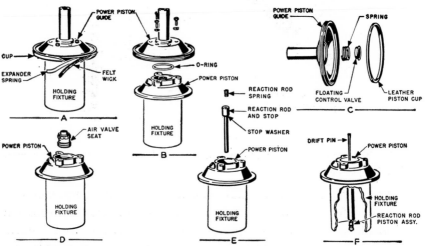

FIG. 16-16. Disassembly of piston and guide. (*Buick Motor Division of General Motors Corporation*)

6. Take leather piston cup, floating control valve, and spring from piston guide (*C* in Fig. 16-16).

7. Remove air valve seat from power piston (*D* in Fig. 16-16) and lift out control spring (if present), reaction rod spring, reaction rod, and dampener spring (if present). (See *E*, Fig. 16-16.)

NOTE: Control and dampener springs were used in earlier production units only (series 1). Discard these springs because they will not be reinstalled.

8. Use a long drift pin to push reaction rod piston assembly out of lower end of piston sleeve (*F* in Fig. 16-16). Remove O ring and cup from piston. *Be extremely careful not to mar the piston surface!*

9. Disassemble the hydraulic cylinder by first removing the four nuts and lock washers attaching it to the housing (Fig. 16-17)

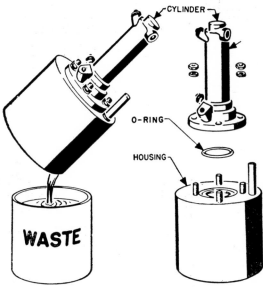

FIG. 16-17. Removal of hydraulic cylinder. (*Buick Motor Division of General Motors Corporation*)

Then lift off cylinder and remove O ring. Mount cylinder in vise, with the flange end up, but do not tighten vise jaws too much as this would damage cylinder. Unscrew and remove cylinder plug assembly (*A* in Fig. 16-18). Disassemble cylinder plug as shown in *B*, Fig. 16-18.

10. Bend a piece of wire—not larger than 0.072 inch in diameter— as shown in *C*, Fig. 16-18, and insert ends into two opposite holes in the bore of the power-piston bearing. Be careful to avoid marring inside surface of the bearing. Then lift bearing assembly from cylinder. Watch the residual valve spring so it doesn't fly out when released by the bearing. Disassemble

[481]

bearing assembly as shown in *D*, Fig. 16-18. Do not remove blue-steel cup-supporting washer unless it is damaged; to remove it, blow air through a small hole in bearing.

11. Complete hydraulic cylinder disassembly by removing residual valve spring retainer, spring, and valve (*E* in Fig. 16-18) and then loosening residual check valve rubber seat with a screw driver so it drops out (*F* in Fig. 16-18).

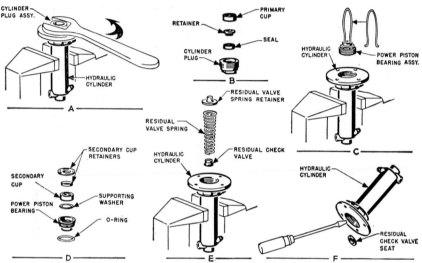

FIG. 16-18. Disassembly of hydraulic cylinder. (*Buick Motor Division of General Motors Corporation*)

§218. Kelsey-Hayes power-brake parts inspection If improper braking action has occurred, wipe all rubber parts, the residual check valve, floating control valve, and air valve seat and examine them for nicks, cuts, or other damage. Such damage might indicate burred or nicked metal parts which should be repaired or replaced on reassembly.

Throw away all the rubber parts.

Use the new parts furnished in the overhaul kit.

Clean all parts in diacetone alcohol or clean brake fluid. Never use gasoline, kerosene, or other cleaning fluid that could contain *even a trace* of mineral oil. This would cause serious damage to the rubber parts in the brake system after reassembly. *Make sure your hands are free of grease.*

[482]

Examine all parts that will be reused to make sure they are free of nicks, burrs, and so on. Compensating ports in end of power-piston sleeve (hydraulic plunger) should be clear. Light score marks on the power-piston guide sleeve, piston sleeve, or cylinder can be polished out with crocus cloth. Be sure to remove all traces of abrasive.

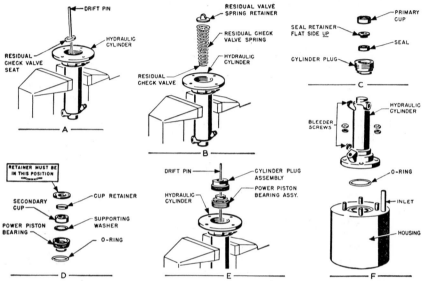

Fig. 16-19. Assembly of hydraulic cylinder. (*Buick Motor Division of General Motors Corporation*)

Before installation, wet all O rings and rubber cups with clean brake fluid, except where O ring or seal is pregreased. *Do not remove this special silicone grease!* It aids the sealing effect.

§219. Kelsey-Hayes power-brake reassembly and installation If

control and dampener springs have been found in the assembly (see §217, item 7), the unit is a series 1 and must be converted by installing all the new parts in the overhaul kit and also a new type of power piston and push rod. Stamp or paint (red or yellow) the letter "K" on the cylinder head to show that the unit is converted. Assemble as follows (refer to Fig. 16-13):

1. Lightly clamp hydraulic cylinder in vise, with flange end up (*A* in Fig. 16-19), and drop new residual check valve seat into place. Guide it in with a drift pin, as shown. Then press new

[483]

residual check valve assembly into small end of valve spring (it will snap into place) and install spring in cylinder with valve square on seat. Put spring retainer on upper end of spring, small end up (*B* in Fig. 16-19). Install new seal, seal retainer with flat side out, and new primary cup in cylinder plug (*C* in Fig. 16-19). Assemble power-piston bearing (*D* in Fig. 16-19) by installing blue-steel washer (if removed); then install new secondary cup (lips outward), cup retainer, and flat retainer (concave side out).

2. Complete the hydraulic-cylinder assembly by installing O ring, piston bearing assembly (cup retainer down), and cylinder plug assembly (*E* in Fig. 16-19). Use a drift pin to hold residual check valve spring down, as shown. Screw plug down and then tighten with wrench, *but do not use force.*

3. Put new O ring around cylinder plug and install cylinder on housing with bleeder screws opposite housing vacuum inlet (*F* in Fig. 16-19). Install lock washers and nuts on studs but do not tighten at this time.

4. Assemble the power piston (refer to Fig. 16-20). First, put expander spring in groove of guide with bent ends in, so center of spring is at one of the slots in the upper flange of the guide. Then insert wedge (supplied with kit) through slot to hold spring in place (*A* in Fig. 16-20).

5. Wrap each end of spring around piston guide and hold it with wedges in two side slots. With ends overlapping under fourth slot, install wedge at this point. This will now hold spring until assembly is complete. Remove first three wedges and throw them away (*B* in Fig. 16-20).

6. Saturate the cup lubricating wick with special power-brake-cylinder oil (supplied with kit) and put wick over spring with the grain of the felt parallel to center line of piston guide. Ends of wick must not coincide with ends of spring (*C* in Fig. 16-20).

7. Mount piston guide in holding fixture with sleeve down and install a new leather cup. Slide service ring down over cup, making sure leather cup does not ride over the edge of the guide and that cup flange lies flat against its face (*D* and *E* in Fig. 16-20).

8. Wet diaphragm of new floating control-valve assembly with brake fluid, put spring over retainer, then install these parts

[484]

on piston hub (*F* in Fig. 16-20). Press diaphragm down over hub on guide and install a new O ring over ridge around valve.

9. Put new reaction cup on reaction piston with lip of cup toward small end of piston. Install new O ring (do not remove silicone grease from ring).

10. Wet reaction cup with brake fluid and install reaction piston assembly in outer end of power piston sleeve (cup lip up as shown in *G*, Fig. 16-20).

11. Now, mount power piston in holding fixture (sleeve down). Put new stop washer on reaction rod (*A* in Fig. 16-21), install

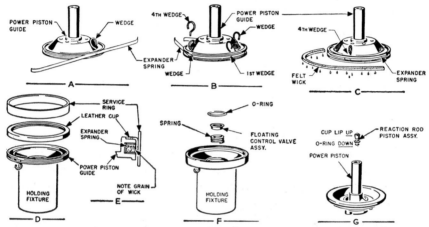

FIG. 16-20. Guide and piston parts. (*Buick Motor Division of General Motors Corporation*)

rod in power piston, and put reaction-rod spring in stop. Put new bumper in cavity in air-valve seat, install new O ring in outside groove of seat (do not remove silicone grease), and put valve seat assembly in power piston above reaction-rod stop and spring.

Caution: Use care when inserting steel seat so you don't damage vacuum valve seat on aluminum piston.

12. Make sure air valve seat moves against spring and is free. Put piston guide over piston and insert push rod through guide to hold the air valve seat down against the reaction-rod spring while starting bolts (*B* in Fig. 16-21). Use the three equally

[485]

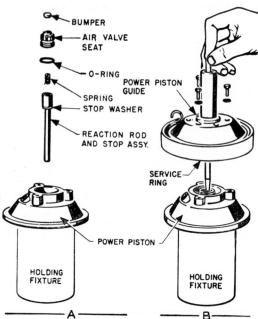

BUMPER
AIR VALVE SEAT
O-RING
POWER PISTON GUIDE
SPRING
STOP WASHER
REACTION ROD AND STOP ASSY.
SERVICE RING
POWER PISTON
HOLDING FIXTURE
HOLDING FIXTURE
A
B

Fig. 16-21. Assembly of piston and guide. (*Buick Motor Division of General Motors Corporation*)

spaced holes in guide — the other holes are air passages. After starting one bolt, remove the expander spring wedge; then install other bolts and tighten all securely (but not so much as to strip threads in aluminum piston). Remove service ring.

13. Put cylinder head on bench, hub end up, install bearing with flat side down, and press a new O ring into bearing groove. Then install new guide seal with felt side up (do not wipe grease from seal). Use arbor press (Fig. 16-22) and apply just enough load to outside edge of seal to press it snugly against the bearing. Do not crush seal!

14. Complete the assembly by installing new O ring and bumper over outside groove of cylinder head, and wet the rubber with special cylinder oil (supplied with kit). Oil the inside of cylinder and leather cup on rim of piston guide with this same oil (Fig. 16-23). Then clamp assembly in vise (Fig. 16-24) and install return spring to seat inside the four cylinder flange bolt heads. Set power-piston-and-guide assembly in place with retaining shoulder engaged in return spring, press the assembly down into the housing about two inches, and pour the remain-

ing special cylinder oil (supplied in kit) into housing and upon piston guide. Do not pour into air holes! See *A*, Fig. 16-24.

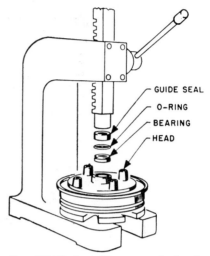

15. While holding piston guide down, install cylinder head. Position with inspection hole screw on same side as the bleeder screws on hydraulic cylinder and with screw holes aligned with housing holes (*B* in Fig. 16-24). Tap head straight down into housing with soft mallet until the three bolts with lock washers can be started. You may have to rotate head by prying with screw driver between air cleaner bosses. Tap head down snug before tightening bolts.

Fig. 16-22. Installing parts in head. (*Buick Motor Division of General Motors Corporation*)

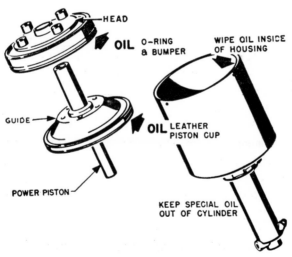

Fig. 16-23. Lubrication of parts with special cylinder oil before installation. (*Buick Motor Division of General Motors Corporation*)

16. Remove assembly from vise, and press guide sleeve end down on bench to hold the piston and guide in fully applied position

[487]

while tightening the hydraulic cylinder stud nuts evenly. Make sure piston moves freely after nuts are tight.

17. Blow out air cleaner core (or install new one) and install core and cover with air inlet tube on same side as bleeder screws (*B* in Fig. 16-24). Install new boot over flange of air cleaner cover.
18. Reinstallation is just the reverse of removal. Be sure to adjust brake pedal stop and push rod, and bleed the system to complete the installation job.

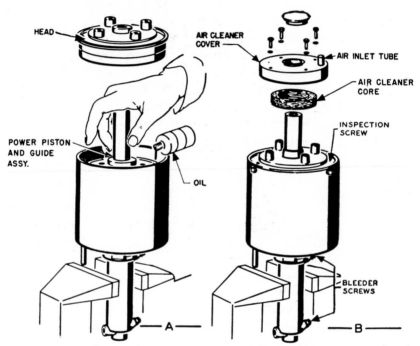

F<small>IG</small>. 16-24. Installation of piston and head. (*Buick Motor Division of General Motors Corporation*)

§**220. Disassembly of Kelsey-Hayes Vacdraulic booster brake**   Refer to Fig. 16-25. The disassembly procedure for this unit (described in §191), is as follows:

1. To have the unit lie flat while working on it, drill four holes in a box or table into which four mounting screws on cover side can enter. Loosen cylinder-end cap and clamp on the air and vacuum inlet hose. Then remove the four Allen-head mounting screws so valve housing can be taken off cylinder.

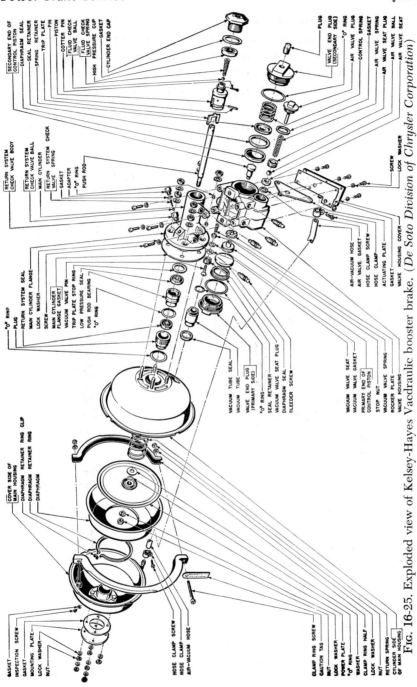

FIG. 16-25. Exploded view of Kelsey-Hayes Vacdraulic booster brake. (*De Soto Division of Chrysler Corporation*)

2. Turn assembly over and clamp cylinder between padded jaws of vise. Then remove clamp-ring screws and ring and remove cover side of the main housing from the cylinder side. You can now remove the hex nut from center of power plate and lift off power-plate and diaphragm assembly.

3. Take out small O ring and flat washer from end of push rod and remove return spring.

4. Now, take unit from vise, invert it, and remove the four hex nuts so cylinder can be taken off main housing.

5. Clamp cylinder between padded jaws of vise with push-rod end up. Screw special protective thimble nut on threads of push rod to protect seals, unscrew return-system seal-retaining plug, and remove it. Grasp end of push rod, and pull the rod, bearing, and piston assembly out of the cylinder.

6. Remove cylinder end cap and inspect the cylinder. Light scratches can be removed with crocus cloth (but clean thoroughly after this with alcohol). Bad scores require cylinder replacement.

7. Remove cotter pin, fluid check valve spring, and ball, and then take bronze bearing from push rod.

§221. Assembly of Kelsey-Hayes Vacdraulic booster brake

1. Remove the secondary cup from piston (be careful not to scratch piston) and replace it with a new one. Drop check-valve ball into position, insert fluid check-valve spring (small end toward ball), and secure with new cotter pin. Bend ends of pin back against piston.

2. Lubricate cylinder and piston with brake fluid, insert push rod and piston assembly from *cap end* of cylinder, install new copper gasket on cap, and screw in cap finger tight.

3. Clamp cylinder in padded vise jaws, push-rod end up, and install stop-plate washer.

4. Remove primary cup from inside of bronze bearing and remove O ring from outside of bearing. Do not scratch bearing! Replace with new cup and O ring.

5. Lubricate bronze bearing and slide it into cylinder over push rod with primary cup down. Press down lightly with thumb.

6. Lubricate inner lip of retaining seal, slide seal and plug as-

sembly over end of push rod, and screw the retaining plug into cylinder. Tighten it with 10 to 12 lb-ft torque.

7. Reposition cylinder in vise and tighten end cap to 110 lb-ft torque.

8. Remove special thimble nut from threads of push rod. Replace O ring seal and cylinder flange gasket between cylinder and main housing. Take cylinder from vise and attach it to main housing with flat side of cylinder facing short studs. Install four lock washers and nuts and tighten nuts to 150 pound-*inches.*

9. Clamp assembly between padded vise jaws (push-rod end up), and install flat washer and then a new small O ring on end of push rod. Install return spring over end of push rod. Center the return spring in boss of power plate and press power-plate and diaphragm assembly down over end of push rod against spring. Secure the assembly with nut and lock washer, tightening nut to 40 pound-*inches.*

10. Assemble two halves of main housing with keys on cylinder side of main housing matching slots in cover side. Be sure that cross-over tube rests in slot in cylinder side of main housing. Install clamping ring with flattened portions of ring covering the cutaway portions of the main-housing flanges. Tighten clamp-ring bolts. Be sure to center the air and vacuum cross-over line between the ears of the clamp ring.

11. Pull vacuum tube out of valve housing, remove O ring and rubber grommet, and replace with new ring and grommet. Lubricate O ring and reinstall vacuum tube (O ring first) into valve housing. Replace the O-rings between valve housing and cylinder with new rings.

12. Reconnect valve housing to air-vacuum hose. Assemble valve housing to cylinder and secure it with four Allen-head screws while holding valve housing tight against the main housing. Tighten air and vacuum hose clamp.

CHAPTER CHECKUP

Because power brakes have been widely adopted on automobiles in recent years, it will be of great value to you for you to understand not only how these units operate, but also what troubles they might have

[491]

and how they are serviced. The chapter you have just completed de
scribes the trouble-shooting and servicing of the most popular types of
passenger-car power brakes. The checkup that follows will give you a
chance to test yourself on how well you remember the important points
covered in the chapter. Don't feel discouraged if any of the questions
seem hard to answer. That simply means that you should read the
chapter again. Taking the test, finding out what points are not clear in
your mind, and then reviewing those points—this is a procedure that
is very good for memorizing the important points in the chapter.

Correcting Trouble Lists

The purpose of this exercise is to help you spot related and unrelated
troubles on a list. In each list below, you will find one item that does not
belong. Write down each list in your notebook, but do not write down
the item that does not belong. Progress Quiz 7, in the middle of the
previous chapter, explains in more detail how to take this test. Refer to
it if you are not sure what to do.

1. Excessive pedal pressure required: defective vacuum-check valve,
   hose collapsed, vacuum fitting plugged, pedal linkage binding, air
   inlet clogged, faulty piston seal, vacuum pump stuck, piston stuck.
2. Brakes grab: reaction or "brake-feel" mechanism damaged, air-
   vacuum valve sticking, ruptured diaphragm.
3. Pedal goes to floor board: broken return spring, hydraulic-plunger
   seal leaking, compensating valve not closing.
4. Brakes fail to release: pedal linkage binding, faulty check valve
   action, compensator port plugged, compensating valve hanging open,
   hydraulic plunger seal sticking, piston sticking, broken return spring.
5. Loss of brake fluid: worn or damaged seals in hydraulic section,
   vacuum fitting plugged, loose line connection.

Servicing Procedures

Write down in your notebook the servicing procedures that are asked
for. Don't copy from the book, but try to explain the procedures as you
would to a friend, in your own words.

1. Explain how to disassemble the Bendix Treadle-Vac power-brake
   unit.
2. Explain how to assemble the Bendix Treadle-Vac power-brake unit.
3. Explain how to disassemble the Kelsey-Hayes power-brake unit.
4. Explain how to assemble the Kelsey-Hayes power-brake unit.
5. Explain how to disassemble and assemble the Vacdraulic booster
   brake.

[492]

SUGGESTIONS FOR FURTHER STUDY

If your local school automotive shop or automotive dealer service shop has power-brake units that you can examine, you will be able to see how the various parts work together. If you are able to disassemble, or watch an automotive mechanic disassemble, one of these units, the relationship of the parts will become clearer. Study any manufacturer's shop manuals you can find on these units. Be sure to write down in your notebook any important facts you run across.

17: Tires and tire service

THIS CHAPTER describes tires and tire service including tire removal and replacement, and tire and tube repair.

§222. Function and construction of tires Tires have two functions: First, they interpose a cushion between the road and the car wheels

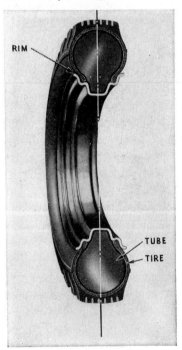

FIG. 17-1. Tire rim and tire cut away so tube can be seen. (*Plymouth Division of Chrysler Corporation*)

to absorb shocks resulting from irregularities in the road. The tires flex, or give, as bumps are encountered, thus reducing the shock effect to the passengers in the car. Second, the tires provide frictional contact between the wheels and the road, so that good traction is secured. This permits the transmitting of power through the tires to the road for rapid acceleration, combats the tendency of the car to skid on turns, and allows quick stops when the brakes are applied.

Tires are of two basic types, solid and pneumatic (air-filled). Solid tires have very limited usage, their use being confined largely to specialized industrial applications. Only pneumatic tires will be considered here. Pneumatic tires are of two types, those using an inner tube and the tubeless type. On the type with an inner tube, both the tube and the tire casing are mounted on the wheel rim, with the tube inside the casing (Fig. 17-1). The inner tube is inflated with air, and this causes the tire casing to resist any change

[494]

of shape. The tubeless tire does not use an inner tube. This tire is mounted on the rim in such a way that the air is retained between the rim and tire casing.

The amount of air pressure used depends on the type of tire and operation. Passenger-car tires are inflated about 22 to 30 pounds (actually pounds per square inch, or psi). Heavy-duty tires on trucks or buses may be inflated up to 100 psi.

Tire casings (and tubeless tires) are made up of layers of cord impregnated with rubber over which the rubber side walls and tread are applied (Fig. 2-18). The layers of cord (called the *plies*)

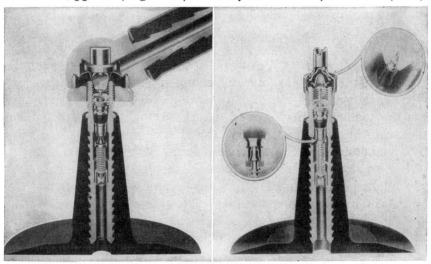

Fig. 17-2. Inner-tube valve in the opened (left) and closed (right) positions. (*A. Schrader's Son Division of Scovill Manufacturing Company, Inc.*)

are formed over a spacing device and rubberized, and the side wall and tread material are applied and vulcanized into place. The term "vulcanizing" pertains to a process of heating the rubber under pressure. This process both molds the rubber into the desired form and gives it the characteristics required. The number of layers of cord (or plies) varies according to the use to which the tire will be put. Passenger-car tires usually have 4 plies. Heavy-duty truck and bus tires may have up to 14 plies, whereas tires for extremely heavy-duty service, such as earth-moving machinery, have been made with 32 plies.

Various shapes of treads are used (Fig. 2-19). The tread designs provide traction and reduce the possibility of skidding.

Air is introduced into the tire (or inner tube) through a valve that opens when the chuck on the air hose is applied as shown to the left in Fig. 17-2. On the tire with an inner tube, the valve is mounted on the tube. On the tubeless tire, the valve is mounted on the wheel rim. Figure 17-2 illustrates one type of tire valve in the opened and closed positions. In the closed position, the valve is held against its seat by spring pressure and the air pressure in the tube. Air can be released from the tube by pressing on the end of the valve stem. A cap is normally screwed down tightly over the end of the valve stem to provide an added safeguard against air leakage and to keep dirt from entering the valve.

§223. Types of tires and tubes   We have already mentioned that the number of plies in tires varies according to the type of service for which the tires are built. Of course, the heavy-duty truck tire is much larger than the passenger-car tire. The typical passenger-car tire today (the low-pressure type) is designed for use on a rim 15 inches in diameter. They are called low-pressure tires (or *extra low-pressure tires*) because they are normally inflated to 22 to 28 psi.

1. *Tire sizes.* Tire sizes are marked on the side of the casing. A tire might be marked 8.00 × 15, for example. This means that the tire fits on a 15-inch rim, and that it is 8 inches larger in radius than the rim (when properly inflated but without load). Thus the diameter of the tire, when inflated but unloaded, is 31 inches (8 + 15 + 8).

2. *Tubeless tires.* Many late-model cars are equipped with tires that do not use tubes. The rim used with this type of tire must be sealed, and it must have a sealed-in tire valve. The tire bead is so constructed that it seals tightly against the rim flange; thus the air pressure will be retained when the tire is inflated.

3. *Puncture-sealing tires.* Some tubeless tires have a coating of plastic material in the inner surface. When the tire is punctured, this plastic material is forced, by the internal air pressure, into the hole left when the nail or other object is removed. The plastic material then hardens to seal the hole.

4. *Tubes.* Three types of rubber, one natural and two synthetic, have been used to make tubes. Today the most common tube material is butyl. You can identify a butyl tube by its blue stripe. The

other synthetic rubber tube (GR-S) has a red stripe. Natural rubber is not striped.

5. *Puncture-sealing tubes.* Some tubes have a coating of plastic material which acts like the plastic material used in the puncture-sealing tire. It flows into and seals any holes left by punctures. In some tubes the plastic material coats the inside of the tube. In others the material is retained between an inner rubber diaphragm and the tube in a series of cells. This latter construction prevents the material from flowing as a result of centrifugal force and thereby from building up in certain spots in the tube. If the material were allowed to build up, it would cause an unbalanced condition.

6. *Safety tube.* The safety tube is really two tubes in one, one smaller than the other and joined at the rim edge. When the tube is filled with air, the air flows first into the inside tube. From there it passes through an equalizing passage into the space between the two tubes. Thus both tubes are filled with air. Now let us see what happens if a puncture or blowout occurs. In this case, the air is lost from between the two tubes. But the inside tube, which has not been damaged, retains its air pressure. It is sufficiently strong to support the weight of the car until the car can be slowed and stopped. Usually, the inside tube is reinforced with nylon fabric so it can take the suddenly imposed weight of the car—without giving way—when a blowout occurs.

§**224. Tire service** Tire service includes periodic inflation to make sure the tire is kept at the proper pressure, periodic tire inspection so that small damages can be detected and repaired before they develop into major defects, tire removal, repair, and replacement. These services are covered in detail below.

§**225. Tire inflation** As we have noted in previous chapters, incorrect tire inflation can cause many types of steering and braking difficulty. Low pressure will cause hard steering, front-wheel shimmy, steering kickback, and tire squeal on turns. Uneven tire pressure will tend to make the car pull to one side. Section 85 covers, in detail, the effects of improper tire inflation on the tires themselves. Low pressure wears the sides of the treads (Fig. 6-3), causes excessive flexing of the sidewalls, and results in ply separation. A tire with insufficient pressure is also subject to rim bruises;

[497]

this could break plies and lead to early tire failure. Excessive pressure also causes uneven tread wear; the tread wears in the center. Also, a tire that is excessively inflated will give a hard ride and is subject to fabric rupture since the pressure may be so high that the tire does not give normally. Thus, when the tire meets a rut or bump, the fabric takes the shock and cannot give, or flex, in a normal manner.

For these reasons, it is very important to maintain proper pressure in the tires. There are a few points you should remember when inflating tires.

1. Don't inflate a tire when it is hot—as it is, for instance, after hard driving on the highway. The increase in temperature increases the air pressure in the tire. If you check pressure with the tire hot, you may find it is high, and your first impulse might be to bleed some of the air out to reduce the pressure. But if you did this, you might excessively reduce cold tire pressure—that is, when the tire cools off, the pressure drops. If you adjust the pressure to the proper value with the tire hot, then when the tire cools the pressure will be too low. Pressures specified by the manufacturers are for cold tires.

2. Always replace the cap after checking air pressure or inflating a tire. The cap helps maintain the air pressure in case the tube valve is leaky. Also, it protects the valve from dirt. If dirt gets into the valve, it may cause the valve to leak. If you release air pressure when you take a cap off, it may be that the valve has become dirty. A new valve core should be installed if the old valve leaks. This simply requires screwing out the old core and screwing in a new one.

§226. Tire inspection   There are certain types of damage and wear you can spot by examining the outside of the tire casing. Thus, abnormal wear, which indicates certain abnormal conditions in the steering, alignment, and brake system (§85) can be easily seen. This abnormal wear is a tip-off that the steering, suspension, or braking system require service. The effects of overinflation or underinflation on tire treads are also obvious. Less obvious are the internal damages from rim bruises or fabric breaks. Sometimes a tire can be bruised badly enough for fabric to break and yet there will be little indication of the trouble on the outside of the casing. Thus,

[498]

the only way to give a tire a thorough inspection is to remove it from the wheel rim so it can be examined inside and out.

Removing the tire from the wheel rim also permits inspection of the tube. Tubes give little trouble if they are installed correctly. However, careless installation of a tube may give trouble. For example, if the tire rim is rusty or if the tire bead (at the rim) is rough, the tube may chafe through. Rust and roughness should be sanded off. Naturally if the tube is pinched between the tire and rim or at the valve stem, it will probably wear through at the pinch and fail. Dirt in the tire casing will also cause chafing of the tube. Another condition that may cause trouble is the installation of too large a tube in a tire casing. This could happen if the wrong tube

A—DEFLATE TUBE. REMOVE FIRST BEAD STARTING NEAR VALVE STEM   B—REMOVE TUBE   C—REMOVE WHEEL

FIG. 17-3. Removing tire from wheel. After the tube is deflated, the bead on the upper side, at A, should be pushed down off the rim flange. The tire bead can then be worked up over the rim as shown at A and B. (*Buick Motor Division of General Motors Corporation*)

were selected. It could also happen if an old tube were used in a new tire because sometimes an old tube has stretched a little. Here is what may happen when you put a tube that is too large in a tire casing: The tube overlaps at some point, and this overlapped area tends to wear both the tire and the tube.

§227. Tire removal The removal and replacement of tires is not difficult on smaller vehicles, but on large, heavy-duty applications special tools are required to remove and handle them. Air must be released from the tube or tire as a first step in tire removal. The bead on one side of the tire should then be pushed in toward the center of the rim (Fig. 17-3). A tire tool or flat stock can be used to pry one part of the bead up over the rim flange (start near valve stem). Care must be exercised to avoid damaging the tire bead or inner tube. After the bead is started over the rim flange with the tool, the remainder of the bead can be worked out over the flange with the hands. The other bead of the tire is removed from over the same side of the rim flange in a similar manner.

Caution: On tubeless tires, do not use tire irons to force the beads away from the rim flanges; this could damage the rim seals on the beads and cause an air leak.

Fig. 17-4. Using special tool to remove tire from safety-rim wheel. The jaws of the tool provide sufficient leverage to lift the bead up and over the hump in the rim. (*Plymouth Division of Chrysler Corporation*)

Chrysler-built cars have so-called "safety-rims" which have a slight hump over which the tire beads must slide (see Fig. 17-1). This hump is designed to keep the tire on the rim in case of a blowout. The hump makes it harder to remove the tire since the tire bead must be slid up and over it. For this reason, a special tool, such as shown in Fig. 17-4, is desirable.

The tire using a tube requires one mounting procedure, the tubeless tire another, as follows:

[500]

1. Tire with tube. Before replacing the tire, inflate the tube until it is barely rounded and put it into the casing. The inside and outside of the tire bead may be coated with a vegetable-oil soft soap to facilitate installation of the tire. Never use grease or oil, for these will damage the rubber. In replacing the tire on the rim, install one bead first, following with the second. Pressing down on the side wall of the tire will facilitate slipping the second bead over the rim flange. After the tire is in place, make sure the beads are up on the bead seats in the rim and that they are uniformly seated all around the rim. Inflate the tube, making sure that it is properly centered in the tire and that the valve stem is square in the rim-valve-stem hole. Deflate and then reinflate the tube. This last operation assures good alignment of tire, tube, and rim.

Caution: If a tire has been deflated, never inflate it while the car weight is on the tire. Always jack up the car before inflating the tire so that the tube can distribute itself around the tire evenly. If this is not done, some parts of the tube will be stretched more than other parts, and this puts a strain on the tube that might cause it to blow out.

2. Tubeless tire. Examine the wheel rim carefully for dents and for roughness or rusting of the rim flanges (where tire beads fit). Straighten out any dents with a hammer. Use steel wool to clean off rim flanges. Use a file to remove roughness of the butt weld (where rim flange attaches to rim). All these areas must be smooth so the tire bead will seal tightly against the rim and not allow air leakage.

Make sure that the valve is sealed tightly in the rim. Most rims have round holes (and require round washers) but some have oval holes (and require oval washers). Rubber valves do not use washers but are snapped into the hole in the rim (vegetable-oil soap makes this job easier).

To replace the tire, install the two beads over the rim, as noted above (for tire with tube). Coating the beads and rim flanges with a vegetable-oil soft soap makes the mounting procedure easier (never use grease or oil since they will damage the rubber). After the tire is mounted on the rim, apply a blast of air to the valve. The valve core should be removed since this will permit the air to enter more freely. The blast of air should force the tire beads outward and into contact with the bead seats on the rim. If it does not and air escapes so that the tire will not inflate, then the beads must be spread by constricting the tread center line. This can be done with a commercial tire-mounting band or with a simple rope tourniquet (Fig. 17-5). As soon as the beads seat, the tire will inflate normally. Remove the band or tourniquet, replace the valve core, and inflate to recommended pressure.

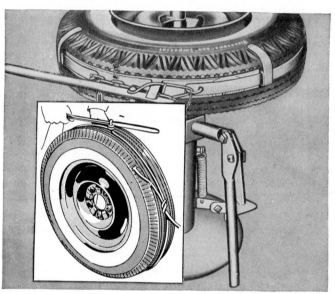

FIG. 17-5. Using a commercial tire-mounting band or a rope torniquet to spread beads during mounting of tubeless tire. (*The American Automobile*)

§228. Rotating tires   The amount of wear that a tire receives varies according to its location on the vehicle. The right-rear tire, for example, wears more than twice as fast as the left-front tire. Of the four tires, the right-rear tire wears most rapidly, the left-rear tire is next, the right-front tire is third, and the left-front tire wears least rapidly of all. To equalize tire wear, it is recommended that tires be rotated every 5,000 miles of operation. The diagram (Fig. 17-6) illustrates one tire-rotation plan. The left-rear tire is moved to the right front, the right-front tire becomes the spare, the spare is installed on the right rear, the right-rear tire is moved to the left front, and the left-front tire is placed on the left rear. This not only interchanges front and rear tires, but it also changes the direction of tire rotation.

§229. Tube and tire repair A number of repairs can be made on tires and tubes, ranging from the patching of nail holes, punctures, or cuts to vulcanizing new tread material to the tire casing. This latter operation is known as *recapping,* since a new cap, or tread, is placed on the tire. Repair procedures vary according to whether the tire is or is not of the tubeless type.

1. Tube repair. Leaks in tubes may be located by inflating the tube (after it is out of the tire) and then submerging the tube in water. Bubbles will leak from punctures or holes. Small punctures can be repaired by use of a vulcanizing kit; this is a patch with a metal back containing fuel. You simply clean the tube around the injury (by buffing and with solvent), remove the protective cover

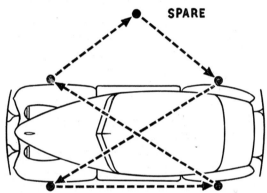

SPARE

Fig. 17-6. Procedure of rotating tires to equalize wear. (*Cadillac Motor Car Division of General Motors Corporation*)

from the patch, clamp it on, and light the fuel. Then when the patch cools, the tube is ready for use.

Small punctures or cuts can also be repaired with a regular tube-vulcanizing hot plate. Larger tube injuries can be repaired only with a hot plate. The hot plate provides the proper curing, or vulcanizing, temperature (of around 300°F). To repair a larger injury to a tube, trim injured edges away so the hole does not have sharp cuts or jagged edges. Then buff the edge of the opening to a 45-degree angle and roughen the area about an inch around the opening. If the injury must be backed (on inside of tube), prepare a patch and apply it to the inside of the tube. Then fill the hole with tube gum and vulcanize it on the hot plate.

NOTE: The cold patch is not generally recommended for tube

repair since it is not as safe a repair as the vulcanized patch. With the cold patch, rubber cement is applied to the tube and allowed to dry until tacky. A second coat is put on, and then the patch is applied.

2. *Tire repair—type using tube.* If a tire has a cut or tear but is otherwise in good condition, it may be repaired by cutting out the material around the injury and buffing the edge (inside and out) to a 45-degree angle. Cement is then applied inside and out, the opening filled with tread gum, a reinforcing fabric applied on the inside, and the repair vulcanized.

If the tread is worn down but the casing is otherwise in good condition, that is, without separated plies or broken or damaged fabric, then a new tread can be vulcanized on the casing. This is a recapping process since a cap of new material is vulcanized on the old casing. This is done on a special recapping machine, such as shown in Fig. 17-7. As a first step, the tire is cleaned and the old tread is roughened by rasping or buffing it. Then a strip of new rubber tread, called *camelback,* is placed around the tread. The casing is put into the recapping machine, the machine is clamped shut, and heat is applied for the specified period of time. This vulcanizes the new material into place.

3. *Tubeless-tire repair.* First examine the tire tread carefully for puncturing objects. This type of tire may carry nails or other puncturing objects for considerable mileage without leaking. Puncturing objects should be removed. Leaks may be located by inflating the tire and submerging the tire and rim assembly in water. Air bubbles will leak from punctures or holes.

NOTE: If air leaks around the spoke welds of the rim, the leaks can be repaired by applying two coatings of cold-patching cement and allowing the cement to dry between coats. Then a strip of rubber is cemented over the welds.

a. *Pressure-gun repair.* If the puncture is less than $\frac{3}{32}$ inch in size, it can be repaired with a pressure gun. If the tire is still on the car, jack up the car so all the weight is taken off the tire. Clean out the hole in the tire with a rasp (after removing puncturing object if it is still in place). Reduce the tire pressure to about 10 pounds. Remove the plug from the gun nozzle and turn the handle until the sealing dough appears. Wipe off the nozzle to make sure only fresh dough will be used. Center the nozzle over the puncture and press

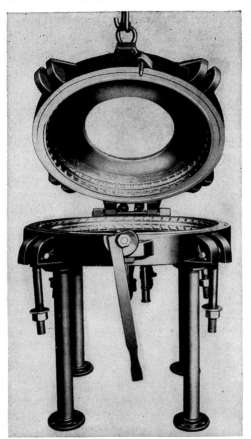

FIG. 17-7. One type of recapping machine. (*Akron Equipment Company*)

it firmly against the tire. Turn the screw handle two full turns (or follow the recommendations of the supplier) to fill the hole. Allow the tire to stand 20 minutes before reinflating it.

b. Rubber-plug repair. The rubber-plug method of tire repair can be used for injuries up to about ¼ inch in size. First, remove the puncturing object. Then use a rasp to clean out the hole. Apply rubber cement to the inside of the hole by coating the needle used to insert the plug with cement. Work the needle around inside the puncture. Repeat until the inside of the hole is well coated. Then select a plug of a size suitable for the hole (it must be at least twice the diameter of the hole). Roll the small end of the plug into the eye of the needle. The end of a ¼-inch plug should be pulled

[505]

through the eye of the needle about ⅜ inch, and the small end of larger plugs should be pulled through almost to the shoulder of the plug. Dip the plug and needle into rubber cement and insert them into the hole. Push the needle in until the short end of the plug snaps through the tire (Fig. 17-8). Remove the needle by pulling it straight out. Trim the plug ⅛ inch above the tread surface (Fig. 17-9). Check for leakage. If no leakage occurs, the tire is ready for service after it is inflated.

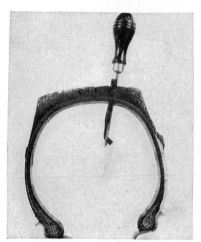 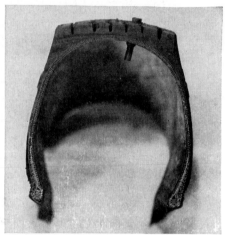

FIG. 17-8. Tire cut away to show needle being used to insert rubber plug in hole in tire. (*The American Automobile*)

FIG. 17-9. Tire cut away to show repair plug in place. (*The American Automobile*)

c. Hot-patch repair. This procedure is for larger holes and requires removal of the tire from the rim. The patch must be applied on the inside of the tire. With the tire off, clean out the injury with a rasp. Fill the injury from outside with sealing dough from the pressure gun (as explained in *a*, Pressure-gun repair, above). Clean the inside of the tire around the injury with gasoline and allow it to dry. Roughen the area with a hand buffer or wire brush. Center the hot patch over the injury and hold it in place, using a special hot-patch clamp (Fig. 17-10). Heat the patch with a match or electrically (according to the equipment being used). Follow the instructions of the patch supplier. After the patch is cured, remount and inflate the tire. Check it for leakage. If no leakage occurs, the tire is ready for service.

[506]

d. Cold-patch repair. This method should not be used on self-sealing tires (which have an inner coating of puncture-sealing material). It can be used, however, on other tubeless tires. The patch is applied on the inside of the tire (as with the hot patch) but does not require heating.

e. Recapping. The tubeless tire is recapped in the same manner as the tire using a tube (see 2, Tire repair, above).

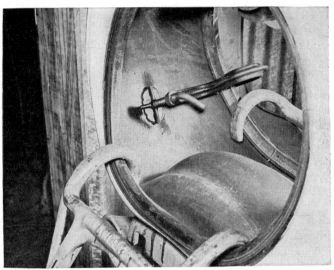

Fig. 17-10. Repairing a tubeless tire by the hot-patch method. (*The American Automobile*)

CHAPTER CHECKUP

Here is your checkup on the chapter you have just finished on tires and tubes. Today tires are more or less taken for granted (unless one goes flat). Yet there is a surprising amount of information on tires that is of importance to the automotive serviceman. Thus, you should know how to inflate a tire properly, the various ways in which tires may wear and what causes the different types of wear, and how to remove, repair, and replace tires. The test that follows will help you to review these facts and remember them.

Completing the Sentences

The sentences below are incomplete. After each sentence there are several words or phrases, only one of which will correctly complete the sentence. Write down each sentence in your notebook, selecting the proper word or phrase to complete it correctly.

1. The typical passenger-car tire has   *two plies*   *four plies* *six plies*   *eight plies*
2. The outside diameter of a 7.50 × 16 tire, when inflated but unloaded, is   *16 inches*   *23.50 inches*   *31 inches*
3. The most commonly used material for tire tubes today is *natural rubber*   *octane rubber*   *butane*   *butyl*
4. For a thorough inspection, a tire should be   *on the car* *on the wheel*   *off the wheel*   *inflated*
5. A butyl tube is identified by a   *blue stripe*   *red stripe* *green stripe*
6. If a tube that is too large for the tire is installed, then   *the tire will overexpand*   *the tire and tube will not fit the rim* *the tube may overlap and wear*
7. Of the four tires on a passenger car, the one that wears most rapidly is the   *right-front tire*   *right-rear tire*   *left-front tire* *left-rear tire*
8. To equalize tire wear, it is suggested that tires be rotated, or shifted from one wheel to another, every   *50 miles*   *500 miles* *5,000 miles*   *50,000 miles*

Servicing Procedures

In the following, you are asked to write down in your notebook the service procedures asked for. Don't copy from the book, but try to explain the procedure in your own words just as you would to a friend.

1. List the points to watch when inflating tires.
2. List types of tire wear and their causes.
3. Explain how to remove a tire from a wheel rim.
4. Explain how to repair a tube.
5. Explain how to repair a tire.

SUGGESTIONS FOR FURTHER STUDY

You can learn a great deal about tire and tube repair by watching a good tire man at work. Notice how he removes and installs tires, and how he makes repairs on various types of tire and tube injury. Examine tires to see how they are constructed. Be sure to write down in your notebook any important points you come across.

18: Chassis lubrication

THIS IS A brief chapter included in this book to emphasize the importance of lubricating various moving parts in the chassis.

§230. Periodic lubrication   The various chassis units, including steering linkage, suspension parts, steering gear, wheel bearings, transmission, and differential, should be lubricated at periodic intervals. It is the usual practice to lubricate many of the chassis components at the same time that the engine oil is changed, or at 1,000 mile intervals. Other chassis components, such as the transmission and differential, require a change of lubricant at less frequent intervals —for example, every 10,000 miles.

To guide the service man, car companies issue lubrication charts, such as shown in Figs. 18-1 and 18-2. As you will note, the charts indicate the points to be lubricated, the type and amount of lubricant to use, and the frequency with which lubrication is required.

In addition to performing the actual lubricating job, the lubrication man also performs other service jobs at the same time. Thus, it is customary to check the battery, tires, lights, fan belt, cooling system, distributor, brake action, clutch, transmission, muffler, spark plugs, and so on. Actually, most of the components of the automobile can be checked, to some extent at least, by the lubrication man while he is "under the hood" or under the car. This is a form of safety insurance since it is often possible to detect trouble in an early stage. It can then be "nipped in the bud" before it develops into serious trouble.

Various lubrication schedules are set up for different makes and models of cars. For best performance and long life of the car, these lubrication schedules should be carefully followed. Study the charts to learn where lubricant is required, how frequently, and the type and amount of lubricant to use.

[509]

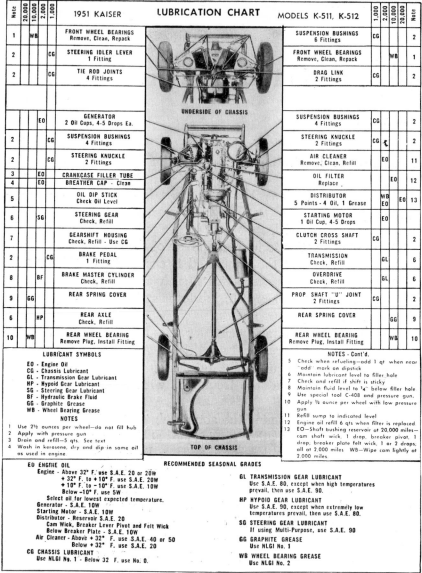

LUBRICATION CHART — 1951 KAISER — MODELS K-511, K-512

Note	20,000	10,000	2,000	1,000	1951 KAISER
1	WB				FRONT WHEEL BEARINGS — Remove, Clean, Repack
2			CG		STEERING IDLER LEVER — 1 Fitting
2			CG		TIE ROD JOINTS — 4 Fittings
		EO			GENERATOR — 2 Oil Cups, 4-5 Drops Ea.
2			CG		SUSPENSION BUSHINGS — 4 Fittings
2			CG		STEERING KNUCKLE — 2 Fittings
3	EO				CRANKCASE FILLER TUBE
4	EO				BREATHER CAP - Clean
5					OIL DIP STICK — Check Oil Level
6	SG				STEERING GEAR — Check, Refill
7					GEARSHIFT HOUSING — Check, Refill - Use CG
2			CG		BRAKE PEDAL — 1 Fitting
8	BF				BRAKE MASTER CYLINDER — Check, Refill
9	GG				REAR SPRING COVER
6	HP				REAR AXLE — Check, Refill
10	WB				REAR WHEEL BEARING — Remove Plug, Install Fitting

UNDERSIDE OF CHASSIS

MODELS K-511, K-512	1,000	2,000	10,000	20,000	Note
SUSPENSION BUSHINGS — 6 Fittings	CG				2
FRONT WHEEL BEARINGS — Remove, Clean, Repack			WB		1
DRAG LINK — 2 Fittings	CG				2
SUSPENSION BUSHINGS — 4 Fittings	CG				2
STEERING KNUCKLE — 2 Fittings	CG				2
AIR CLEANER — Remove, Clean, Refill		EO			11
OIL FILTER — Replace			EO		12
DISTRIBUTOR — 5 Points - 4 Oil, 1 Grease	WB EO		EO		13
STARTING MOTOR — 1 Oil Cup, 4-5 Drops	EO				
CLUTCH CROSS SHAFT — 2 Fittings	CG				2
TRANSMISSION — Check, Refill		GL			6
OVERDRIVE — Check, Refill		GL			6
PROP SHAFT "U" JOINT — 2 Fittings	CG				2
REAR SPRING COVER			GG		9
REAR WHEEL BEARING — Remove Plug, Install Fitting			WB		10

TOP OF CHASSIS

LUBRICANT SYMBOLS

EO - Engine Oil
CG - Chassis Lubricant
GL - Transmission Gear Lubricant
HP - Hypoid Gear Lubricant
SG - Steering Gear Lubricant
BF - Hydraulic Brake Fluid
GG - Graphite Grease
WB - Wheel Bearing Grease

NOTES

1 Use 2½ ounces per wheel—do not fill hub
2 Apply with pressure gun
3 Drain and refill—5 qts. See text
4 Wash in kerosene, dry and dip in same oil as used in engine

NOTES - Cont'd.

5 Check when refueling—add 1 qt. when near "add" mark on dipstick
6 Maintain lubricant level to filler hole
7 Check and refill if shift is sticky
8 Maintain fluid level to ¼" below filler hole
9 Use special tool C-408 and pressure gun
10 Apply ½ ounce per wheel with low pressure gun
11 Refill sump to indicated level
12 Engine oil refill 6 qts when filter is replaced
13 EO—Shaft bushing reservoir at 20,000 miles—cam shaft wick, 1 drop, breaker pivot, 1 drop, breaker plate felt wick, 1 or 2 drops; all at 2,000 miles WB—Wipe cam lightly at 2,000 miles.

RECOMMENDED SEASONAL GRADES

EO ENGINE OIL
Engine - Above 32° F. use S.A.E. 20 or 20W
+ 32° F. to + 10° F. use S.A.E. 20W
+ 10° F. to - 10° F. use S.A.E. 10W
Below -10° F. use 5W
Select oil for lowest expected temperature.
Generator - S.A.E. 10W
Starting Motor - S.A.E. 10W
Distributor - Reservoir S.A.E. 20
Cam Wick, Breaker Lever Pivot and Felt Wick
Below Breaker Plate - S.A.E. 10W
Air Cleaner - Above + 32° F. use S.A.E. 40 or 50
Below + 32° F. use S.A.E. 20

CG CHASSIS LUBRICANT
Use NLGI No. 1 - Below 32 F. use No. 0.

GL TRANSMISSION GEAR LUBRICANT
Use S.A.E. 80, except when high temperatures prevail, then use S.A.E. 90.

HP HYPOID GEAR LUBRICANT
Use S.A.E. 90, except when extremely low temperatures prevail, then use S.A.E. 80.

SG STEERING GEAR LUBRICANT
If using Multi-Purpose, use S.A.E. 90

GG GRAPHITE GREASE
Use NLGI No. 1

WB WHEEL BEARING GREASE
Use NLGI No. 2

Fɪɢ. 18-1. Lubrication chart for Kaiser. (*Kaiser Motors Corporation*)

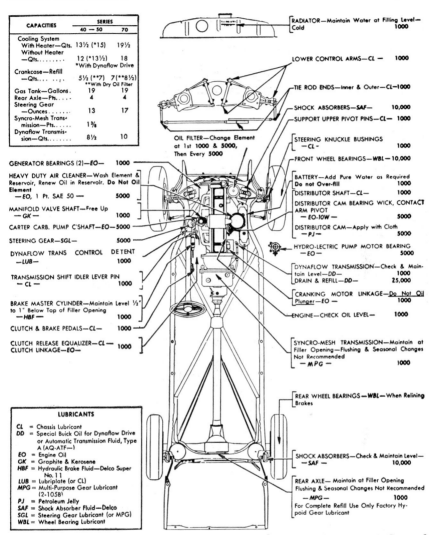

CAPACITIES	SERIES	
	40 — 50	70
Cooling System With Heater—Qts.	13½ (*15)	19½
Without Heater —Qts.........	12 (*13½)	18
	*With Dynaflow Drive	
Crankcase—Refill —Qts....	5½ (**7)	7(**8½)
	**With Dry Oil Filter	
Gas Tank—Gallons.	19	19
Rear Axle—Pts.....	4	4
Steering Gear —Ounces.......	13	17
Syncro-Mesh Trans-mission—Pts......	1⅜	
Dynaflow Transmis-sion—Qts........	8½	10

RADIATOR—Maintain Water at Filling Level—
Cold   1000

LOWER CONTROL ARMS—CL —   1000

TIE ROD ENDS—Inner & Outer—CL—1000

SHOCK ABSORBERS—SAF—   10,000

SUPPORT UPPER PIVOT PINS—CL— 1000

STEERING KNUCKLE BUSHINGS
—CL-   1000

FRONT WHEEL BEARINGS—WBL—10,000

BATTERY—Add Pure Water as Required
Do not Over-fill   1000

DISTRIBUTOR SHAFT—CL—   1000

DISTRIBUTOR CAM BEARING WICK, CONTACT
ARM PIVOT
—EO-10W—   5000

DISTRIBUTOR CAM—Apply with Cloth
—PJ—   5000

HYDRO-LECTRIC PUMP MOTOR BEARING
—EO—   5000

DYNAFLOW TRANSMISSION—Check & Maintain Level—DD—   1000
DRAIN & REFILL—DD—   25,000

CRANKING MOTOR LINKAGE—Do Not Oil
Plunger—EO —   1000

ENGINE—CHECK OIL LEVEL—   1000

SYNCRO-MESH TRANSMISSION—Maintain at
Filler Opening—Flushing & Seasonal Changes
Not Recommended
—MPG—   1000

REAR WHEEL BEARINGS—WBL—When Relining
Brakes

SHOCK ABSORBERS—Check & Maintain Level—
—SAF —   10,000

REAR AXLE— Maintain at Filler Opening
Flushing & Seasonal Changes Not Recommended
—MPG—   1000
For Complete Refill Use Only Factory Hy-
poid Gear Lubricant

OIL FILTER—Change Element
at 1st 1000 & 5000,
Then Every 5000

GENERATOR BEARINGS (2)—EO—   1000

HEAVY DUTY AIR CLEANER—Wash Element &
Reservoir, Renew Oil in Reservoir. Do Not Oil
Element
—EO, 1 Pt. SAE 50 —   5000

MANIFOLD VALVE SHAFT—Free Up
—GK—   1000

CARTER CARB. PUMP C'SHAFT—EO—5000

STEERING GEAR—SGL—   5000

DYNAFLOW TRANS CONTROL DE TENT
—LUB—   1000

TRANSMISSION SHIFT IDLER LEVER PIN
—CL—   1000

BRAKE MASTER CYLINDER—Maintain Level ½"
to 1" Below Top of Filler Opening
—HBF—   1000

CLUTCH & BRAKE PEDALS—CL—   1000

CLUTCH RELEASE EQUALIZER—CL— 1000
CLUTCH LINKAGE—EO—

LUBRICANTS

CL = Chassis Lubricant
DD = Special Buick Oil for Dynaflow Drive
     or Automatic Transmission Fluid, Type
     A (AQ-ATF—1
EO = Engine Oil
GK = Graphite & Kerosene
HBF = Hydraulic Brake Fluid—Delco Super
      No. 11
LUB = Lubriplate (or CL)
MPG = Multi-Purpose Gear Lubricant
      (2-105B\
PJ = Petroleum Jelly
SAF = Shock Absorber Fluid—Delco
SGL = Steering Gear Lubricant (or MPG)
WBL = Wheel Bearing Lubricant

FIG. 18-2. Lubrication chart for Buick. (*Buick Motor Division of General Motors Corporation*)

CHAPTER CHECKUP

Write the answers to the following questions in your notebook:

1. Make a list of items requiring lubrication every 1,000 miles, together with the type of lubricant required.
2. Make lists of the items requiring lubrication at longer intervals (as noted in the charts), together with the type and amount of lubricant used.
3. Make a list of items that could be checked by the lubrication man while he is lubricating the chassis.

SUGGESTIONS FOR FURTHER STUDY

Oil companies, as well as automobile manufacturers, supply their dealers with complete sets of charts as a guide to lubrication procedures. If you have a chance, study some of these charts. Also, note the manner in which the lubrication man does his job while he is lubricating a car. Notice particularly the lubricating equipment he uses. Write down in your notebook any interesting points you learn.

19: Car frame and body

THIS CHAPTER describes the construction, servicing, and repair of the car frame and body. Actually, this chapter should be considered as an introduction to body repair. Body repair is a complex subject; for a complete exposition of body repair, the reader is referred to one of the textbooks that has been published on the subject.

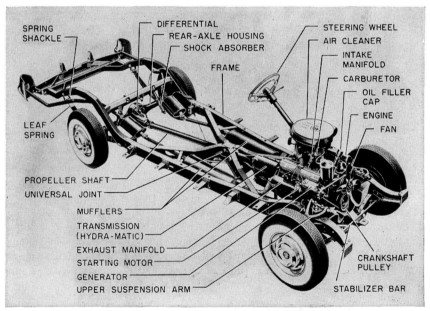

Fig. 19-1. Passenger-car frame with engine, wheels, and steering system attached. This assembly is often called the *chassis.* (*Cadillac Motor Car Division of General Motors Corporation*)

§231. Car frame   The car frame is designed to support all body and engine parts and is in turn supported by the front- and rear-wheel springs. The frame is normally made up of specially formed channel or U-shaped members that are riveted or welded together. Figure 19-1 illustrates an automobile frame with the wheels, engine, and steering systems attached. This assembly is often referred to as the chassis. Figure 2-3 illustrates typical frames. It will be noted that the frame members are designed to receive and support all attached parts.

§232. Frame service   Almost the only service required on frames results from accidents in which the frame has been twisted or broken. It is possible to repair such damage, if it is not too severe,

FIG. 19-2. Checking frame alignment with frame gauges. Sights will line up as shown by white line if frame has proper forward alignment. (*Bear Manufacturing Company*)

by straightening the bent members and replacing or welding those that have been broken. In order to determine whether or not the frame has been bent, frame alignment can be checked by any of several methods. One method of checking the frame for forward alignment is shown in Fig. 19-2. In using this method, frame gauges are hung from the car in three different places. If the sights on the centers of the gauges do not line up, the frame is out of line.

A more complete check of frame alignment can be made by using a plumb bob to transfer to the floor a pattern of the car frame. This operation must be very carefully performed in order to obtain accurate measurements. The floor should be level and clean. Paper can be pasted or tacked to the floor if desired. Using the plumb bob, mark on the floor the various frame points between which measurements are to be taken (Fig. 19-3). Then roll the car out of the way and measure between the points marked on the floor. Every car

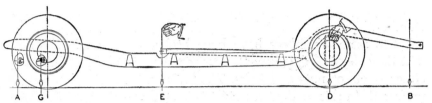

Fig. 19-3. Checking frame alignment with a plumb bob. (*Buick Motor Division of General Motors Corporation*)

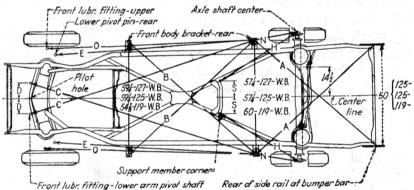

Fig. 19-4. Measurements to be taken when checking for frame alignment. (*Oldsmobile Division of General Motors Corporation*)

manufacturer supplies in his car shop-manual a frame diagram that shows the measurements to be taken and the proper frame dimensions (Fig. 19-4).

If the frame is out of line, it is possible to straighten it satisfactorily, provided the lack of alignment is not too great. The recommendations of the various car manufacturers differ in the matter of straightening frame members. Some state that frame members should be straightened cold, without the application of heat. It is their contention that application of heat weakens the frame mem-

[515]

bers excessively. Other car manufacturers state that heat may be applied, provided the temperature of the steel is kept below 1200°F. Steel, at this temperature, is a deep cherry-red color. Heat above this temperature will seriously weaken the steel. A torch can be used to apply heat to the member to be straightened. Special straightening tools are usually required. These include heavy I beams placed alongside the distorted frame member, chains to be attached between the beam and the frame member, and jacks to apply straightening pressure on the chain against the frame member.

When frame members have been broken or so badly distorted that they require replacement, new members can be installed with either rivets or nuts and bolts. The hot-riveting method is usually preferred. In this method the rivet is heated and riveted into place.

When the front-suspension cross member has been damaged, it is the usual practice to replace it. This part is manufactured to extremely close tolerances and, if it is once bent, it is practically impossible to restore it to perfect alignment. If it is not in proper alignment, the front wheels cannot be properly aligned, and poor steering control and rapid tire wear are apt to result.

On vehicles that do not have independent front suspension, the front axle is bent to correct front-wheel alignment. This has already been discussed in §125.

§233. Car body The car body is attached to the frame by numerous nuts and bolts, all the bolts being insulated with rubber washers or shims to prevent the transfer of vibration and noise from the frame to the body. A few of the various types of body bolts are shown in Fig. 19-5.

The body is designed to contain and protect the engine and accessories, as well as the passengers. In addition, it is shaped to reduce the resistance to the air as it moves forward. This shaping of the car to reduce air resistance is called *streamlining*. Streamlining makes use of curves, rather than angles and flat surfaces. An early-model car and a later, streamlined car are pictured in Figs. 19-6 and 19-7. In the early-model car, the vertical front sections of the radiator and the windshield offer considerable resistance to the car movement through the air. In addition, air eddies form in back of the car, tending to produce a drag that impedes forward motion.

Fɪɢ. 19-5. Various types of body bolts that attach the body to the car frame. (*Buick Motor Division of General Motors Corporation*)

At intermediate and high speeds, considerable power is required to overcome this air resistance on a car with the type of body shown in Fig. 19-6.

The car shown in Fig. 19-7 is streamlined, with sloping lines that permit the car body to move more smoothly through the air. The sloping lines tend to push the air up and around the car, as shown by the curved lines. Note that air eddies are not formed behind the car body as on the early-model car.

[517]

The car body is made up of a number of pressed-steel panels, which are welded together to form the complete body (Fig. 19-8). Reinforcing members are placed at proper intervals in the body. Attaching brackets are welded to the body to attach doors, trim,

FIG. 19–6. Outline of early-model car body, showing resistance to its passage through the air.

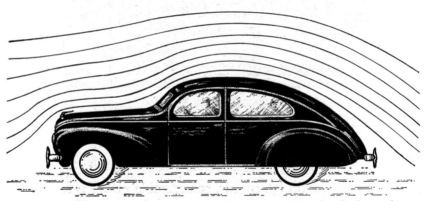

FIG. 19-7. Modern car design, showing air movement over car body as the car moves forward.

instrument panel, hood, trunk lid, headlining, and so on. In case of accidents, panels can be replaced if they are so badly damaged that they cannot be straightened.

Doors, engine hood, and trunk or rear-compartment lids are attached to the body by hinges (Figs. 19-9 and 19-10). The hinges

[518]

FIG. 19-8. Typical passenger-car body. (*Buick Motor Division of General Motors Corporation*)

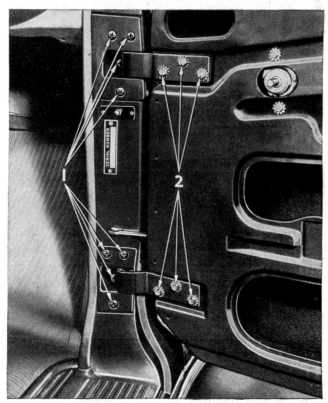

FIG. 19-9. Door hinges. Screws may be loosened to adjust the fit of the door. 1, hinge-to-body screws; 2, hinge-to-door screws. (*Plymouth Division of Chrysler Corporation*)

[519]

have slotted holes by means of which adjustments can be made. Door hinges usually incorporate a hold-open mechanism that causes the door to hold open when it is fully opened. This prevents the door from closing accidentally when passengers are entering or alighting from the car. One type of hold-open mechanism is illustrated in Fig. 19-11. When the door is opened wide as shown, the

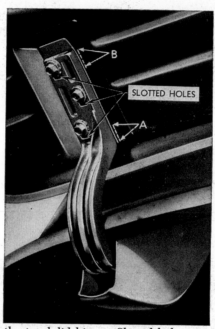

Fig. 19-10. One of the trunk-lid hinges. Slotted holes permit adjustment of lid fit to body. Lid may be moved in or out with respect to body by placing shims at *B* or *A* respectively. (*Chevrolet Motor Division of General Motors Corporation*)

high section of the bar (No. 3) rides up over the ridge in the door cover plate (No. 2). Some pressure against the door is required to force the high section of the bar (No. 3) to life up over the ridge and permit the door to close.

The doors contain the window-regulator mechanism, door latch, and lock. Figure 19-12 illustrates a rear-door window regulator being removed from the door. It consists of a small gear attached to the window crank, a gear sector, and a lever, the free end of which is attached to the window-glass support. A spring provides spring-loading of the lever to retain the window at the height to

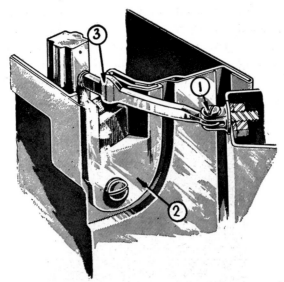

FIG. 19-11. Details of one type of door hold-open mechanism: 1, holding screw; 2, door cover plate; 3, check-link bar. (*Oldsmobile Division of General Motors Corporation*)

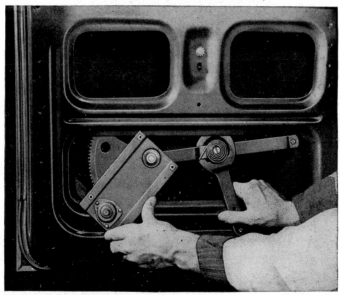

FIG. 19-12. Window regulator being removed from door. (*Plymouth Division of Chrysler Corporation*)

which it is adjusted. The other windows in the body are regulated by similar mechanisms.

A typical seat construction is shown in Fig. 19-13. The coil springs are held in a framework to which the padding and upholstery are attached. Some cars make use of sponge-rubber seats. The rear-seat support is normally attached to the car body, but the front seat often incorporates an adjusting device that permits adjustment of

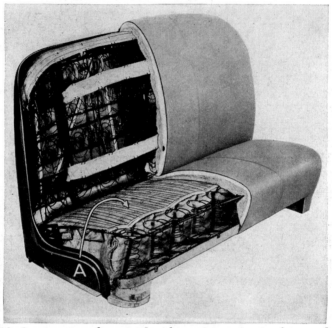

Fig. 19-13. Construction of seat and cushion. A is spring insulator pad. (*Chevrolet Motor Division of General Motors Corporation*)

the front seat backward or forward. The seat adjuster is attached to the floor and to the bottom of the seat by screws. A control rod, to which a lever is attached, unlocks the seat adjuster when the lever is raised. This permits the seat to roll forward or backward as desired. When the lever is released, a latch falls into place to lock the seat into position.

Some seat adjusters are now operated electrically by small motors that use battery current. On these, there is a switch that can be moved into one position or another so as to cause the seat to move forward or back, and up or down. Gearing from the motor shaft to the seat adjuster causes this motion. There are limit switches included to turn off the motors when the limit of travel (up or down, or back or forward) is reached. There is little in the way of special service that these devices require.

Another type of seat-adjuster control makes use of an electric motor that drives a hydraulic pump. In this system, generally used on convertibles, hydraulic pressure operates pistons in cylinders to

FIG. 19-14. Using door bar to take excessive bow at *A* out of door. (*Buick Motor Division of General Motors Corporation*)

FIG. 19-15. Using door bar to put more bow into door. (*Buick Motor Division of General Motors Corporation*)

raise and lower the convertible top and the windows. In addition, there is a cylinder to move the seat back and forth. These devices are discussed in detail in another book in the McGraw-Hill Automotive Mechanics Series (*Automotive Electrical Equipment*).

§234. Body service Body service embraces a variety of operations that require a specialized knowledge of sheet-metal working and welding. Some minor operations, such as replacing window regulators, locks, or latches, can be performed without special tools.

[523]

Complete body service includes correcting the fit of doors, rear-compartment or trunk lid, and engine hood. It also includes straightening doors, realigning the body after an accident, replacing body parts, removing dents or bulges in body panels, refinishing the body, replacing glass, and servicing window regulators, locks, latches, and ventilators.

§235. Door, rear-compartment-lid, and hood service

The first step in correcting the fit of a door is to determine where the door is not

FIG. 19-16. Using a hammer and spoon to align door flange. (*Buick Motor Division of General Motors Corporation*)

fitting snugly. This may be done by placing chalk marks about six inches apart around the outer body edge against which the door closes and then closing the door. When the door is reopened, the chalk contact on the weather strip of the door will show the fit.

Of course, it may not be necessary to use chalk marks to check the door fit, since lack of alignment will often be readily noticeable. Adjustment usually can be made, if the door is not distorted, by loosening the hinge-attaching screws (Fig. 19-9) and moving the door up or down or back and forth, as required.

If the door is actually distorted, correction may be made by use of a special door-straightening bar, which will take excessive bow out of, or put more bow into, the door (Figs. 19-14 and 19-15).

If the door flange does not fit snugly to the body, it can be brought down by use of a surfacing spoon and a hammer (Fig. 19-16). The door flange should first be covered with several layers of tape to prevent damage to the finish. Then, by moving the spoon along the flange and striking it with the hammer, the flange can be brought down to fit.

If the lower edge, or skirt, of the door does not fit snugly against the body, it may be bent inward by placing a piece of wood between the door and the doorpost at the latch and pushing in on the bottom of the door. The top of the door may be adjusted inward by clamping it to the body at the top and then pulling the door out, at the window. The straightening of bent or crumpled door panels will be covered in a later section.

Fig. 19-17. Checking alignment of center section of car body. (*Plymouth Division of Chrysler Corporation*)

Fit of the rear compartment, or trunk, lid to the body may be adjusted by loosening the hinge-attaching screws and shifting the lid by means of the slotted holes (Fig. 19-10). Fit of the lid flange may be corrected by use of a spoon and a hammer in a manner similar to the procedure used for correcting door-flange fit (Fig. 19-16). Tape the flange to avoid damaging the finish.

§236. **Body alignment** For checking body alignment after an accident, chalk marks should be placed at various points on the body posts and an extension measuring bar used to take comparative measurements from the various markings (Figs. 19-17 to 19-19). This will determine how much, if any, misalignment the body has. By a series of checks from side to side, top to bottom, and front to back, the amount and location of misalignment can be determined.

By use of body-straightening jacks, pressure may be applied in the proper places to bring the body back into alignment, provided

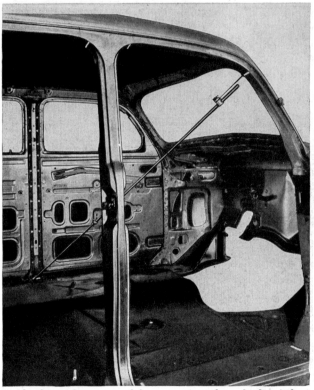

Fig. 19-18. Checking alignment of front section of car body. (*Plymouth Division of Chrysler Corporation*)

it is not too far out of line. All glass should be removed during the aligning operation, to avoid breakage. Figures 19-20 to 19-22 illustrate typical uses of the straightening jack to increase the dimensions being checked in Figs. 19-17 to 19-19. These dimension increases are required if it is found, in checking, that they are too small in comparison to similar measurements taken from the base of the center post on the near side of the car body.

[526]

§237. Panel repair When metal panels have been dented or distorted, they may be straightened and refinished (if the proper tools are available). If the damage is severe, the old panel may be removed and a new panel welded into place.

A variety of tools is available to remove dents from body panels (Fig. 19-23). The simplest consists of hammers and dolly blocks.

Fig. 19-19. Checking alignment of rear section of car body. (*Plymouth Division of Chrysler Corporation*)

Dolly blocks are steel blocks of various shapes and contours that are held on one side of the distorted panel while the other side is pounded with a hammer.

There are available air-driven body and fender reshapers, which quickly and easily straighten out dents in body or fender panels (Fig. 19-24). The reshaper consists of a pair of dolly blocks attached to a frame. The upper dolly block is operated by air as an air hammer, and the lower dolly block pivots on the frame to maintain alignment with the other block. When the two dolly blocks are placed on the two sides of a distorted panel and the air hammer is operated, the panel is quickly flattened out. Dolly blocks of various contours are available to fit different fender and body contours.

FIG. 19-20. Aligning center section of car body. (*Plymouth Division of Chrysler Corporation*)

The hot-shrinkage technique is useful in straightening out panels that have large dents in them. When distortion has taken place—for example, when a dent has been made in a panel—the metal has been stretched, and it must be shrunk to bring it back into shape. The hot-shrinkage method makes use of the fact that application of heat and then cold to the panel will cause the metal to contract, or shrink. This method requires a rawhide or wood mallet, a special shrinking dolly block, and an acetylene torch.

The first step in hot shrinking is to rough out the dented section so that it bulges outward above the normal curvature of the surface. This operation may be accomplished with dolly block and a hammer. Then a small section in the center of the bulge is heated to cherry-red color with the acetylene torch. Excessive temperature should be avoided, since this would make the metal brittle. When

Fig. 19-21. Aligning front section of car body. (*Plymouth Division of Chrysler Corporation*)

the spot reaches a cherry-red heat, place the shrinking dolly block under the hot spot and use the hammer to pound the outside surface of the heated spot down onto the low-crown surface of the shrinking dolly block. Only a few blows will be required. Then, quickly take a sponge filled with water and place it on the heated spot to cool it. This causes a decided shrinking of the metal sheet. The pounding and quenching must be performed quickly. Repeat this action of heating, pounding, and quenching over the entire surface

[529]

of the bulge, but do not overlap the areas. Work from the center out. The bulge will be brought down to proper contour by this action. It will, however, be rough and will require further attention with a dolly block and a hammer before it is ready for finishing work.

When a body panel has been dented in not too deeply and without too much irregularity, it is sometimes possible to remove

FIG. 19-22. Aligning rear section of car body. (*Plymouth Division of Chrysler Corporation*)

the dent without working from the inside. A piece of welding rod is welded to the center of the dent and formed into a handle, and the dent is pulled out while heat is applied with the torch. The welding rod is then cut off close to the body and the remaining stub driven in, level with the panel. The small remaining cavity can then be filled with surfacing material or solder, as explained below, and sanded smooth.

After a panel surface has been restored to its natural contour,

[530]

rough places must be filed or sanded off. Garages doing considerable body work usually have power-driven sanders such as that shown in Fig. 19-25. The sanding disk can be changed for a buffing wheel for finish work.

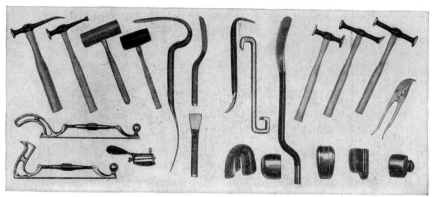

FIG. 19-23. Set of body tools including hammers, spoons, file holders, and dolly blocks. (*Kent-Moore Organization, Inc.*)

If the panel surface is excessively rough, with deep file marks or gouges, a special surfacing material can be used to fill the gouges. This material will bond to the metal surface and can be sanded smooth. Paddle soldering also can be used where the marks or gouges are quite deep. To paddle-solder a surface, the surface is first cleaned with muriatic acid to remove all paint and oil and then is heated with the acetylene torch. Solder is applied and smoothed with a wooden paddle or with rags. This not only fills deep gouges but will also fill small dents. Roughness is sanded off.

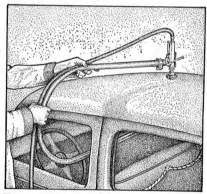

FIG. 19-24. Air-driven body-and-fender reshaper in action.

In addition to the above panel- and fender-repair procedure, there is a special plastic-type substance—supplied in rolls and somewhat like cloth—for repairing these body parts. The substance is unrolled and cut with knife or scissors to fit the repair and is then dipped into a liquid. Next, it is

[531]

applied to the cleaned and sanded surface to be repaired and is molded by hand into approximately the original contour of the damaged surface. After a few hours, the substance has set and has become very hard and tough. It can then be sanded to a final finish and painted just as though it were metal.

FIG. 19-25. Power-driven sander. (*Kent-Moore Organization, Inc.*)

If new panels are welded into place, the weld marks will stand up above the natural body contour. These weld marks should be driven below the contour surface and the channel filled with solder.

§238. Body painting Before a repaired panel is repainted, all trace of soldering flux must be washed off and the panel then washed with gasoline (do not use ethyl gasoline). Before a body is painted, all traces of rust or scaling paint must be sanded off, so that either well-bonded paint or the metal is exposed. A primer coat is first sprayed on with a spray gun (Fig. 19-26); this is followed by a finish coat. Two general types of finish materials are used in the auto-body shop, lacquer and enamel. Enamel can be of the air-drying type, or it can be baking enamel. Baking enamel is baked, after it is sprayed on, by application of heat; infrared lamps (Fig. 19-27) may be used for this purpose.

§239. Glass work To replace a windshield, first remove the center-strip molding (where used), the garnish molding, and the rubber weather strip. The windshield can then be pushed into the car.

Masking tape should be placed over the instrument panel to prevent damage to the finish. Before installing a new windshield, clean out all the old sealing compound, lay a bead of sealing compound around the glass opening, install weatherstrip on the glass, and place the glass in the opening. Be sure that sealing compound is in all cracks. Replace the garnish and center-strip molding. Rear car windows are replaced in a similar manner. In case of any breakage that does not seem to have been caused by impact of a flying object or by a car accident, it is well to check the glass opening to make sure there is not a distorted or a raised section that strains the glass and causes it to break.

Door glass is replaced by removing the door handles, garnish molding, door-trim pad, and panel-hole covers. The screws that attach the lifter mech-

FIG. 19-26. Spray gun for applying paint to car body. (*Alexander Milburn Company*)

anism can then be removed, so that the window can be tipped in and lifted out. Replacement is the reverse of removal.

§240. Window regulators, locks, and door latches The removal and replacement of window regulators, door latches, and locks is usually easy and obvious. Removal of the garnish molding, door handles, trim panels, and glass allows easy access to the window-regulator mechanism, lock, or door latch, which can then be detached and lifted out. For replacement of these parts the removal procedure is reversed.

[533]

§241. Windshield wipers Windshield wipers are of two types, electrically operated and vacuum-operated. The vacuum-operated type, which is the more commonly used, is operated either by vacuum from the engine intake manifold, or by vacuum from a vacuum pump. The vacuum pump is an integral part of the fuel pump. The vacuum-operated windshield wiper uses a small vacuum-actuated motor which moves the windshield-wiper blades back and forth

Fig. 19-27. Bank of infrared lamps for applying heat to painted car body. (*North American Electric Lamp Company*)

across the windshield. Figure 19-28 illustrates the mounting arrangement of this type of wiper, with its control. The control has three hose connections: one to the intake manifold, or vacuum pump, a second to the "run" connection on the wiper, and a third to the "park" connection on the wiper.

Normally, this type of wiper requires little service aside from occasional replacement of the wiper blades. If the sweep, or stroke, adjustment is not correct, so that the sweep is farther to one side than to the other, the wiper blade and arm assembly may be removed from the wiper shaft and reinstalled in a slightly different position. This will provide a more balanced stroke. If the stroking is short and uneven, it may be that the chain of one or both transmission and link assemblies is loose. This may be corrected by loosening the nut at the bottom of the transmission and link and moving the nut and bolt downward, to take up the slack in the chain.

The electrically operated windshield wiper uses an electric motor with a gearing arrangement and linkages to the wiper blades. There

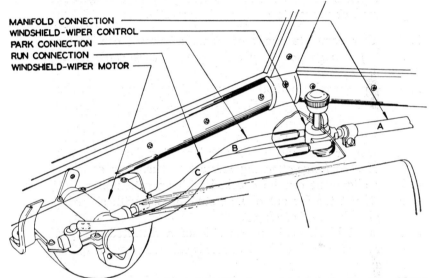

MANIFOLD CONNECTION
WINDSHIELD-WIPER CONTROL
PARK CONNECTION
RUN CONNECTION
WINDSHIELD-WIPER MOTOR

FIG. 19-28. Vacuum-operated windshield wiper and control. (*Pontiac Motor Division of General Motors Corporation*)

is little in the way of special service or maintenance these wipers require. About once a year the pivots should be supplied with a drop of oil. In addition, new wiper blades may be required when the old ones become worn. After long service, moving parts—such as the gearing, pivots, motor bearings, armature, and brushes—may require replacement or servicing.

CHAPTER CHECKUP

Car frame and body work is a specialty for which special training and tools are required. The body man usually devotes full time to body repair; he does not engage in other repair or servicing activities. Nevertheless, the man with a well-rounded education in the field of automotive mechanics should have an understanding of how body-repair work is done. The chapter you have just completed gives you a brief introduction to the subject. The checkup that follows covers high points of the chapter. When you take the test, you will review these high points and at the same time will find out how well you remember them.

Completing the Sentences

The sentences below are incomplete. After each sentence there are several words or phrases, only one of which will correctly complete the sentence. Write down each sentence in your notebook, selecting the proper word or phrase to complete it correctly.

1. A rather complete check of frame alignment can be made with a   *frame gauge*   *plumb bob*   *carpenter's level*   *carpenter's square*
2. The preferred method of replacing frame members is by the   *hot-riveting method*   *cold-riveting method*   *welding method*
3. To improve the fit of an undistorted door, it should be moved up or down, or back and forth, after loosening the   *frame bracket screws*   *hinge-attaching screws*   *window regulator screws*
4. Body alignment can be checked with an extension measuring rod and, if not too far out of line, straightened with a   *body bar*   *dolly block*   *body jack*
5. The steel block held on one side of a distorted panel while the other side is struck with a hammer is called a   *body block*   *reshaper*   *dolly block*
6. Where the metal in a panel has been stretched, it can be shrunk to bring it back into shape by the   *hot-shrinkage method*   *cold-shrinkage method*   *paddle-soldering method*
7. Two general types of body finish paint are   *masking and enamel*   *lead-base and enamel*   *enamel and lacquer*
8. Two types of windshield wipers are   *electric and hydraulic*   *hydraulic and vacuum*   *electric and vacuum*

Servicing Procedures

Write down in your notebook the procedures asked for below. Don't copy from the book, but explain the procedures in your own words just as you would to a friend.

1. Explain how to check frame alignment, and list important points to watch when straightening or replacing a frame member.

[536]

2. What are some important points the body designer must keep in mind?
3. Explain how to improve the fit of a door that is not distorted; a door that is distorted.
4. Explain how to check and correct body alignment with a measuring bar and body jack.
5. Explain how to use the hot-shrinkage method to bring a body panel back into shape.

SUGGESTIONS FOR FURTHER STUDY

There are several books devoted exclusively to frame and body repair and painting. If you are especially interested in this subject, you may find one or more of these books at your local public or school library. You can also purchase these books from your local bookstore. If you have a chance, you can spend some time at a local body shop, watching the body men at work repairing and repainting bodies. Be sure you write down in your notebook any important facts you learn.

20: Air conditioning

THIS CHAPTER discusses the theory of refrigeration and air conditioning and the construction and operation of the air-conditioning equipment used in automobiles. The chapter that follows discusses the servicing and repair of this equipment.

§242. Air conditioning   An air conditioner does two things when it "conditions" or treats the air: (1) it takes heat from the air (by refrigeration), thus lowering the temperature of the air, and (2) it takes moisture from the air, thus drying the air. The air conditioner both cools and dries the air.

Air conditioners have been used for many years in public buildings, theaters, restaurants, and homes. A few installations of air-conditioning equipment were made on passenger cars a number of years ago. But it has been only recently that the major car companies have made air conditioning generally available, as accessory equipment, on their cars.

The terms "refrigeration" and "air conditioning" sound rather formidable. Of course, there is a lot of science and engineering behind them, but in essence they are not hard to understand. All of us are familiar with electric refrigerators. We see them in our homes, in restaurants, food stores, soda fountains, and so on. An air conditioner is nothing more than a refrigerator with an air-circulating system. But before we talk about the air-circulating system, let us discuss refrigerators.

§243. Methods of cooling   If you hold a piece of ice in your hand, your hand gets cold. This is because the ice takes heat from your hand. Likewise, if you put a liquid such as water or alcohol on your hand, and then blow on it, your hand feels cold. Why? Because the liquid evaporates and removes heat from your hand. In the same way, when we are hot and perspire, the perspiration evaporates and removes heat from our body, so that we are cooled.

[538]

Thus, to cool an object, you remove heat from it.

1. Cooling by evaporation. We noted, in §10, that heat, or the temperature of an object, is nothing more nor less than the speed of molecular motion. When the molecules that make up an object move fast, the object is hot. When the molecules move slowly, the object is cold. In ice, the molecules are moving rather slowly and in restricted paths. They "hang together" so that ice is a solid. But if the ice is heated, it melts; the molecules move faster and break out of their restricted paths, and the ice turns into water. Further heating causes the water to boil. As this happens, the molecules are set into such fast motion that they "jump" clear of the water: the water turns to vapor.

When you put a liquid on your hand, it begins to evaporate—that is, the molecules forming the liquid begin to leave your hand. To jump clear, however, they must be moving rather fast. They cannot, of themselves, suddenly "decide" to begin moving fast. They must be given a push. This push comes from the molecules of the skin. The skin molecules are moving, too. Liquid molecules and skin molecules, both in motion, are constantly colliding. During such collisions, the skin molecules are slowed down while the liquid molecules are speeded up. This speeding up gives the liquid molecules enough velocity to allow them to jump clear: the liquid evaporates. But note that the skin molecules are slowed down. This means that the skin is cooled (slower molecular motion means a lower temperature).

2. Cooling by melting. When a solid is turned into a liquid, a cooling effect results. Ice, for example, is widely used as a cooling agent. When ice melts, as in a refrigerator, it takes heat away from the surrounding air, thus cooling the contents of the refrigerator. In the solid, ice, the molecules are moving slowly. But as the solid turns to liquid, the molecules move much more rapidly. This speed-up must come from the air molecules around the ice—that is, as the air molecules and ice molecules collide, the air molecules are slowed down and the ice molecules speeded up. In other words, the air is cooled and the ice is warmed. When the ice molecules are sufficiently speeded up, they break out of their restricted paths: the ice melts or turns to water. This change of state (from solid to liquid) has a big cooling effect since the air molecules lose a great deal of their velocity as they collide with the ice molecules.

[539]

Remember, cooling means that the molecules are slowed down.

§244. **More on evaporation**   Since the refrigerating devices used in home refrigerators and car air conditioners operate on the principle of evaporation of a liquid, let us talk some more about evaporation. If you filled a glass of water, and then watched it for a day or two, you would notice that the water level would gradually drop as the water evaporated. You could speed up the evaporation by applying heat to the water. When you apply heat, you speed up the molecular movement. The molecules become more lively; more of them "jump" clear and escape from the glass. If you heated the water

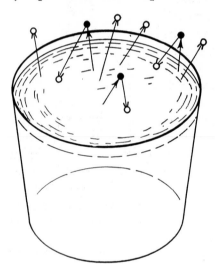

Fig. 20-1. Glass of water illustrating evaporation. The molecules of water (hollow circles) and the molecules of air (solid circles) are shown enormously enlarged. Molecules of water that collide with molecules of air may be "bounced" back into the water.

to 212°F (at sea level), it would begin to boil—that is, the water molecules would begin to move so rapidly that the water would be violently agitated and the evaporation would go on at a lively rate.

You could also speed up evaporation by placing the glass of water in a vacuum. A vacuum is, as you will recall from §6, an absence of air or other substance. During evaporation of water, as noted above, water molecules are constantly gaining enough speed to leave the water. With air above the water, some of the water molecules will collide with air molecules and, in effect, will be knocked back into the water (Fig. 20-1). But this would not occur if the air were removed from above the water. With the air removed, evaporation of the water would thus be speeded up.

Air can be removed from around the glass of water by sealing it into a jar (Fig. 20-2) and using a vacuum pump (§7) to draw the air from the jar. When this happens, the water will begin to evaporate more rapidly. Soon, however, if the vacuum pump stops, the rate of evaporation will slow down again. The reason is that the space around the glass becomes partly filled with water molecules. These free water molecules collide with molecules leaving the surface of the water, knocking some of them back into the water. After a time, the space will become so saturated, or filled, with water molecules that for every molecule leaving the water, another molecule gets knocked back into the water. In other words, evaporation, in effect, ceases.

But if the vacuum pump is started again, the free water molecules will be pumped out and evaporation will start once again.

Thus, evaporation of a liquid depends not only on the heat that goes into the liquid, but also on the amount of pressure, or vacuum, above the liquid. When there is a high vacuum, there are few free molecules to block the escape of molecules from the liquid. But as vacuum decreases, more free molecules are present to block the escape of molecules from the liquid.

Fig. 20-2. Glass of water sealed into a glass jar. When air is pumped out of jar, water evaporation increases.

§245. Effect of pressure on evaporation If we reversed the vacuum pump, and pumped free water molecules back into the sealed jar, we would create a pressure in the jar. This would produce a very curious result. For, under the proper conditions of increased pressure, water molecules would be forced *back into* the glass of water. Here is how that could happen. We pump free water molecules into the sealed jar. There are thus many water molecules moving about in the jar. Many collisions take place and, as a result, more water molecules get knocked *back into* the glass of water than leave the glass of water.

Actually, under such conditions, water would condense all over the inside surface of the jar and all over the glass itself—that is, the water molecules would become so crowded (as more and more were pumped into the jar) that collisions would be more frequent. Soon molecules would begin to stick together in clumps (driven together by the collisions). These clumps would form the beads of condensed water on the inside surfaces of the jar.

§246. Heat and pressure   One more thing must be considered. That is the heat resulting from the increased pressure. We have already noted, in §§10 and 11, that increasing the pressure increases the heat. Whenever a gas—such as air or water vapor—is subjected to pressure, the molecules are moved closer together. More molecular collisions take place, the molecules are set into faster motion by these more frequent collisions. (Faster motion means higher temperature.) Thus, in the experiment described in the previous section, we would find that the temperature in the sealed jar would increase. The water molecules are set into fast motion. The walls of the jar are bombarded by these fast-moving molecules of water vapor. Thus, the molecules of the substance composing the jar are bombarded into faster motion—that is, the jar begins to get hot. However, there is air outside the jar. The air molecules, as they move about, come into contact with the outer surface of the jar. The jar molecules have been set into fast motion; and they, in turn, set the air molecules into fast motion.

Now, what have we said? We have said that heat is produced inside the jar by compressing water vapor in the jar. Part of this heat passes to the jar itself. Then heat passes from the jar to the surrounding air. All of this was described in terms of molecular motion in the previous paragraph.

Since the jar is cooler than the compressed water vapor, water molecules are slowed down as they strike the inner surface of the jar. In fact, many are slowed down so much that they are no longer vapor: they are water. Thus, water condenses on the inside of the jar, as mentioned above.

Note: The above discussion on heat and heat transfer is only part of the story. Heat also is transferred by radiation; that is, by a movement of heat energy. Any modern physics textbook contains information on this subject.

§247. Condensation   Water may also condense on any cold surface. For example, all of us have seen moisture condense on the outside of a glass of ice water. On a damp day, so much water will condense that it will run off the glass. The same thing is happening here as was mentioned in the previous section. Water molecules in the air strike the cold surface of the glass. The water molecules give up part of their speed of motion (part of their heat) to the cold, or slow moving, glass molecules. In giving up some of their speed of motion, they are slowed down so much that they cannot "get away" from the surface of the glass. Thus, water molecules collect on the cold surface of the glass. In other words, water condenses on the glass.

§**248. Boiling points** Water boils at 212°F at sea level. At higher altitudes, where the atmospheric pressure is lower (§5), the boiling point is also lower. Thus, water will boil at 187°F on the top of Pikes Peak, a mountain in Colorado that is 14,108 feet high. The reason is that at the lower pressure there are fewer air molecules to knock water molecules back into the water. Water molecules can escape more easily (water can boil at a lower temperature). The lower the air pressure on the water, the lower the temperature at which the water boils.

Normally, we tend to think of a boiling liquid as being hot. This is only natural since we boil water every day and, to us, boiling water is *hot*. However, there are many liquids that boil at temperatures we would consider very cold. For instance, sulfur dioxide (SO_2) boils at a temperature of 14°F at sea level. Below that temperature it is a liquid. If the pressure is reduced, its boiling point is lowered.

Pure ammonia (not the diluted ammonia used in households) boils at a temperature of −28°F, or 28° *below zero* (at atmospheric pressure). Another substance with a low boiling point is Freon-12, or dichlorodifluoromethane. It boils at −22°F (at atmospheric pressure). We mention Freon-12 because it is the substance, the liquid, used in many refrigerators and in automobile air conditioners. It is called a *refrigerant*. Any substance used in a refrigerator to produce the cooling effect through a cycle of evaporation and condensation (as explained below) is called a refrigerant.

§**249. Refrigeration** We have now covered the fundamentals of refrigeration. All we have to do is to put those fundamentals together to learn how a modern electric refrigerator operates. In learning this, we will learn also how the car air conditioner works. The refrigerating unit in an automobile air conditioner works in exactly

[543]

the same way as an electric refrigerator. There is only one additional device in the conditioner to circulate the air.

§250. A simple refrigerator   We could make a simple refrigerator that would work for a short time by putting a jug of refrigerant such as Freon-12 in the top of a closed compartment (Fig. 20-3).

Fɪɢ. 20-3. A simple refrigerator. Evaporation of Freon-12 removes heat from the cabinet. (*Hotpoint, Inc.*)

Note that the mouth of the jug is outside the cabinet, or refrigerating compartment. Since the Freon-12 boils at −22°F, as already noted, it will begin to boil as soon as it is put into the refrigerating compartment. The boiling action removes heat from the refrigerating compartment since, as explained above, when a liquid is changed to a vapor, it absorbs heat. The only place the boiling Freon-12 can obtain heat is from the refrigerating compartment. It therefore cools this compartment by removing heat from it. The refrigerating action will continue as long as there is any refrigerant left to evaporate from the jug.

The refrigerator in Fig. 20-3 obviously has several drawbacks. In the first place, it is wasteful to let all the refrigerant escape. It is expensive and, besides, it might be dangerous to have refrigerant gases floating freely about the house. Furthermore, since the Freon-12 boils at −22°F, it would try to pull everything in the refrigerating compartment down to this temperature so that all the food would be frozen.

To eliminate these drawbacks, actual refrigerators use the same refrigerant over and over again, taking the gas, or vapor, and turning it into liquid again. The liquid is then put back into the "jug" so it can boil away once more. This is a more or less continuous action, controlled so that the refrigerant will not boil away too rapidly and thus cool the refrigerator too much.

§251. Refrigerator operation   To provide continued use of the refrigerant, and also to control it so that the proper temperature will be maintained, a closed refrigerating system is used. (Fig. 20-4). The "jug" or evaporator is inside the refrigerator cabinet. It is connected by two tubes to a pumping mechanism driven by an electric motor (the pumping mechanism is driven by the engine in an automobile). There is also a temperature control inside the cabinet. The control has a set of contact points that close when the temperature goes too high. As this happens, the motor circuit is closed so the motor starts and drives the pump and fan.

When the pump starts, it produces a partial vacuum in the upper part of the evaporator and thus pumps off evaporated refrigerant. This reduces the pressure above the liquid refrigerant. The refrigerant therefore begins to boil. As it boils, it removes heat from the refrigerating cabinet. The vaporizing refrigerant is continually pumped from the evaporator, thereby maintaining the low pressure which permits the refrigerant to continue to boil. So long as the pump is working, it continues to remove evaporated refrigerant, and thus heat, from the evaporator.

In the pump, the vapor is compressed, or put under pressure.

[545]

Actually, the pressure may approach 200 psi (pounds per square inch). This high pressure "pushes" the molecules close together. They are set into violent motion by the increased number of collisions. In other words, the vapor temperature is increased; it may go well above 100°F. The hot, compressed vapor then passes from the

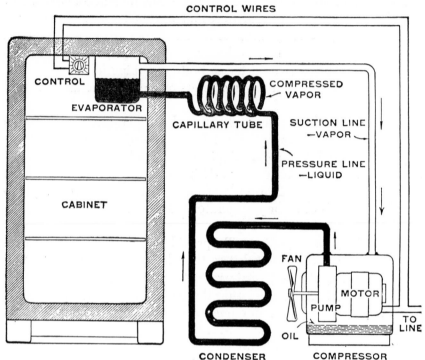

Fig. 20-4. Simplified diagrammatic scheme of an electric refrigerator. (*Hotpoint, Inc.*)

pump into the condenser. The condenser is a long tube, usually equipped with radiating fins or plates. As the hot vapor enters the tube, it begins to cool off (to transfer some of its heat—molecular motion—to the tube and radiating fins or plates). The refrigerator shown in Fig. 20-4 is equipped with a fan to help the cooling action.

By the time the vapor has passed through the condenser, it has cooled enough (molecules have slowed down enough) for it to start to condense, or turn to liquid.

It then passes through the capillary tube and, in liquid form, enters the evaporator again. The capillary tube is simply a small-diameter tube through which the liquid can pass but slowly. It acts as a sort of throttle to hold back the liquid. This means that the

[546]

pressure on the pump side of the capillary tube is high while it is low on the evaporator side. The pump is allowed to build up a comparatively high pressure in the condenser while the pressure in the evaporator can remain comparatively low. Thus, the high pressure causes the refrigerant to condense in the condenser and the low pressure in the evaporator permits the refrigerant to evaporate.

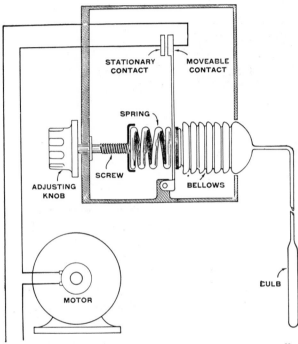

FIG. 20-5. Simplified drawing of a bellows thermostat for controlling refrigerator temperature. (*Hotpoint, Inc.*)

The above series of events continues as long as the control holds it contact points closed. However, as soon as the temperature falls low enough, the control opens its contact points, the motor shuts off, and the pumping action stops.

§252. Refrigerator control Figure 20-5 is a simplified drawing of a temperature control used in refrigerators. The bulb and bellows are connected by a tube. The bulb contains a liquid having a low-temperature boiling point. The bulb is placed in the refrigerator cabinet so it is subjected to refrigerator temperature. As this temperature goes up, the liquid starts to boil, creating pressure in the bellows. The pressure expands the bellows, causing it to move against, and compress, the spring. As the bellows expands and the spring compresses, the moveable contact is moved toward the stationary contact. When the preset operating temperature is reached, the pressure due to the boiling liquid in the bulb is great enough for the bellows to close the contacts. Now the motor is connected to the main circuit; it begins to drive the pump so that refrigeration starts.

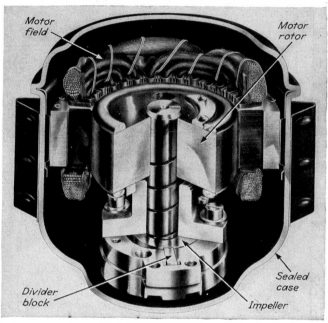

Fɪɢ. 20-6. Cutaway view of a rotary compressor. (*Frigidaire Division of General Motors Corporation*)

Note that the temperature setting can be changed by the adjusting knob. When the knob is turned so as to place more spring pressure on the bellows, the temperature must go higher before the contacts will close. This is because a higher pressure in the bellows will be required—that is, a higher bulb temperature in needed. When the adjusting knob is turned the other way so as to reduce the spring pressure against the bellows, then the bellows can close the contact points at a lower temperature.

§253. Refrigerator pump or compressor   A variety of pumps (commonly called *compressors*) have been used in refrigerators and air conditioners. One of the more widely used compressors is shown in cutaway view in Fig. 20-6. This unit is electrically driven by an electric motor that is built into the same case as the compressor. Figure 20-7 shows in schematic view the maner in which this unit works. There is an eccentric mounted on the end of the motor drive shaft. Mounted on the eccentric is an impeller. The impeller is essentially nothing more than a roller that rolls around in a cylinder. As the eccentric rotates, the impeller rolls around and around in the cylinder. The cylinder has two openings, or ports, an intake port and an exhaust port. Between the two ports there is a divider

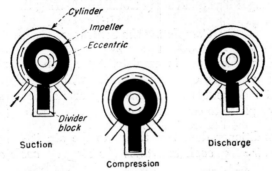

Suction   Discharge

Compression

Fig. 20-7. Eccentric action of compressor shown in previous illustration. (*Frigidaire Division of General Motors Corporation*)

block that is spring-loaded and therefore presses tightly against the impeller at all times. Thus, as the impeller rolls around in the cylinder, it first creates a vacuum so that refrigerant is "pulled" into the expanding space between the impeller and cylinder (left in Fig. 20-7). Then, further movement of the impeller seals off the intake port. The continuing movement of the impeller compresses the refrigerant vapor and forces it out of the exhaust port. Meanwhile, the intake port on the other side of the divider block has been uncovered and another charge of vapor is entering the expanding space between the impeller and cylinder. The cycle of events continues as long as the compressor is operated.

CHECK YOUR PROGRESS

Progress Quiz 8

Before you continue your studies of air conditioners, let us stop and check up on the progress you have been making. Air conditioning is a new subject to many automotive men. But it is very important. More and more cars are being equipped with air conditioning. Even though you do not plan to specialize in this field, you must have some knowledge of the subject. Here's the reason. Since the compressor and other conditioner units are mounted in and around the engine compartment, you may find it necessary to remove and reinstall these components when working on the engine. Removing the compressor is not quite the same as removing the generator. There is more to it than merely disconnecting a couple of wires. Thus, you should know what air conditioning is "all about" before you attempt such jobs. The quiz that follows gives you a chance to check your memory on the important points covered in the past few pages. Reread these pages if you have any trouble answering the questions.

Completing the Sentences

The sentences below are incomplete. After each sentence there are several words or phases, only one of which will correctly complete the sentence. Write down each sentence in your notebook, selecting the proper word or phase to complete it correctly.

1. An air conditioner does two things to the air; it   *warms and dries the air   cools and dries the air   cools and moistens the air*
2. Essentially, the process of cooling means   *evaporation   melting   removal of heat   removal of moisture*
3. From the molecular standpoint, cooling means that the molecules   *jump clear   are slowed down   stop   turn to liquid*
4. Rate of evaporation of a liquid depends upon   *temperature and pressure   vacuum and pressure   heat and cold*
5. As the pressure on a liquid is lowered, the boiling point (or temperature) of the liquid is   *raised   lowered   held steady*
6. In a refrigerator, refrigeration is produced by a cycle of   *evaporation and condensation   boiling and freezing   refrigerant loss*
7. Heat is removed from the refrigerator by the evaporation of refrigerant in the   *condenser   compressor   evaporator   control*
8. Heat that the refrigerant takes on in the evaporation-compression part of the refrigerator circuit is later disposed of when the refrigerant enters the   *condenser   compressor   evaporator   control*

9. The high-pressure side of the system (in compressor and condenser) is separated from the low pressure side (in evaporator) by the
    control bulb   *bellows*   *intake port*   *capillary tube*
10. In the refrigerator control, expansion of the bellows and closing of the contacts, is caused by   *increasing pressure in bulb*
    falling pressure in bulb   *reduced temperature in evaporator*

§254. Automobile air conditioner   We have described the operation of a typical electric refrigerator. Now, let us see how the various components of the refrigerator can be assembled into an automobile in order to "refrigerate" the occupants of the car. There are es-

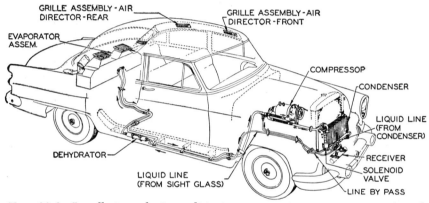

FIG. 20-8. Installation of air-conditioning system in passenger car. (*Buick Motor Division of General Motors Corporation*)

sentially only two differences in the operation of a refrigerator and a car air conditioner. First, we don't pull the car temperature down to 35 to 40 degrees, as in the refrigerator. And, second, we use a blower system to circulate the air in the car, circulating it between the evaporator (where cooling takes place) and the passenger compartment of the car.

    Figure 20-8 is a schematic view of an air conditioner installation on a car. The three essentials of the system we have already discussed. These are the compressor, condenser, and evaporator (see Fig. 20-4). There are certain additional items, including the receiver, solenoid valve, sight glass, and air-circulating system. Let's see how these units operate.

    NOTE: The air-conditioning system shown in Fig. 20-8 and discussed below is only one of several being used in automobiles. It

[551]

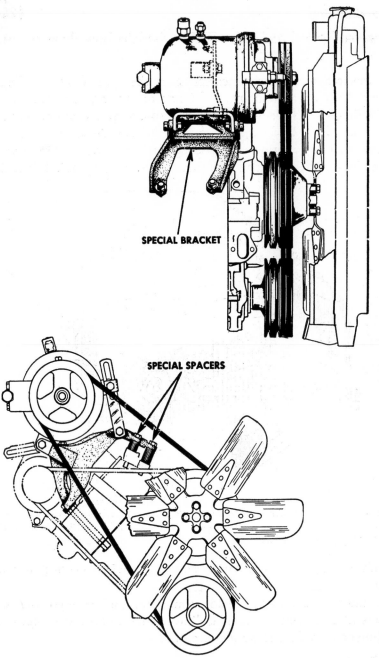

SPECIAL BRACKET

SPECIAL SPACERS

FIG. 20-9. The compressor is mounted on one side of the engine (a V-8 engine is shown) and is driven by V belts from a pulley on the engine crankshaft. (*Oldsmobile Division of General Motors Corporation*)

[552]

is, however, typical and will serve to describe how these systems function.

§**255. Compressor** The compressor is of the type shown in Figs. 20-6 and 20-7. It is mounted on the side of the engine as shown in Fig. 20-9 and is driven by two V belts from a special pulley on the engine crankshaft. In the system shown, the compressor is driven all the time that the engine is operating. In other systems the compressor drive pulley contains a clutch (electrically operated) which

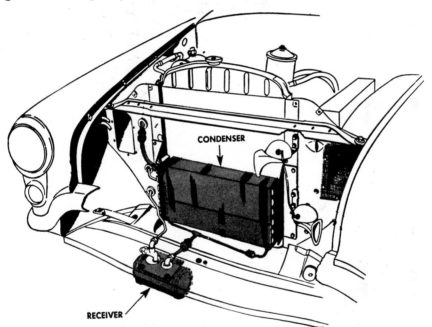

FIG. 20-10. The condenser and receiver are mounted at the front of the car. The condenser is in front of the engine radiator. (*Oldsmobile Division of General Motors Corporation*)

declutches the compressor from the pulley when cooling is not wanted.

The function of the compressor is to compress the vaporized refrigerant after it leaves the evaporator. The compressed vapor is then delivered to the condenser (see §251).

§**256. Condenser** The condenser, as well as the receiver (explained in following section), is mounted at the front of the car (Fig. 20-10). The condenser consists essentially of a series of tubes on which fins have been mounted. The compressed vapor passes through the tubes. Air passes around the fins and between the tubes. In this way, heat is removed from the compressed vapor. As the vapor is cooled, it begins to condense, or return to liquid form. The mounting of the condenser at the front of the radiator, as shown in Fig. 20-10, places it in the air stream so that adequate amounts of air will pass through it. Figure 20-11 shows, in more detail, the con-

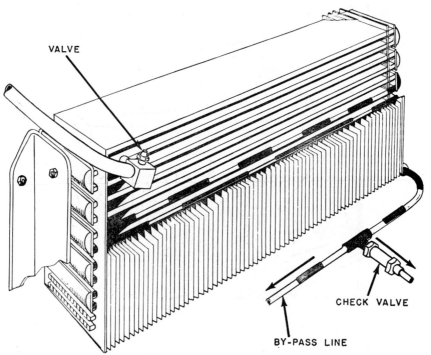

VALVE

CHECK VALVE

BY-PASS LINE

Fig. 20-11. Construction of the condenser. The upper fins have been cut away so the tubes can be seen. (*Oldsmobile Division of General Motors Corporation*)

struction of the condenser. In this illustration, the fins have been cut away from the upper tubes so that the location of the tubes can be seen. The valve (upper left in Fig. 20-11) permits flushing of the system with liquid refrigerant in case this service is needed (as it might be if a part is replaced or if refrigerant has escaped). The check valve (lower right) prevents liquid refrigerant from reversing direction and passing back into the condenser from the receiver. This is discussed in a following section.

[554]

§**257. Receiver**   The receiver (Fig. 20-12) is simply a tank in which excess liquid refrigerant is stored. As the highly compressed vapor cools and condenses in the condenser, it runs from the condenser into the receiver. There will also be a certain amount of refrigerant vapor in the receiver; this maintains the high pressure in the system on the liquid refrigerant in the bottom of the tank. On the exit side, a tube extends almost to the bottom of the tank. When the system is in operation, liquid refrigerant passes up this tube and through a tube extending to the evaporator (at back of car).

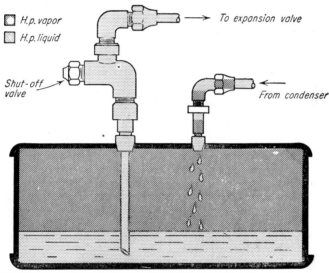

H.p. vapor

H.p. liquid

To expansion valve

Shut-off valve

From condenser

Fɪɢ. 20-12. Construction of the receiver. The receiver is simply a storage tank to store excess liquid refrigerant. (*Oldsmobile Division of General Motors Corporation*)

The shutoff valve (upper left in Fig. 20-12) is for use during service work on the system. When it is closed (by use of a special tool), no refrigerant can escape from the receiver. This valve is omitted in some later models.

§**258. Check valve**   On some models, there is a check valve (Fig. 20-11) between the condenser and the receiver. The purpose of the valve is to keep liquid refrigerant from surging back into the condenser from the receiver. This back surge could occur when the refrigerating system shuts off. Under some conditions, if liquid refrigerant surged all the way back to the compressor, it could cause

[555]

damage to the compressor. Figure 20-13 is a sectional view of the check valve. It consists essentially of a spring-loaded disk resting against a seat. When the compressor is operating and causing refrigerant, under pressure, to pass from the condenser to the receiver, it passes through the check valve in the direction shown by the

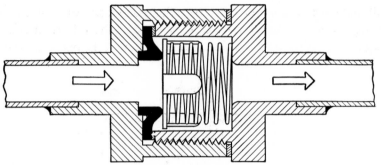

Fig. 20-13. Sectional view of the check valve. (*Oldsmobile Division of General Motors Corporation*)

arrows. Thus, the pressure forces the disk off its seat so the refrigerant can pass through. However, if pressure drops—for example, when the compressor is shut off—then the pressure will be higher on the receiver side of the check valve. Now this pressure forces the disk against its seat, shutting the valve.

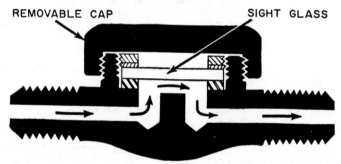

Fig. 20-14. Sectional view of sight glass. (*Oldsmobile Division of General Motors Corporation*)

§259. Sight glass   The sight glass (Fig. 20-14) is in the line from the receiver to the evaporator. Its sole purpose is to give the service man a means of checking the refrigerant in the system. It consists of a small glass window under a removable cap. Refrigerant has to pass under this window on its way to the evaporator. If there is insufficient refrigerant in the system, then bubbles will be seen in the refrigerant. That is, with insufficient refrigerant, the liquid refrigerant level in the receiver will be low. In this case, the pickup tube will send both liquid refrigerant and vapor into the line. The vapor will be seen as bubbles passing under the sight glass.

§**260. Solenoid bypass valve**   The solenoid bypass valve is the controlling valve in the refrigerating system. When it is closed (or energized), refrigeration takes place. When it is opened, there is

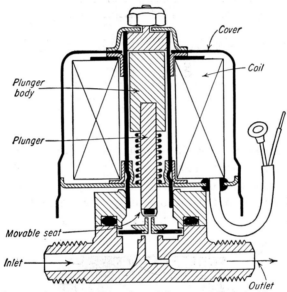

Fig. 20-15. Sectional view of the solenoid bypass valve. (*Oldsmobile Division of General Motors Corporation*)

no refrigerating action. The solenoid bypass valve is shown in sectional view in Fig. 20-15. It contains a coil of wire and a plunger. A valve is mounted on the lower end of the plunger. When the coil is energized (by being connected to the car battery), it magnetically attracts the plunger. This causes the plunger to move down into the coil. The movement closes the valve. Now, let us see how the opening and closing of the valve affect the refrigerating action.

We have already noted that the compressor is being driven by the engine all the time that the engine is operating. When the solenoid bypass valve is closed, normal refrigerating action takes place. During this action, refrigerant circulates as shown in Fig. 20-16.

[557]

It passes, under high pressure, to the condenser, where it is cooled and condensed. Then it moves into the receiver. Refrigerant, in liquid form, passes from the receiver, through the sight glass and dehydrator filter (which removes dirt and moisture) to the expansion valve. The expansion valve (§261) serves the same purpose as the capillary tube described in §251. That is, it holds back the high pressure from the condenser and admits liquid refrigerant to the

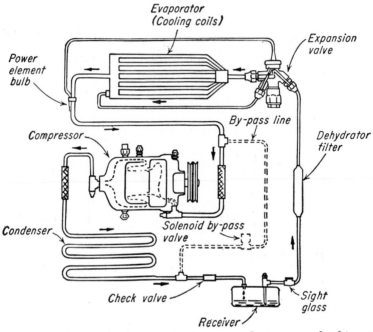

Fig. 20-16. Circulation of refrigerant in the system during normal refrigeration. (*Oldsmobile Division of General Motors Corporation*)

evaporator in a relatively small stream and at low pressure. As the liqiud refrigerant passes into the evaporator at low pressure, it begins to evaporate. We have already seen how this evaporation "soaks up" heat. The evaporated refrigerant is then pumped back through the compressor and redelivered, at high pressure, to the condenser.

When the solenoid bypass valve is opened (or de-energized by being disconnected from the car battery), then a bypass line between the condenser and the compressor is opened (Fig. 20-17). This means that the pressure in the system is relieved. Refrigerant can circulate freely between the condenser and the compressor. Since no pressure can build up, and since no refrigerant is sent the "long way around" (receiver-expansion valve-evaporator), no cooling action takes place.

In a later section we will learn how the solenoid bypass valve is controlled. In essence, the control is similar to that used in the

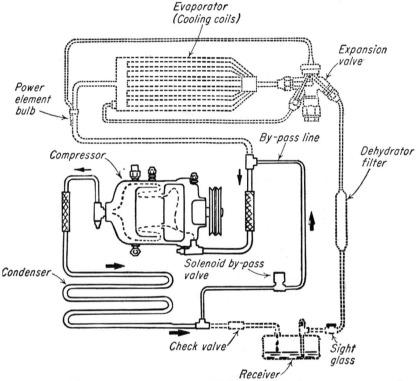

FIG. 20-17. When the solenoid bypass valve opens, refrigerant can circulate through the bypass (from condenser back to compressor) and no refrigerating action takes place. (*Oldsmobile Division of General Motors Corporation*)

ordinary domestic electric refrigerator (§252). That is, once the control is set for a certain temperature, an automatically operating thermostatic device takes over. This device then closes the solenoid bypass valve for cooling, and opens the bypass valve when the temperature has dropped to the preset value.

NOTE: Some systems do not use a bypass valve. Instead, refrigeration is controlled by a solenoid-operated clutch in the compressor drive pulley. Thus, when the system is not refrigerating, the pulley is declutched so that the compressor does not operate. But when the control system calls for cooling, then the pulley clutch engages so the compressor is driven, and the system therefore goes into operation.

§261. Expansion Valve   The entire refrigerating action depends on pressure difference. That is, pressure must be built up in the com-

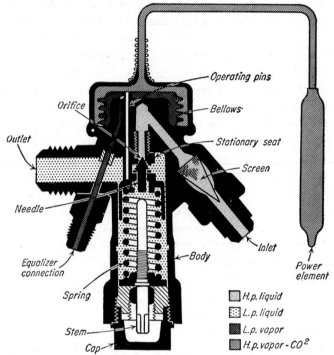

Fig. 20-18. Sectional view of expansion valve. (*Oldsmobile Division of General Motors Corporation*)

pressor-condenser side of the system. But pressure must be low in the evaporator so the liquid refrigerant can evaporate. Thus, there must be a point in the system where high pressure is reduced to low pressure; and this pressure reduction must take place just before the refrigerant enters the evaporator. In some systems, a capillary tube (§251) produces this pressure differential, or reduction. In the system we are discussing, an expansion valve does the job. The ex-

[560]

pansion valve (Fig. 20-18) not only produces the pressure reduction, but it also changes the amount of refrigerant flowing to the evaporator to suit the requirements of the system.

The operation of the expansion valve depends upon opposing vapor and spring pressures. Control is produced by the "power element," a sealed bulb and tube filled with carbon dioxide gas (CO_2) under pressure. The bulb is attached to the exit line from the evaporator (Fig. 20-16). Thus, it is exposed to the temperature of the refrigerant vapor as it leaves the evaporator. If the temperature of the vapor is too low, it means that too much refrigerant is being allowed to enter the evaporator. When this happens, the temperature of the power element bulb is lowered. This, in turn, reduces the CO_2 pressure. Thus, there will be less pressure in the bellows at the top of the expansion valve. With less pressure here, the valve spring tends to close the needle valve (since the operating pins—there are three pins—are allowed to move up as the bellows pressure is reduced). This reduces the amount of refrigerant that can enter the evaporator.

The equalizer connection admits low-pressure vapor from the exit side of the evaporator into the underside of the bellows. This pressure assists the action of the power element bulb in controlling the amount of refrigerant flowing into the evaporator. When the amount is too great, then the pressure on the exit side is raised. This increased pressure, acting in the bellows, tends to allow the needle valve to close. Thus, both temperature and pressure at the exit side control the position of the needle valve and therefore the amount of refrigerant entering the evaporator.

In operation, the needle valve never completely closes. It is simply positioned so as to admit the proper amount of refrigerant to suit the operating conditions.

§262. Evaporator

In the system under discussion, the evaporator is located at the back of the car, just behind the rear seat (Fig. 20-19). In some other systems, the evaporator is at the front of the car. The evaporator consists of tubing and radiating fins. There is a pair of intake air grills on the deck in back of the rear seat and, beneath these, a pair of blowers. The blowers take air in through the air grills, pass this air through the evaporator, and then discharge the cooled air through a pair of outlet ducts in the car.

[561]

Figure 20-20 shows the location of the intake air grills and outlet air ducts in the system under discussion. Note also (Fig. 20-20) that there are two air scoops, one on each side of the car, for bringing outside air into the car. The outside air is lead by tubes away

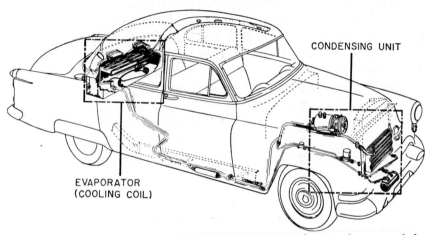

FIG. 20-19. Air conditioner system in passenger car, showing location of the evaporator. (*Oldsmobile Division of General Motors Corporation*)

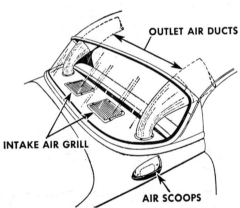

FIG. 20-20. Intake air grills and outlet air ducts in car air conditioner. (*Oldsmobile Division of General Motors Corporation*)

from the scoops and into the air stream passing through the evaporator. Thus, the outside air is cooled before it enters the passenger compartment. Knobs control dampers in each of the tubes from the scoops so that the amount of outside air being brought

[562]

into the car can be regulated. Figure 20-21 shows one of the blowers used to provide air circulation through the evaporator.

§263. Electric control circuit   Figure 20-22 shows the electric circuit used with the car air conditioner. This circuit contains the controls for the solenoid bypass valve (§260)—both manual and thermostatic. It also contains the controls for the two blowers. The blowers turn on whenever the main control switch on the instrument panel (Fig. 20-23) is turned away from "Off." When the switch is turned to "Vent" (ventilation), only the blowers turn on; and they circulate

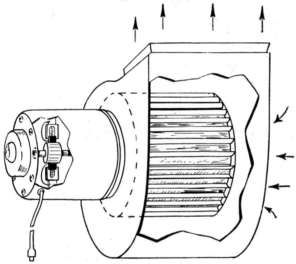

Fig. 20-21. Blower used in air conditioner. Case is partly cut away so blower rotor can be seen. (*Oldsmobile Division of General Motors Corporation*)

air, taking in outside air (in amount for which the scoop-regulating knobs have been set) through the air scoops. Each blower has a speed regulator knob (on instrument panel—Fig. 20-23).

When the switch is turned to "On," then the blowers operate and at the same time the refrigerating system comes into operation. The amount of cooling that will result depends upon the position of the temperature control lever. The temperature control lever operates a variable resistance which puts more or less resistance into a circuit to a heater coil on the thermostat. The thermostat consists of a tube of mercury in which contacts are set. When the control lever is turned to the right ("Cooler"), full line voltage is imposed on the

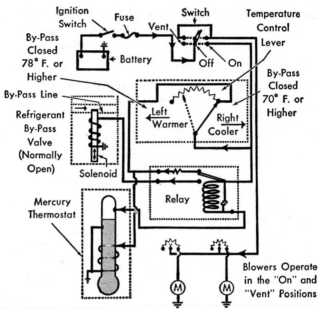

FIG. 20-22. Electric circuit of air-conditioning system. This circuit provides control of the system and, at the same time, operates the two blower motors. (*Cadillac Motor Car Diviion of General Motors Corporation*)

FIG. 20-23. Control switches for air conditioner. (*Cadillac Motor Car Division of General Motors Corporation*)

heater coil. Heat from the heater coil, plus the warmth of the car, heats the mercury so it evnands and rises (just as increasing temperature sends the mercury in a thermometer up in the thermometer tube). When the mercury reaches the upper contact, the relay winding is grounded through the mercury. This completes the relay-winding circuit. The relay closes its lower points. Now, the solenoid bypass valve is energized and the refrigerant bypass line is closed. [564]

This means that refrigeration takes place (Fig. 20-16). If the temperature control lever is set at any other position ("toward Warmer"), there will be less voltage on the thermostat heater coil. This means that the car temperature must be somewhat higher to make the thermostat complete the relay-winding circuit. Thus, operating temperature will be higher.

A somewhat different type of thermostatic control, shown in Fig. 20-24, is used on several models of the air conditioner described in the past few pages. This thermostatic control is the pressure type.

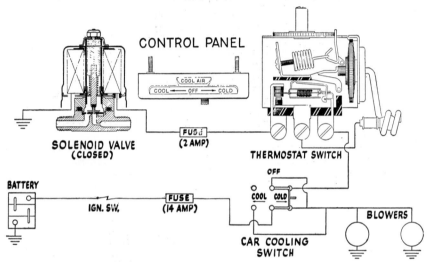

Fɪɢ. 20-24. Electric control circuit of air-conditioning system that uses pressure-actuated thermostat. (*Oldsmobile Division of General Motors Corporation*)

It contains a tube filled with gas under pressure. The gas exerts more or less pressure on a diaphragm as the temperature changes. Increasing temperature increases the pressure. When the pressure reaches the value for which the thermostat is set, it forces a plunger out which causes a set of contacts to snap "On." This connects the coil in the solenoid bypass valve to the battery so the valve closes. Now, with the bypass closed, refrigeration takes place (Fig. 20-16). There is a small light bulb around which the tube is wound (right in Fig. 20-24). This bulb furnishes a small amount of heat which causes the system to "anticipate" the moment when refrigeration will be required—that is, it furnishes part of the heat needed to

[565]

actuate the thermostat. The rest of the heat comes from the increasing temperature in the car. In some models, the light bulb is omitted.

In either control system (Fig. 20-22 or 20-24), as the temperature in the car is reduced to the preset value, the thermostat operates to cause the solenoid bypass valve (or clutch solenoid) to be disconnected. This opens the bypass line (or declutches compressor drive pulley) so that refrigeration stops (Fig. 20-17).

§264. Drying the air   As the air is moved through the evaporator, it is not only cooled, but also dried. As we mentioned in §247, water will condense on a cold surface. We have all seen condensation form on the outside of a glass of ice water. Thus, as the air is moved through the evaporator, moisture in the air condenses on the cold evaporator coils and fins. This water drips off into a drip pan. Drip tubes then carry off the water and allow it to run out of the car. The dried air "feels" cooler to us because it permits easier evaporation of perspiration from our skin. When air is very moist (or humidity is high), we feel much warmer even though the temperature is not high. This is because the moist air has greater resistance to accepting more moisture. The perspiration evaporates slowly and we therefore feel hot. But when this moisture is removed from the air, perspiration evaporates more easily and we feel cooler.

Thus, the air conditioner not only cools the air, but also dries, or dehumidifies, it. It is the combination of these two functions that conditions the air so that we feel comfortable in it.

CHAPTER CHECKUP

With the widespread adoption of air conditioning for automobiles, everyone in the automotive field has become interested in the subject. Some, perhaps, plan to specialize in car air-conditioning service and will be taking special courses in the subject. Others may be interested only to the extent of wanting to learn something about how the system operates. But anyone who works on cars should have a basic understanding of the system. They should know how various components are removed and reinstalled on the car. It is necessary for them to know this because, for example, the compressor must be removed before many service operations can be carried out on the engine. Regardless of your own personal plans for your future in the automotive field, you will want to make sure you understand how air conditioners work and also how the components

[566]

Air Conditioning

are removed and replaced (as explained in the following chapter). Thus, you will want to check yourself on how well you understood the chapter you have just finished by taking the test that follows.

Unscrambling the Lists

When the two lists below are unscrambled and combined, they will form a list of the components in the air-conditioning system and their functions. To unscramble the lists, take one item at a time from the list to the left, and then find the item from the list to the right that goes with it. Write down the results in your notebook.

compressor	causes cooling by evaporation of refrigerant
condenser	storage tank for liquid refrigerant
receiver	prevents surging of refrigerant back to condenser
check valve	to check refrigerant for bubbles
sight glass	controls refrigerant circuit
bypass valve	removes heat from condensed vapor
expansion valve	compresses refrigerant vapor
evaporator	provides pressure drop at evaporator

Completing the Sentences

The sentences below are incomplete. After each sentence there are severals words or phrases, only one of which will correctly complete the sentence. Write down each sentence in your notebook, selecting the proper word or phrase to complete it correctly.

1. Other things being equal, the drier the air, the   *faster water will evaporate*   *slower water will evaporate*   *greater the air pressure*

2. Other things being equal, the lower the air pressure, the   *faster water will evaporate*   *slower water will evaporate*   *higher the temperature*

3. Condensation of a vapor on a cold surface is due to the vapor losing some of its heat; that is, its molecules   *speed up*   *slow down*   *stop moving entirely*

4. In the refrigerating system, the pressure is relatively low in the   *compressor*   *condenser*   *evaporator*

5. When the compressor is operating, the pressure is high in the   *condenser*   *evaporator*   *cabinet*

6. The purpose of the receiver in the car air conditioner is to store excess refrigerant in the form of   *low-pressure vapor*   *liquid*   *gas*

7. When the solenoid bypass valve is closed, then   *there is no refrigerating action   refrigerating action takes places   the bypass circuit is open*
8. In the car air conditioner, the device that reduces the high pressure (compressor-condenser) to law pressure (evaporator) is called   *sight glass   check valve   bypass valve   expansion valve*
9. In the air conditioning system described in the chapter, air is circulated through the evaporator by   *two blowers   a blower   a compressor*
10. The thermostatic control starts and stops the refrigerating action by causing the closing and opening of the electric circuit between the battery and the   *compressor   bypass valve   check valve   expansion valve*

Purpose and Operation of Components

In the following, you are asked to write down the purpose and operation of various components in the air-conditioning system. If you have any difficulty writing down your explanations, turn back in the chapter and reread the pages that will give you the answer. Don't copy; try to tell it in your own words just as you might explain it to a friend. This is a good way to fix the explanation in your mind. Write in your notebook.

1. Explain, in terms of molecular action, how cooling is achieved by evaporation.
2. Explain, in terms of molecular action, why lowering the pressure increases the rate of evaporation.
3. Explain, in terms of molecular action, why compressing a vapor and then cooling it causes condensation.
4. Describe the complete refrigerating cycle, starting with the evaporation of the refrigerant in the evaporator.
5. Explain how a refrigerator control operates.
6. What is the purpose of the receiver?
7. What is the purpose of the check valve?
8. What is the purpose of the sight glass?
9. What is the purpose of the solenoid bypass valve?
10. What is the purpose of the expansion valve? Explain how it works.
11. Describe the operation of one of the air-conditioner controls described in the chapter.
12. Why does dry air feel cooler to us than moist air?

[568]

Air Conditioning

SUGGESTIONS FOR FURTHER STUDY

If you are especially interested in refrigeration and air conditioning, you might wish to study a book that deals with this subject alone, and in detail. Your local library or book store probably has books on the subject which will give you a great deal of information. For specific car air-conditioning information, refer to special manuals issued by the car and air-conditioner manufacturers. These manuals are supplied to the service men in the car-dealer shops. Your local school automotive shop may also be able to obtain these manuals. If you can borrow these manuals and study them, you will be able to find out the details of the air-conditioner systems used on automobiles: how they are constructed, how they operate, and how they are serviced. Write down in your notebook any important facts you learn.

21: Servicing air conditioners

THIS CHAPTER describes various troubles that might occur with automotive air conditioners, how to diagnose these troubles to find their causes, and how to correct the causes of trouble. Further, it explains how to remove various components of the system. Even though you might not plan on performing actual service operations on air-conditioning equipment, you may find it necessary to remove and replace certain conditioner components (such as the compressor) while you are doing other automotive work. For example, many engine-servicing operations require removal of the compressor. The following pages describe the various removal, servicing, and replacement procedures on air-conditioning equipment.

§265. Trouble-shooting the system *You must not attempt any service work on air conditioners—and that includes diagnostic checks—unless you have the proper equipment and know exactly how to use it. Furthermore, you must be fully aware of the dangers inherent in working with high-pressure equipment and with liquid refrigerants (see §266).*

Bearing the above caution in mind, the following chart will help you to locate possible causes of trouble in the air-conditioner system. Troubles (and their causes) are not listed in the order of frequency of occurrence.

AIR-CONDITIONING TROUBLE-SHOOTING CHART

Complaint	Possible Cause	Check or Correction
1. Poor cooling	a. Blowers not operating	Check electrical system, switches, blower motors
	b. Relay on thermostat contacts stuck	Clean points or replace relay on thermostat

Complaint	Possible Cause	Check or Correction
	c. Air flow through evaporator restricted	Check filter for dirt, and check scoops, air ducts, return grills for restrictions
	d. Not enough refrigerant	Check for leaks, add refrigerant
	e. Too much refrigerant	Bleed off refrigerant
	f. Expansion valve out of adjustment or defective	Adjust or replace
	g. Power element (from expansion valve) defective or improperly mounted	Power element must mount tight on low-pressure line but must be insulated from high-pressure (liquid) line
	h. Receiver-to-evaporator line clogged	Replace line
	i. Insufficient air flow through condenser	Clean condenser core and radiator. *Do not use steam!*
	j. High engine temperatures	Check engine cooling system
	k. Air in system	Bleed off air
	l. Solenoid bypass valve stuck open	Repair or replace
	m. Clutch solenoid or clutch out of adjustment or defective	Adjust, repair, replace as necessary
	n. High-pressure line restricted	Replace line
	o. Compressor defective	Replace
2. Excessive cooling	a. Solenoid bypass valve stuck closed	Free plunger or replace valve

Complaint	Possible Cause	Check or Correction
	b. Relay or thermostat points stuck	Clean points, replace relay or thermostat
	c. Temperature control rheostat shorted	Replace
3. Noises	*a.* Tubing loose	Tighten clamps, make sure tubing does not rub
	b. Blowers	Check motor mounting, blower attaching screws (on shaft), motor bearings
	c. Compressor	If from mounting, tighten, if from pulley clutch (on units so equipped) replace clutch. If internal, replace compressor
	d. Expansion valve hisses	Shortage of refrigerant, or restrictions in line
4. Water leaking in trunk	*a.* Drain hose not connected	Connect
	b. Drain pan dirty	Clean
	c. Evaporator case sweating	Insulate case properly

NOTE: When pressures are checked with the special equipment described on later pages, and incorrect pressures are found, possible causes and corrections may be as follows:

5. Excessive pressure on high-pressure side	*a.* Air or excess refrigerant	Purge air and refrigerant to remove excess
	b. Clogged condenser core restricts air circulation	Clean core with air or brush. *Do not use steam!*
	c. Line restricted (high side)	Replace line

Complaint	Possible Cause	Check or Correction
	d. High engine temperature	Check engine cooling system
	e. Insufficient air flow through evaporator	Check as noted in item 1c, above
	f. Expansion valve out of adjustment or faulty	Adjust or replace
6. Insufficient pressure on high-pressure side	*a.* Insufficient refrigerant	Add refrigerant
	b. Bypass valve stuck open	Free plunger, replace valve
	c. Bypass valve leaks	Replace valve if valve and seat are worn or defective
	d. Expansion valve out of adjustment or faulty	Adjust or replace
	e. Compressor faulty	Replace
7. Excessive pressure on low-pressure side	*a.* Expansion valve-action faulty	Check power-element bulb contact (see item 1g, above) Adjust or replace valve
	b. Bypass valve leaky or stuck open	Clear valve, replace if defective
	c. Compressor defective	Replace
8. Insufficient pressure on low-pressure side	*a.* Line restricted	Replace kinked or restricted lines
	b. Shortage of refrigerant	Add refrigerant
	c. Expansion valve out of adjustment or faulty	Adjust valve, replace if defective

§**266. Essential cautions you must observe**   There is no more danger in working with air conditioners than in working with any component of the car—provided you observe normal caution. Listed here are the things to look out for when you work on air conditioners or handle refrigerant:

[573]

1. Undercoating. Never apply undercoating to any connections in the refrigerating lines. Mask all flare joints and connections before applying undercoating.

2. Steam cleaning and welding. Heat in any form *must not be applied* to any refrigerant line or any component of the air-conditioning system. It must be remembered that the refrigerating system contains refrigerant under pressure. Heating the refrigerant increases the pressure excessively and may cause serious damage. Do not steam clean any tube or component. When welding, remove components or move refrigerating tubing out of the way.

3. Handling the refrigerant. The refrigerant normally used in automotive air-conditioning systems is Freon-12. This is considered to be about the safest refrigerant commercially available. But you can be hurt if you handle it carelessly. Note the following:

    a. Always wear glasses or goggles when handling refrigerant or servicing air conditioners. You could damage your eyes seriously by getting refrigerant in them. If you get Freon-12 in your eyes, apply a few drops of sterile mineral oil as an irrigator. Wash eyes with boric acid solution if eyes still hurt. See an eye specialist at once.

    b. Do not discharge Freon-12 in a room where there is an exposed flame. If Freon-12 vapor comes into contact with an open flame, it is converted into a dangerously toxic gas. Of course, small amounts would not be particularly harmful. But to be on the safe side, if you have to discharge Freon-12 from a system, it is best to do it outside in the open air. If you do it inside, be sure the room is well ventilated and that there is no open flame in the room.

    c. Freon-12 is supplied in high-pressure drums. There is no special danger if the drums are handled carefully. But remember the following:

        Do not overheat the drum (by leaving it in the sun, applying hot water or a torch, putting drum on stove or radiator, and so on). *An overheated drum may explode and this could injure or kill you!* The drum must never be heated above 125°F.

        For the same reason, do not drop the drum or handle it carelessly.

Do not carry the drum around in the passenger compartment of a car.

Do not leave drum uncapped. The cap protects the valve and safety plug.

4. Handling tubing. Refrigerant tubing, or lines, should not be crushed or kinked; this would restrict the flow of refrigerant and reduce cooling action. Lines must be kept sealed and dehydrated in stock, just as received from the factory. Do not remove caps until just before installation. When tightening fittings, use two wrenches to avoid damaging the tubes.

If lines have to be disconnected for any reason, close the ends of the line with caps or masking tape.

5. Refrigerating oil. A special oil is used in the refrigerating system to provide lubrication of the compressor. This oil is sealed into the system and does not need replacement unless it is lost (by removing refrigerant, by accident, and so on). The new oil comes in special containers which are sealed to prevent the entrance of moisture. The new oil should not be exposed to the air any longer than absolutely necessary since it will absorb moisture. Moisture in the system may freeze and clog the refrigerant flow.

6. Vacuum pump. A special vacuum pump (shown in Fig. 21-3) must be used to remove any air or moisture that has entered the system when the system has been opened for replacement of any part.

§**267. Service operations** Service operations on the automotive air-conditioning system include periodic inspection checks, preparing the system for winter operation, preparing it for summer operation, pumping down the system (pumping refrigerant into receiver), evacuating the system before adding refrigerant, adding refrigerant, adding oil as necessary, purging the system of air or excess refrigerant, removing and replacing various components, repairing some of the components, and adjusting the expansion valve. These operations are covered in the following sections.

§**268. Periodic inspection** Periodically, the system should be checked to see if it is operating normally. First, note whether or not the compressor drive belts are tight. If they are not tight enough, they will slip when the system is in operation. Then listen to the solenoid bypass valve to make sure it opens and closes when the cooling switch is turned on and off. (On models using a solenoid-operated clutch, note clutch action.) If the car interior is too cool to permit operation of the air conditioner, heat it with the car heater.

A leak detector should be used to check the system for leakage

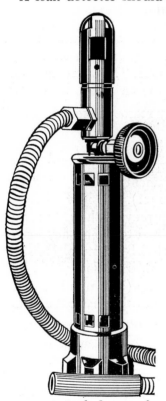

of refrigerant. This device (Fig. 21-1) is a small torch that burns a special fuel—anhydrous methyl alcohol. It has a long tube that is open at one end and connected to the base of the torch at the other. When the torch is lighted, air is drawn through the tube. If the open end of the tube is placed close to a point where refrigerant (Freon-12) is leaking, then refrigerant will be drawn through the tube and will pass through the flame. As the refrigerant passes through the flame, it will change the color of the flame. The flame will turn green, brilliant blue, or purple. By moving the open end of the tube around and holding it close to the connections in the system, you can locate any leak.

Caution: Do not breathe the fumes or black smoke that the torch gives off when a leak has been located; *they are poisonous.*

Fig. 21-1. Leak detector for detecting leakage of Freon-12 and locating source of leakage. (*Oldsmobile Division of General Motors Corporation*)

Note: There is also a liquid leak detector which is used to check connections after they have been broken and reconnected. This liquid is daubed on the connection and will form bubbles if refrigeration is escaping.

Check both blower fans and control knobs to make sure they operate normally.

Connect a jumper wire from the battery to the solenoid bypass valve (or clutch solenoid) so system will operate continuously. Operate on fast idle for fifteen minutes. Remove cover from sight glass and check for bubbles. Use a flashlight to make sure you can see the refrigerant passing under the sight glass. If there are bubbles, it means there is insufficient refrigerant in the system and more should be added.

If there is evidence of oil leaks, the oil level in the compressor should be checked and oil added if necessary.

§269. **Seasonal changes** During the cooler months, when the air conditioner is not needed, the compressor drive belts should be removed so the compressor will not be driven. This saves the compressor from unnecessary wear. The outside air ducts should also be closed.

Then, when the warmer season comes, the air conditioner should be put back into operation, as follows:

Leak-test system. Check for traces of oil. Repair leaks, add refrigerant and oil as necessary. Install compressor belts and check for proper belt tension. Test operation of system by connecting a jumper wire to the solenoid bypass valve (or clutch solenoid) and then watching sight glass for bubbles (as explained in previous section). Note blower-fan action. Open outside air ducts. Check outlet air temperature with temperature outside of car to make sure system is bringing temperature down properly.

§270. **Pumping down the system** This operation is used on those systems having a shutoff valve and check valve at the receiver. It has the purpose of saving as much of the refrigerant as possible during servicing operations. Most of the refrigerant is pumped into the receiver and held there while other components of the system are removed and replaced. On the system which does not have a shutoff valve and check valve at the receiver, all of the refrigerant must be lost when any line, except those at the compressor, must be disconnected. Pumping down the system is done as follows:

1. Put on your goggles to protect your eyes! *This is important.*
2. Assemble and connect gauge set (Fig. 21-2). Note that the gauge connector has three connections, one for the high-pressure side of the system, one for the low-pressure side, and a third, center one, through which refrigerant may be discharged, the system evacuated, and refrigerant added.
3. With gauge set connected to compressor, remove cap from

shutoff valve at receiver outlet and use special key to shut
off the valve. Then remove caps from high- and low-pressure
shutoff valves on compressor (so you can shut off these valves
in a hurry if you have to).

4. Energize solenoid bypass valve by connecting jumper wire
   from battery (disconnect solenoid wire at connector and connect it to jumper wire).

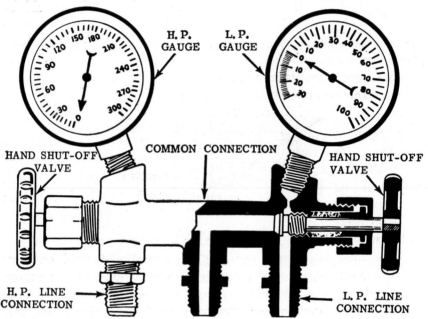

Fig. 21-2. Gauge set for checking high pressure and low pressure in refrigerating system. (*Oldsmobile Division of General Motors Corporation*)

5. Purge the air from the gauge lines by removing the plug
   from the center fitting on the gauge set and then slightly
   cracking the low- and high-pressure valves on the gauge set.
   Then close the valves tightly.

6. Start and operate engine at slow idle and turn control switch
   on. Watch high-pressure gauge carefully. If it reaches 275
   pounds (or psi), shut off engine and discharge refrigerant by
   opening the valve on the high-pressure side of the gauge set.
   Allow compressor to operate until the low-pressure gauge reads
   zero. (But high pressure must not exceed 275 pounds.)

7. Stop engine and close high-pressure shutoff valve at compressor (with special key).
8. The low-pressure gauge will now show more than zero. Purge refrigerant that remains in low-pressure side by turning the low-pressure valve in the gauge set. Allow 1 or 2 pounds to remain. Then shut off low-pressure gauge valve on gauge set for 5 minutes. If pressure builds up above 5 pounds release some more refrigerant to reduce pressure to 1 or 2 pounds. Then shut off low pressure valve on the compressor.

§271. Evacuating the system Whenever the refrigerating system has been opened for any reason, it must be evacuated with a special vacuum pump so as to remove all air and moisture from it. To evacuate the system, proceed as follows.

1. Put on your goggles to protect your eyes! *This is important.*
2. Install gauge set, vacuum pump, gauge lines, connector, Freon-12 drum, and valve as shown in Fig. 21-3. Before using vacuum pump, make sure dust cap on discharge side is removed. Also, make sure there is sufficient oil in pump. Oil should be changed every 250 hours of operation (see pump instructions).
3. On those systems having a shutoff valve at the receiver, it is possible to evacuate only the low-pressure side of the system without having to evacuate the high-pressure side. On other systems, the complete system must be evacuated at once. To evacuate the low-pressure side of the line, make sure the low-pressure valve at the compressor is open and that the shutoff valve at the receiver and the high-pressure valve on the compressor are closed. Then open the low-pressure gauge valve on gauge set and start vacuum pump. Open the two-way shutoff valve at the vacuum pump (slowly, so as to avoid forcing oil out of pump). Operate at 28 inches vacuum for 10 minutes. Close shutoff valve at pump and shut off pump. Open Freon-12 drum valve and allow system to come up to drum pressure. Close drum valve. Check low-pressure side of system with leak detector (if leak is suspected). Two gauges should read equally. Evacuate system once again as already described. This charging and second evacuation of the system picks up any air or moisture that may have remained in the

[579]

system. Close low-pressure gauge valve. The system is now ready for a partial charge of refrigerant.

4. To evacuate the entire system, the low-pressure and the high-pressure valves at the compressor, as well as the shutoff valve at the receiver, must be open. Open low and high-pressure gauge valves at the gauge set. Then connect and start the vacuum pump and proceed to evacuate the system as explained in the previous paragraph. System is then ready for a complete charge of refrigerant.

§272. Charging the system If the system requires refrigerant, it should first be tested for leaks. Refrigerant is always added to the low-pressure side in vapor form. This requires heating of the Freon-12 drum. *But extreme care must be used in heating the drum in order to avoid the danger of drum explosion.* The best way to heat the drum is to put it into a bucket of hot water. *The water temperature must not be above 125°F.*

Refrigerant is added to the system by weight—that is, the appropriate number of pounds must be put in. Thus, the drum (and the bucket of water) must be put on a scales and the reduction in the weight of the drum noted as refrigerant is withdrawn. Proceed as follows.

1. Put on your goggles to protect your eyes! *This is important.*
2. A partial charge is added when the system has lost only part of its refrigerant, or when the low-pressure side has been evacuated (§271). To add a partial charge:
   a. Evacuate low-pressure side of system (§271). Leave drum and pump connected as shown in Fig. 21-3.
   b. Open high-pressure valve at compressor. Low-pressure valve and shutoff valve at receiver must also be open. Operate engine at slow idle and open the low-pressure valve on gauge set. High-pressure valve on gauge set must be closed.
   c. Open drum valve slightly (90 pounds maximum). Drum must not be heated above 125°F and pressure in drum (as noted on the low-pressure gauge) must not exceed 90 pounds.
   d. With system in operation, watch sight glass until no more bubbles appear. Then note the exact weight of the drum and bucket of water, as recorded on the scales. Add one more pound of Freon-12 to the system. Then shut off drum valve.

Close low-pressure valve on gauge set. Operate engine at intermediate speed and note action of system for 5 minutes. If any bubbles appear, add one more pound of refrigerant. Then close valves on compressor, remove tubes, gauge set,

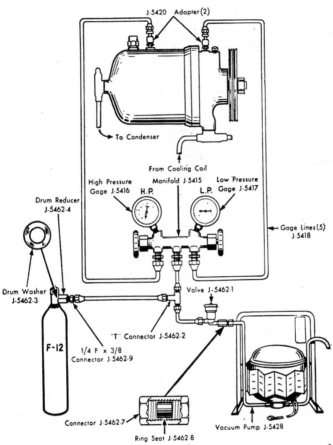

Fig. 21-3. Gauge set, Freon-12 drum, and vacuum pump connected to compressor, ready to check pressures, evacuate the system, and add refrigerant. (*Oldsmobile Division of General Motors Corporation*)

and so on. Cap gauge connections on compressor with nuts.

3. A complete charge is needed when the system has been completely evacuated (§271). After evacuation, leave all connections as shown in Fig. 21-3, open the two valves on the compressor and the low-pressure valve on gauge set; then open

[581]

the drum valve wide. Freon-12 vapor will flow into the system under its own pressure. The amount that enters should not exceed 7 pounds, by weight. Watch scales and shut drum valve when the drum has lost 7 pounds of Freon-12.

If 7 pounds will not enter the system, operate the engine at slow idle until 7 pounds have entered. Then close drum valve.

Operate the engine at intermediate speed and note action of system and sight glass. If system operates satisfactorily, stop engine, remove gauge lines (after closing compressor valves) and cap gauge connections with nuts.

§273. Checking and adding oil   The compressor has an original charge of 20 to 22 ounces of 525 viscosity refrigerator oil (Frigidaire). To check oil level, the compressor is equipped with a special Schrader valve, capped with a flare nut and deadhead.

1. Checking oil level. Run engine at 35 to 40 mph (miles per hour) for 10 minutes with cooling-control switch on and blowers on high speed. Use a big electric fan in front of car grill to get a flow of air over condenser; this prevents high engine and condenser temperatures.

Stop engine and remove flare nut and deadhead from oil test fitting. Hold a white cloth close to the fitting and depress the valve core. Oil should continue to blow out with Freon-12 vapor. If no oil comes out after the first spurt, there is insufficient oil.

2. Adding oil—minor loss. If you suspect that only a little oil is lost, add 4 ounces of special 525 refrigerator oil, as follows. With engine stopped, shut off high- and low-pressure shutoff valves at compressor with special key. Depress valve core (in oil-lever test valve) to purge Freon-12 until the hiss is barely audible. This indicates that most of the Freon-12 has escaped. Wait a few minutes and then repeat the purging. Then, remove the high-pressure relief valve, pour in 4 ounces of special oil, and replace valve, using a new copper gasket. Open high-pressure shutoff valve and purge air from compressor by depressing the valve core in the high-pressure gauge fitting of compressor. Recheck oil level, as above. Add another 4 ounces of oil, if necessary. Then open valves and replace nuts and deadhead on fittings. Leak-test all connections that have been disturbed.

3. *Adding oil—major loss.* If most or all of the oil has been lost (by a break in the line, a compressor-shaft-seal leak, and so on), add oil as follows after repairs have been completed. Close both high- and low-pressure shut-off valves on compressor. Depress valve core on the high-pressure gauge fitting of compressor to purge all refrigerant from compressor. Remove valve-flange mounting screws and take shutoff valves from compressor. Then remove belts and compressor from mounting bracket and take compressor to work bench. (See §276 for complete removal procedure.)

Turn compressor upside down so oil drains out. Drain oil into a clean container and examine it for dirt, metal chips, water, sludge, and so on. If an excessive amount of water is found, a new high-pressure-line dehydrator filter should be installed. Pour 16 ounces of special oil into the high-pressure relief-valve opening. Replace valve with new copper gasket. Install compressor on engine, reconnect high- and low-pressure valves using new O rings and gaskets, and reinstall belts. Open high-pressure shutoff valve and purge air from compressor by depressing the valve core in the high-pressure gauge fitting. Open low-pressure shutoff valve. Leak-test all connections and test system.

§**274. Purging system of air or excess refrigerant** Air or too much refrigerant produces excessive pressures in the system and insufficient cooling. Air will end up in the condenser and take up space that will then block normal vapor circulation and cooling. Check and purge system as follows:

1. *Checking for air or excess refrigerant.* Connect high-pressure gauge of gauge set to high-pressure fitting on compressor (Fig. 21-3). With engine off, open high-pressure valve on gauge set slightly to purge air from gauge, then shut valve. Clip thermo-well (Tool J-5422) to inlet tube to condenser. Fill well cavity with water and insert thermometer into cavity (see Fig. 21-4). Operate engine and compressor for 5 minutes at intermediate speed. Do not allow pressure to exceed 275 pounds (see §270, 6). Stop engine and close low-pressure shutoff valve on compressor and shutoff valve on receiver. Then note the high-pressure gauge and thermometer readings as the system cools down. Figure 21-5 is a chart showing the relationships of various pressures and temperatures. If the pressure falls as the condenser cools, and the pressure-temperature relation-

ship conforms to that shown in the chart, then the inadequate cooling is due to an overcharge of refrigerant. On the other hand, if the pressure stays up even though the temperature falls, the trouble is due to air in the system.

2. *Purging refrigerant.* To purge excess refrigerant, it is necessary only to allow refrigerant to escape by slightly opening the high-pressure valve on the gauge set. Cover the connection with a

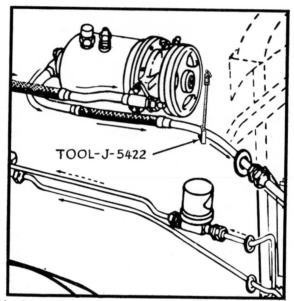

Fig. 21-4. Checking refrigerant temperature in the high-pressure line from the compressor to the condenser. (*Oldsmobile Division of General Motors Corporation*)

cloth so refrigerant and oil will not get on the car or on other parts. After allowing some refrigerant to escape, recheck the system. With the correct amount of refrigerant, pressure will build up rather slowly as the compressor starts and excessive pressures will not be attained.

3. *Purging air.* To purge air, proceed as when purging refrigerant. However, open the high-pressure valve on the gauge set only briefly and then recheck the system. Note the pressure and temperature. Repeat this as many times as necessary to bring the pressure and temperature into line (see chart, Fig. 21-5).

[584]

Temp, °F	Pressure, psi	Temp, °F	Pressure, psi	Temp, °F	Pressure, psi
−8	5.4	42	39.0	92	103.0
−6	6.3	44	41.0	94	106.3
−4	7.2	46	43.0	96	110.0
−2	8.2	48	45.0	98	113.3
0	9.2	50	47.0	100	117.0
2	10.2	52	49.0	102	121.0
4	11.3	54	51.0	104	124.0
6	12.3	56	53.0	106	128.1
8	13.5	58	55.4	108	132.1
10	14.6	60	58.0	110	136.0
12	15.9	62	60.0	112	140.1
14	17.1	64	62.5	114	144.2
16	18.4	66	65.0	116	148.4
18	19.7	68	67.5	118	153.0
20	21.0	70	70.0	120	157.1
22	22.4	72	83.0	122	161.5
24	23.9	74	75.5	124	166.1
26	25.4	76	78.3	126	171.0
28	27.0	78	81.1	128	175.4
30	28.5	80	84.1	130	180.2
32	30.1	82	87.0	132	185.1
34	32.0	84	90.1	134	190.1
36	33.4	86	93.2	136	195.2
38	35.2	88	96.4	138	200.3
40	37.0	90	97.6	140	205.5

Fig. 21-5. Relationship between Freon-12 pressure and temperature in refrigerant line. (*Cadillac Motor Car Division of General Motors Corporation*)

§275. Removing and replacing components of system On the type of system which has a check valve and a shutoff valve at the receiver, many of the components of the system can be removed and replaced without excessive refrigerant loss. On systems not having these valves, all of the refrigerant will be lost when the system is opened to replace a component. The exception to this is the compressor. It may be removed and replaced without losing all the refrigerant since the lines entering the compressor have shutoff valves. Removal and replacement of various components are covered in following sections.

Caution: Always wear goggles when working on the system since your eyes must be protected when you are working with refrigerant.

§276. Removing compressor   If the compressor requires servicing, the pressure in it should be released as it is removed from the car. If the compressor is being removed for engine work, then it will not be necessary to release compressor pressure. The two removal methods are detailed below.

1. *Removing compressor for servicing.* Remove shutoff valve caps from high- and low-pressure valves at compressor. Turn both valves clockwise until they are tight with special key. This shuts system off from compressor.

Caution: Do not operate compressor with valves shut off as this would damage the compressor.

Remove protective covers from low- and high-pressure gauge fittings on compressor and relieve pressure in compressor by depressing valve cores. Disconnect lines from compressor by removing bolts attaching line fittings. Cover openings and fittings with masking tape to protect them from dirt. Remove belts and compressor attaching bolts and take compressor off engine.

2. *Removing compressor for engine work.* When removing the compressor for engine work, it is not necessary to relieve the pressure in the compressor. However, if the automatic shutoff valves under the line fittings in the compressor do not happen to close when the fittings are removed, then the pressure will be lost from the compressor. If you hear a continuing hiss when you remove a line fitting, you will know that the automatic shutoff valve has not closed. This means that you should purge the refrigerant from the compressor as you do when you remove the compressor for service (item 1, above).

§277. Replacing compressor seal   If the compressor seal has become defective, it can be replaced as follows (see Fig. 21-6):

1. Take pulley off shaft and remove seal retaining plate and bellows seal. Then use special tool to take out Nitralloy ring.

[586]

Remove any paint or corrosion from shaft. Flush seal cavity in compressor with new Frigidaire oil and wipe the surface of the shaft and cavity with clean, lint-free cloth. Wet a piece of clean, lint-free cloth with lighter fluid, allow the cloth to dry until it is just damp, and then wipe the shaft and shaft shoulder thoroughly to remove all traces of oil. The compressor is now ready for the installation of the new seal.

Caution: Do not touch the polished surfaces of the new Nitralloy seal with your fingers. Any trace of sweat or oil on these surfaces may cause damage and leakage. Do not put any oil on the neoprene seal; it must be dry when installed.

2. To install the new seal, remove the new Nitralloy ring from the protective foil and insert it in the special seal-centering tool so that the synthetic rubber is visible. Tighten set screw in centering tool. Put lighter fluid on a clean, lint-free cloth and wipe the entire rubber surface (including inner diameter and radius) of the seal to remove all trace of protective oil coat. Rubber must be *clean* and *dry*.
3. Slide centering tool, with seal ring, over shaft. Make sure rubber rests firmly against shoulder of shaft. To make sure of this, loosen set screw in centering tool, take tool off shaft (leaving seal in place), reverse tool, and use small end of tool to push against inner rubber ring. Wipe the face of the bellows seal with a clean, lint-free cloth and apply a small amount of Frigidaire oil to the first three convolutions and the face of the bellows seal (see Fig. 21-6).
4. Put retaining-ring lead seal against compressor and then use the centering tool (small end) to install bellows seal assembly on shaft. Leave tool in place for the time being. Install retaining ring with six attaching screws (make sure lead seal is in place). Tighten screws evenly. Then remove centering tool.

§278. Replacing compressor Reinstall compressor on engine with attaching bolts and nuts. Put belts in place and tighten to proper tension. Use new O rings (lubricated lightly with Frigidaire oil), and attach fittings and high- and low-pressure line fittings to compressor. Use special key and open high- and low-pressure valves all the way. Be sure they are turned *all the way open.* Test the connections that have just been made with liquid lubricant. If leaks occur, remove connections and install new O rings and gaskets.

If the pressure has been lost from the compressor, air must be purged from compressor. This is done by first opening the high-pressure-line valve (after installation is complete) and then purging the air by depressing the valve core in the high-pressure gauge connection for a few seconds. Then open the low-pressure-line valve, operate the engine for a few minutes (with compressor running), and then repeat the purging operation.

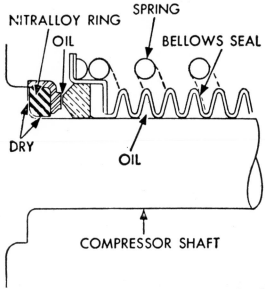

FIG. 21-6. Sectional view of seal on compressor shaft. (*Oldsmobile Division of General Motors Corporation*)

§279. Adjusting expansion valve   The expansion valve must not be adjusted unless you are reasonably sure it is out of adjustment (producing inefficient cooling by either starving or flooding the evaporator). Adjustment is relatively simple under normal circumstances. To adjust, use a 1-inch socket wrench and remove cap nut from expansion valve (support valve to prevent damage to it or lines). Then use special valve key and close the valve by turning it clockwise. Then open the valve by turning key five complete turns (counterclockwise).

If this adjustment does not produce satisfactory operation, the following, more complete, adjustment is required. Connect gauge set to compressor (Fig. 21-3). Attach thermometer to low-pressure line coming from evaporator so mercury bulb is in contact with line. Tape securely and pack insulation around tubing and bulb of thermometer. Start engine and operate at fast idle for about 15 minutes. Check sight glass; there should be no bubbles. Then read low-pressure gauge and temperature of low-pressure line simultaneously. For any given pressure, temperature should be as shown in Fig. 21-7.

If the low-pressure-line temperature is too low, the expansion valve is too far open. Close it one-half turn and recheck as in the previous paragraph. If the temperature is still too low, close valve another half turn. Repeat until pressure-temperature relationship is correct.

Low pressure, psi	Low pressure line temp. ?F
5	2 to 17
10	15 to 30
15	25 to 40
20	34 to 49
25	41 to 56
30	48 to 60

Fig. 21-7. Relationship of pressure in low-pressure side to temperature of low-pressure line from evaporator. (*Cadillac Motor Car Division of General Motors Corporation*)

If the temperature is too high, the expansion valve is not open enough. Open it one-half turn and recheck. Open another half turn if it is still too high and repeat, as necessary, to establish correct pressure-temperature relationship.

§280. **Replacing expansion valve** If the valve cannot be adjusted to obtain normal operation, it should be replaced. On those systems where it is possible, pump down the system (§270). On other systems, purge refrigerant from system. Then disconnect power-element bulb from low-pressure line and remove the equalizing, low-pressure, and high-pressure line flares from valve (in that order). Then remove the expansion valve clamp and take valve off.

Have new valve ready at hand to replace the old one immediately (and thus avoid danger of moisture or dirt getting into system).

Install new valve, connect lines, and clamp. Clamp power-element bulb to the *top* or *side* of the *low-pressure* line.

Caution: High-pressure line must not touch power-element bulb.

If system has been pumped down, evacuate the low-pressure side and recharge it (§§271 and 272). If the entire charge of refrigerant has been lost, evacuate the entire system and recharge it (§§271 and 272).

§281. Replacing other components   Other components of the system, including the evaporator, dehydrator-filter, solenoid bypass valve, sight glass, condenser, check valve and receiver, are replaced in a somewhat similar manner to that used to replace the expansion valve—that is, on those systems where it is possible, the system is pumped down. On other systems, purge the system of refrigerant. Then remove and replace the component requiring replacement. Finally, evacuate the system (or low-pressure side if it has been pumped down), and then recharge it.

CHAPTER CHECKUP

The chapter you have just completed covers the highlights of servicing one type of car air conditioner. While the basic servicing procedures cover all types, there are variations in design and construction which make necessary some variation in servicing. If you do not plan to specialize in air-conditioning work, then the main servicing procedure you should know about is how to remove and replace the compressor. However, if you do plan to specialize in this subject, you should know not only all the details covered in the chapter, but the operation and maintenance procedures on other types of equipment. The material in the chapter gives you a good start in this direction. To find out how well you remember the material, take the following test.

Completing the Sentences

The sentences below are incomplete. After each sentence there are several words or phrases, only one of which will correctly complete the sentence. Write down each sentence in your notebook, selecting the proper word or phrase to complete it correctly.

1. When Freon-12 comes into contact with an open flame, it is converted into   *a harmless gas*   *a dangerously toxic gas*   *a liquid*

Servicing Air Conditioners

2. A drum of Freon-12 must never be heated above *125°F 175°F 212°F 300 F*

3. The purpose of the vacuum pump used in servicing the air-conditioning system is to *pump down the system evacuate the system hydrate the system*

4. When the system is pumped down, most of the refrigerant is pumped into the *compressor condenser evaporator receiver*

5. The purpose of evacuating the system is to remove *all traces of refrigerant all air and moisture all low-pressure refrigerant*

6. When completely charging a system with Freon-12, the amount that should be added, by weight, is *2 pounds 5 pounds 7 pounds 70 pounds*

7. If the expansion valve is out of adjustment and starves the evaporator, then the result will be *excessive cooling excessively low temperature of evaporator insufficient cooling*

8. The only servicing operation to be performed on the compressor discussed in the chapter is replacement of the *rotor bearings seal*

9. When you remove the compressor to service it, you should *purge it of refrigerant maintain pressure in it disassemble it completely*

10. High and low pressures in the system are measured by use of a special *vacuum gauge pressure gauge gauge set*

Servicing Procedures

Write down in your notebook the servicing procedures that are asked for. Don't copy from the book, but try to explain the procedure in your own words just as you would tell it to a friend.

1. What are the main causes of poor cooling?
2. What would cause excessive cooling?
3. Make a list of possible causes of noise in the cooling system.
4. What could cause excessive pressure on the high-pressure side?
5. What could cause insufficient pressure on the high-pressure side?
6. What could cause excessive pressure on the low-pressure side?
7. What could cause insufficient pressure on the low-pressure side?
8. Explain how you check the pressures in the system.
9. List the essential cautions you must observe in working on an air conditioner and in handling refrigerant.
10. Explain how the two types of leak detector are used

11. Explain how to pump down a system.
12. Explain how to exacuate a system (low-pressure side and complete system).
13. Explain how to charge a system (partially and completely).
14. Explain how to check oil level and how to add oil.
15. Explain how to purge excess refrigerant or air from a system.
16. Explain how to remove and replace a compressor.
17. Explain how to adjust an expansion valve. How to remove and replace it.

SUGGESTIONS FOR FURTHER STUDY

If you wish to learn more about servicing of automobile air conditioners, study the various car shop manuals and special manuals issued for this equipment by the car companies. If the service shop of a local car dealer is servicing air-conditioning equipment, try to be on hand so you can observe how the various operations are performed. Be sure to write down everything you learn in your notebook.

Glossary

THIS GLOSSARY of automotive terms used in the book is designed to provide a ready reference for the student. The definitions may differ somewhat from those given in a standard dictionary. They are not intended to be all-inclusive but have the purpose of serving as reminders so the student can quickly refresh his memory on automotive terms about which he may be doubtful. More complete definitions and explanations of the terms are found in the text.

Air brake A braking system which uses compressed air to supply the effort required to apply the brakes.

Air conditioning Conditioning air by cooling and drying it.

Air pressure Atmospheric pressure (14.7 pounds per square inch at sea level) or pressure of air produced by pump, by compression in engine cylinder, and so on.

Antifriction bearings Bearings having rolling contact between the moving surfaces, as in ball and roller bearings.

Atmospheric pressure Pressure of the atmosphere, or air, due to the pressing downward of its weight. Average value is 14.7 pounds per square inch at sea level.

Axle A crossbar supporting a vehicle on which one or more wheels turn.

Backlash In gearing, clearance between meshing teeth of two gears which will permit backward rotation of driven gear in direction opposite to driving rotation. Generally, the amount of free motion, or lash, in a mechanical system.

Ball-and-nut steering gear Recirculating ball-and-nut steering gear.

Ball-joint suspension A type of front suspension which does not use a steering knuckle. Instead, the wheel spindle is attached directly to the upper and lower suspension arms through ball joints.

Ball stud Stud with a ball on end, commonly used in steering linkage to connect pitman arm to linkage, or to connect tie rods.

Bleeding A process by which air is removed from a hydraulic system (brake or power-steering) by bleeding off part of the fluid or operating the system to work out the air.

[593]

Body The assembly of sheet-metal sections, together with windows, doors, seats, and other parts, that provides an enclosure for the passengers, engine, and so on.

Body panels Sheets or panels of steel which are fastened together by welding to form the car body.

Boiling point The temperature at which a liquid begins to boil.

Brake A device for slowing or halting the motion of any object or mechanism.

Brake drums Metal drums mounted on the car wheels: brake shoes press against the drums to slow or stop drum and wheel rotation for braking.

Brake fade A reduction, or fading out, of braking effectiveness caused by overheating from excessively long and hard brake application— for instance, when coming down a long hill or mountain.

Brake feel The reaction of the brake pedal against the driver's foot, that tells him how heavily he is applying the brakes.

Brake fluid A special non-mineral-oil fluid used in the hydraulic braking system.

Brake lines The tubes or hoses connecting the master and wheel cylinders in a hydraulic brake system.

Brake lining The asbestos type of material used to line the brake shoes. The lining takes the wear when the shoe is pressed against the brake drum.

Brakes The mechanism that enables the driver to slow or stop the car by depressing a foot pedal; this action results in the application of a braking or retarding force at the car wheels.

Brake shoes Arc-shaped metal pieces, lined with heat-resistant fiber, which are forced against the revolving drums to produce braking action.

Butyl A type of synthetic rubber used in making tire tubes.

Bypass valve In the car air conditioner, the solenoid bypass valve.

Camber Tilting of the wheels from the vertical; when tilt is outward, camber is positive.

Capillary tube A tube with a small inside diameter. In refrigerators, the capillary tube is used to produce a pressure differential between the condenser and evaporator.

Casing The tire casing, made of fabric or cord, to which rubber is vulcanized. It is the outer part of the tire assembly.

Caster Tilt of kingpin forward or backward from the vertical. Backward tilt from the vertical is called positive caster.

Charging the system The process of adding refrigerant to the refrigerating system.

[594]

Glossary

Chassis The assembly of mechanisms that make up the major operating part of the vehicle. It is usually assumed to include everything except the car body.

Check valve A valve that operates to check, or prevent, excessive pressure rise or other undesirable action (check valve in power-steering system, for example).

Clutch solenoid In some car air conditioners, a solenoid that operates a clutch on the compressor drive pulley. When the clutch is engaged, the compressor is driven and cooling takes place.

Coil spring A spring made up of an elastic metal such as steel, formed into a wire or bar, and wound into a coil.

Compressor The mechanism in a refrigerator which pumps vaporized refrigerant out of the evaporator, compresses it to a relatively high pressure, and then delivers it to the condenser.

Condensation A change of state during which a vapor, or gas, turns to liquid.

Condenser The device in a refrigerator to which vaporized refrigerant at high pressure is delivered; as it passes through the condenser, the refrigerant cools and condenses.

Cornering wear A type of tire-tread wear caused by taking turns at excessive speeds.

Dehumidification The process of dehumidifying, or drying. In the air conditioner, the air is dehumidified as it passes through the evaporator, since water condenses from the air onto the evaporator coils.

Dehydrator-filter A filtering device in the line between the condenser and evaporator through which all liquid refrigerant must pass. The device removes dirt and moisture from the refrigerant.

Direct-acting shock absorber Type of shock absorber which shortens or lengthens in action. Also called a telescope shock absorber.

Dolly blocks Blocks of metal, variously shaped and contoured, used to straighten body panels and fenders. The dolly block is held on one side of the panel while the other side is struck with a special hammer.

Drum lathe A special lathe for turning brake drums; this is required when drums are out of round, rough, or scored.

Dynamic balance Balance of an object when it is in motion (for example, dynamic balance of a wheel).

Electric brakes A type of braking system which uses an armature-electromagnet combination at each wheel; as the electromagnet is energized, the magnetic attraction between the armature and electromagnet causes the brake shoes to move against the brake drum.

Evacuating the system A procedure required whenever any component in the refrigerating system (except compressor) has been removed and replaced. The procedure uses a vacuum pump which pumps out air and moisture from the system.

Evaporation A change of state during which a liquid turns to a vapor, or gas.

Evaporator The device in a refrigerator inside of which refrigerant evaporates; this action causes the refrigerant to take heat from the refrigerator.

Expansion valve A valve between the condenser and evaporator, located at the evaporator, which provides a pressure differential; the high pressure on the condenser side is reduced to low pressure on the evaporator side.

Fade See brake fade.

Flushing With regard to hydraulic braking system, the washing out of the hydraulic lines and the master and wheel cylinders with a special flushing compound to remove dirt or impurities that have gotten into the system.

Four-wheel steering Type of steering system in which all four wheels of a vehicle are turned for steering.

Frame The assembly of metal structural parts and channel sections that supports the engine and body and that is supported by the car wheels.

Frame gauges Gauges hung from the car frame to check frame alignment.

Freon-12 A widely used refrigerant.

Friction The resistance to motion between two bodies in contact with each other.

Friction bearings Bearings having sliding contact between the moving surfaces. Sleeve bearings, such as those used in connecting rods, are friction bearings.

Front-end geometry The angular relationship between the front wheels, wheel attaching parts, and car frame. Includes camber, caster, kingpin inclination, toe-in, and toe-out on turns.

Gasket A flat strip, usually of cork or other material, placed between two surfaces to provide a tight seal between them.

Gravity The attractive force between objects that tend to bring them together. A stone dropped from the hand falls to the earth because of gravity.

Grinder A machine for removing metal by means of an abrasive wheel or stone.

[596]

Glossary

Hill-holder A device incorporated into some brake systems; it is interconnected to the clutch so that depressing the clutch maintains brake application.

Hood That part of the car body which fits over and protects the engine.

Hotchkiss drive The type of rear suspension in which the springs absorb the rear-end torque.

Hot-shrinkage A method of straightening panel; the panel is heated and then cooled with a water-soaked sponge.

Hydraulic brakes A braking system that uses hydraulic pressure to force the brake shoes against the brake drums as the brake pedal is depressed.

Hydraulic pressure Pressure exerted through the medium of a liquid.

Hydraulics That branch of physics dealing with the motion of and pressures in liquids.

Idling speed The speed at which the engine runs, without load, when the accelerator pedal is released.

Included angle Camber angle plus kingpin inclination angle.

Inner tube The inside rubber tube assembled in the tire casing; it contains the air at sufficient pressure to inflate the casing and adequately support the vehicle weight.

Kinetic friction Friction between two bodies in relative motion.

Kingpin The steel pin on which the steering-knuckle pivots; it attaches the steering knuckle to the knuckle support or axle.

Kingpin inclination Inward tilt of the kingpin from the vertical.

KPI Kingpin inclination.

Lathe A machine tool used to shape objects. Its distinguishing feature is that it rotates the object while a cutting tool is brought to bear upon it so that material is cut from the object.

Leaf spring A spring made up of a series of flat steel plates of graduated length, assembled one on top of another.

Leak detector A device or substance that can be used to detect leakage of gas.

Linkage power steering A type of power steering in which the power steering units (power cylinder and valve) are an integral part of the steering linkage.

Lock nut A second nut turned down on a holding nut to prevent loosening.

Major brake adjustment Adjustment of brakes which involves complete realignment of brake shoes to drums and requires relocation of adjustment of shoe anchors as well as adjusting screws.

[597]

Manometer   A device for measuring gas or vapor pressures. Specifically, so far as this book is concerned, a U-shaped, water-filled tube used to check the Gemmer power-steering gear for internal leaks.

Master cylinder   The liquid-filled cylinder in the hydraulic braking system where hydraulic pressure is developed by depression of the brake pedal.

Mechanical brakes   Brakes operated by mechanical linkage (cables and levers) between the brake pedal and the brakes at the car wheels.

Minor brake adjustment   Adjustment of brakes to compensate for brake-lining wear.

O ring   A type of sealing ring, made of special rubberlike material, which is compressed into grooves to provide the sealing action.

Parking brakes   Mechanically operated brakes that operate independently of the service brakes on the vehicle. They may be set for parking the car.

Piston   A movable part, fitted to a cylinder, which can receive or transmit motion as a result of pressure changes (fluid, vapor, gas) in the cylinder.

Pitman arm   That part of the steering gear which is linked to the steering knuckle arms of the wheels; it swings back and forth for steering.

Pitman-arm stop   On some cars (particularly those using linkage power steering), stops to prevent excessive pitman-arm, and thus steering-linkage, movement.

Pitman shaft   The shaft to which the pitman arm is attached in a steering gear.

Plies   The layers of fabric in a tire casing. Each layer is a ply.

Power brakes   Brakes that use vacuum and atmospheric pressure to provide most of the effort required for braking action.

Power cylinder   Operating cylinder which produces power to actuate a mechanism. Both power brakes and power-steering units have power cylinders.

Power rack   In the Saginaw power-steering unit, a rack that meshes with a sector on the pitman shaft and transmits to the shaft power from the power cylinder.

Power steering   A device that uses hydraulic pressure to multiply the driver's effort as he turns the steering wheel, so that his steering effort is reduced.

Preload   In bearings, the amount of load originally imposed on a bearing before actual operating loads are imposed. This is done by bearing adjustments and assures alignment and minimum looseness in system.

Psi   Pounds per square inch; usually used to indicate pressure of a liquid or gas.

[598]

Pumping down the system A procedure whereby most of the refrigerant in the refrigerating system can be pumped into one part (such as receiver) and held there while other system components are removed and replaced. This saves refrigerant.

Puncture-sealing tires and tubes Tires and tubes coated on the inside with a plastic material. Air pressure in the tire or tube forces that material through holes made by punctures. It hardens on contact with the air to seal the puncture.

Purging the system The process of opening a valve to allow some of the refrigerant in the refrigerating system to escape. Its purpose is to remove excessive refrigerant or air, or to eliminate refrigerant from components or from the entire system when parts must be removed.

Reamer A metal-cutting tool with a series of sharp cutting edges that remove material from a hole when the reamer is turned in it.

Recapping A form of tire repair in which a cap of new material is placed on the old tread and vulcanized into place.

Receiver In a car air conditioner, a metal tank for holding excess liquid refrigerant. Liquid refrigerant is delivered from the condenser to the receiver. From there, it passes to the evaporator as needed.

Recirculating ball-and-nut steering gear A type of steering gear in which there is a nut (meshing with a gear sector) assembled on a worm; balls circulate between the nut and worm threads.

Refrigerant A substance used in a refrigerator, which circulates between the condenser and evaporator to produce cooling through a cycle of evaporation and condensation.

Refrigeration Cooling by removal of heat.

Relief valve A valve that opens when a preset pressure is reached. This relieves, or prevents, excessive pressures.

Run-out, of wheel Lack of alignment of wheel to axle so that wheel wobbles; certain parts of wheel "run-out" or move out of alignment, as wheel rotates.

Safety rim A type of wheel rim (used on Chrysler-built cars) having a hump on the inner edge of the ledge on which the tire bead rides. The hump helps hold the tire on the rim in case of a blowout.

Seat adjuster A device to permit forward or backward (and sometimes upward and downward) movement of the front seat.

Sector One section of a gear. Specifically, the gear sector on the pitman shaft, in many steering gears.

Shackle Swinging support by which one end of a leaf spring is attached to car frame.

Shimmy Rapid oscillation; in wheel shimmy, for example, the front

[599]

wheel tries to turn in and out alternately and rapidly. This causes the front end of the car to oscillate, or shimmy.

Shock absorber The assembly on the vehicle that checks excessively rapid spring movement and oscillation.

Sight glass In a car air conditioner, a viewing glass set in the refrigerant line; it provides a visual check of refrigerant passing from the receiver to the evaporator. If bubbles are seen, it means there is insufficient refrigerant in the system.

Solenoid bypass valve In the car air conditioner, a valve placed in a bypass line between the condenser and compressor, operated by a solenoid. When open, refrigerant can bypass between the condenser and compressor so no refrigeration takes place. When closed, refrigeration results.

Spline Slot or groove cut in a shaft or bore; a splined shaft onto which a hub, wheel, gear, and so on, with matching splines in its bore is assembled so the two must turn together.

Spring An elastic device that yields under stress, or pressure, but returns to its original state or position when the stress or pressure is removed.

Sprung weight That part of the car which is supported on springs (the frame and body, for example).

Stabilizer shaft An interconnecting shaft between the two lower suspension arms which reduces body roll on turns.

Starting motor The electric motor in the electric system that cranks the engine, or turns the crankshaft, for starting.

Static balance Balance of an object while it is at rest or not moving.

Static friction Friction between two bodies at rest.

Steering arm The arm attached to the steering knuckle to turn the knuckle, and wheel, for steering.

Steering gear That part of the steering system, located at the lower end of the steering shaft, that carries the rotary motion of the steering wheel to the car wheels for steering.

Steering geometry See toe-out during turns.

Steering kickback Sharp and rapid movements of steering wheel as front wheels encounter obstructions in road; the shocks of these encounters "kick back" to steering wheel.

Steering knuckle The front-wheel spindle which is supported by the kingpin so it, and wheel, can be turned for steering.

Steering shaft Shaft extending from steering gear to the steering wheel.

Steering system The mechanism that enables the driver to turn the wheel axles (usually the front) and thus turn the wheels away from the straight-ahead position so the car can be guided.

[600]

Glossary

Steering wheel The wheel at the top of the steering shaft in the driver's compartment which is used to guide or steer the car.

Streamlining The shaping of an object that moves through a medium (such as air or water), or past which the medium moves, so that less energy is lost by the parting and reuniting of the medium as the object moves through it.

Suspension arm In the front suspension, one of the arms pivoted at one end to the frame and, at the other, to the wheel (steering-knuckle) support.

Sway bar See stabilizer.

Telescope shock absorber See direct-acting shock absorber.

Thermostat A device that is sensitive to temperature changes; it produces mechanical movement with temperature change. In a refrigerator, this movement opens or closes contact points to provide control of the refrigerator.

Tie rods In the steering system, the rods that link the pitman arm to the steering-knuckle arms.

Tire The casing and tube assembled on a car wheel to provide pneumatically cushioned contact and traction with road.

Toe-in The turning in of the front wheels. Wheels are closer together at the front than at the back of the wheels.

Toe-out during turns Difference in angles between the two front wheels and the car frame during turns. Inner wheel in a turn turns out, or toes-out more. Also called steering geometry.

Torque Turning or twisting effort, usually measured in pounds-feet.

Torque-tube drive The type of rear suspension in which the torque tube surrounding the propeller shaft absorbs the rear-end torque.

Torque wrench A special wrench with a dial that indicates the amount of torque to a nut or bolt being turned.

Tracking The following of the rear wheels directly behind, or in the tracks of, the front wheels.

Trouble-shooting The detective work necessary to run down the cause of a trouble. Also implies the correction of the trouble by elimination of cause.

Unsprung weight That part of the car which is not supported on springs (the wheels and tires, for example).

V-8 A type of engine with two banks of cylinders set at an angle with each other to form a V.

Vacuum An absence of air or other substance.

Vacuum-suspended power brake A type of power brake in which both sides of the piston are subjected to vacuum; the piston is "suspended" in vacuum.

Valve A device that can be opened or closed to allow or stop the flow of a liquid, gas, or vapor from one to another place.

Valve-operating block A block in the Gemmer power-steering unit which moves to operate the valves.

Valve spool A spool-shaped valve in the power-steering unit.

Vise A gripping device for holding a piece while it is being worked on.

Vulcanization A process of treating raw rubber by heat and pressure; the treatment forms the rubber and gives it the desired characteristics of toughness and flexibility.

Welding The process of joining pieces of metal by fusing them together with heat.

Wheel cylinders In the hydraulic braking system, hydraulic cylinders placed in the brake mechanisms at the wheels; hydraulic pressure from the master cylinder causes the wheel cylinders to move the brake shoes into pressure contact with the brake drums for braking.

Wheel tramp Tendency for the wheel to move up and down so it repeatedly bears hard, or "tramps," on the pavement. Sometimes called high-speed shimmy.

Window regulator A device for opening and closing the window; usually operated by a crank.

Windshield wiper A mechanism which utilizes a rubber blade to wipe the windshield; it is either vacuum or electrically operated.

Worm Type of gear on the lower end of the steering shaft.

Index

Index

Index

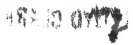